PERTH HIGH STREET

ARCHAEOLOGICAL EXCAVATION

1975–1977

Fascicule 4
Living and working in a medieval Scottish burgh
Environmental remains and miscellaneous finds

Environmental remains
the late G W I Hodgson, C Smith, A Jones,
M Fraser, A K G Jones, the late D Heppel,
R Cerón-Carrasco, A S Clarke, I H M Smart,
R B Longmore and D McKay

Miscellaneous finds
A MacGregor, C Smith, M A Hall, J L Brown,
the late J B Kenworthy
J Hunter, G Dalgleish
and the late N Q Bogdan

TAYSIDE AND FIFE ARCHAEOLOGICAL COMMITTEE

PERTH

2011

This fascicule is one of four in a special series and is available by post from John Sheriff, Hon Treasurer TAFAC, 21 Burleigh Crescent, Inverkeithing, Fife, KY11 1DQ.

Monograph One
Excavations in St Andrews 1980–89 A decade of archaeology in a historic Scottish Burgh

Monograph Two
The salt and coal industries at St Monans, Fife in the 18th and 19th centuries

Monograph Three
Perth: the archaeology and development of a Scottish burgh

Monograph Four
Dundee rediscovered: the archaeology of Dundee reconsidered

Monograph Five
Excavations at Brown Catherthun and White Catherthun hillforts, Angus, 1995–1997

Monograph Six
Excavations at St Ethernan's Monastery, Isle of May, Fife 1992–7

Monograph Seven
First Contact: Rome and Northern Britain

Submission of potential monographs
Offers of monographs are welcomed, and intending contributors should first contact the Assistant Editor, 34 Glenfarg Terrace, Perth PH2 0AP.

Front cover Artist's impression, by Maureen Rooney Mitchell, of medieval fleshers' stalls.
(© Maureen Rooney Mitchell)

Back cover A group of stone whorls from the Perth High Street excavations.
(© Alder Archaeology Ltd)

Editor's note
TAFAC would like to acknowledge the support of Historic Scotland, Perth and Kinross Heritage Trust, the Guildry Incorporation of Perth, The Strathmartine Trust and Marks and Spencer plc in aiding the publication of this Fascicule.

Published with assistance from the Perth Common Good Fund

2011
© The individual authors.

ISBN 978 0 9561783 5 0

Typeset by Christina Unwin *e-mail* christina@wave.demon.co.uk

Printed and bound by Farquhar and Son Ltd, Perth

Contents

Illustrations   vi

Tables   viii

Foreword *Olwyn Owen* Historic Scotland   ix

Obituary *Nicholas Quentin Bogdan* 18 June 1947–15 August 2002   x

THE ENVIRONMENTAL REMAINS

1 The history of the environmental remains   3
Catherine Smith

2 The mammal bone   5
the late George W I Hodgson, Catherine Smith and Angela Jones

3 The bird bone   45
Catherine Smith and A S Clarke

4 The fish bone   53
Andrew K G Jones

5 The human bone   59
I H M Smart and R B Longmore

6 The mollusca   60
The late David Heppel, Catherine Smith and David McKay

7 The feathers   63
Ruby Cerón-Carrasco

8 The botanical remains   66
Mhairi Fraser and Catherine Smith

9 Conclusions: the environment of medieval Perth   81
Catherine Smith

THE MISCELLANEOUS FINDS

10 The worked bone   97
Arthur MacGregor, with Mark A Hall, Catherine Smith and the late Nicholas Q Bogdan

11 The glass   117
John Hunter, George Dalgleish and the late Nicholas Q Bogdan

12 The stone objects   127
Catherine Smith, J Lawson Brown and Mark A Hall

13 The flint   139
the late James B Kenworthy

References   147

Appendix 1 *Glossary*   155

Acknowledgements   157

Index   161

CD Insert data tables

List of tables on CD

1 *Bone size range summary*
1.1 Cattle
1.2 Sheep/goat
1.3 Sheep and goat skull measurements
1.4 Goat
1.5 Pig
1.6 Horse
1.7 Red deer
1.8 Dog skull measurements
1.9 Dog
1.10 Cat skull measurements
1.11 Cat
1.12 Domestic fowl
1.13 Domestic/Greylag goose

2
2.1 *Numbers and percentages of mammal bones found in middens*
2.2 *Numbers and percentages of mammal bones found in buildings*
2.3 *Numbers of mammal bones found in pits*

3 *Expected and actual numbers and percentages of cattle and sheep/goat bones*
   3.1 in middens
3.1.1 Midden M1.1c (Phase IId)
3.1.2 Midden M1.3 (Phase IIi)
3.1.3 Midden M1.4c (Phase IIIa–IVcc)
3.1.4 Midden M1.4d (Phase IVb,IVc)
3.1.5 Midden M1.4f (Phase IVc)
3.1.6 Midden M1.4g (Phase IVb,IVc)
3.1.7 Midden M1.5 (Phase Va,Vaa)
3.1.8 Midden M.2.1b (Phase Ic)
3.1.9 Midden 3a (Phase Vb–Vc)
3.1.10 Midden 3c (Phase Vd)
3.1.11 Midden M4a (Phase Vaa–Vc)
3.1.12 Midden M4c (Phase Vd,Vdd)
3.1.13 Midden M7 (Phase Vc)
3.1.14 Midden M8a (Phase Va,Vaa)
3.1.15 Midden M9a (Phase IVc,IVcc)
3.1.16 Midden M9b(b) (Phase IVc,IVcc)
3.1.17 Midden M10 (Phase IId–IIg)
3.1.18 Midden M14b(b) (Phase Ie)

   3.2 in buildings
3.2.1 Building B1(a) (Phase IVcc)
3.2.2 Building B1(b) Phase Va)
3.2.3 Building B2 (Phase IVa,IVaa)
3.2.4 Building B3 North (Phase IVa,IVaa)

3.2.5 Building B3 South (Phase IVa,IVaa)
3.2.6 Building B4 (Phase IIc)
3.2.7 Building B5 (Phase IIa–IIff)
3.2.8 Building B6 (Phase Ie–IIa)
3.2.9 Building B8 (Phase (Icc,Id)
3.2.10 Building B10 (Phase Icc)
3.2.11 Building B11 (Phase IVaa)
3.2.12 Building B12 (Phase IIe–IIg)
3.2.13 Building B13 (Phase IIh)
3.2.14 Building B15 (Phase Ic,Icc)
3.2.15 Building B16 (Phase Id–Ia)
3.2.16 Building B16a (Phase Id–IIa)
3.2.17 Building B17 (Phase Ib)
3.2.18 Building B18 (Phase IVa–IVb)
3.2.19 Building B19 (Phase IIIa–IIIc)
3.2.20 Building B20 (Phase <IIId–IVaa)
3.2.21 Building B21 (Phase IIff)
3.2.22 Building B23 (Phase IIb–IIIf
3.2.23 Building B26 (Phase IIg–IVaa)
3.2.24 Building B27 (Phase <IIc–IIff)
3.2.25 Building B28 (Phase Ia–Ic))
3.2.26 Building B34 (Phase Va)
3.2.27 Building B50(a) (Phase IVc-Vc(–Vdd))
3.2.28 Building B50(b) (Phase IVcc–(–Vdd))
3.2.29 Building B51 (Phase Vd,Vdd)
3.2.30 Building B53 (Phase 1) (Phase Vb)
3.2.31 Building B53 (Phase 2) (Phase Vbb)
3.2.32 Building G (Phase VI–VIf)
3.2.33 Building T (Phase VI)
3.2.34 Building V (Phase VI)

4 *Distribution of horse bones*
4.1 in middens
4.2 in buildings
4.3 in paths
4.4 in miscellaneous features
4.5 in Areas 5 and 6

5 *Distribution of dog bones*
5.1 in middens
5.2 in buildings
5.3 in paths
5.4 in miscellaneous features
5.5 in Areas 5 and 6

6 *Distribution of cat bones*
6.1 in middens
6.2 in buildings
6.3 in paths
6.4 in miscellaneous features
6.5 in Area 5

7 *Distribution of bird bones*
7.1 in middens
7.2 in buildings
7.3 in pits
7.4 in paths
7.5 in miscellaneous context groups
7.6 in Areas 5 and 6

Illustrations

Illus 1 Location map of Scotland, showing burghs where excavations of medieval sites mentioned in the text have taken place

Illus 2 Plan of medieval Perth showing locations of major excavations mentioned in the text

Illus 3 Skeleton of young female Soay sheep used for comparison with medieval material

Illus 4 Sheep (above) and goat (below) scapulae: note differences in morphology of scapula neck

Illus 5 Sheep (above) and goat (below) metatarsals and metacarpals

Illus 6 Gilded copper alloy spur with animal head decoration, Context 5014, A11316

Illus 7 Detail of underside of decorated spur

Illus 8 Copper alloy prick spur, Context 7299, A04–0551

Illus 9 Conjectured appearance of the Scots sow, the unimproved pig prevalent in Scotland from the Iron Age to the Early Modern period

Illus 10 Three dog skulls from PHSAE: frontal and lateral views

Illus 11 Skull and long bones of bow-legged dog

Illus 12 Partial skeleton of small dog, Context 5019, A10702 and A10696, Phase IIa

Illus 13 Cat skulls from Perth High Street

Illus 14 Cat tibiae from Perth High Street

Illus 15 From left: red deer distal tibia and roe deer maxilla

Illus 16 Modern red deer stag (Camperdown Country Park, Dundee)

Illus 17 Cattle left horn cores, showing variations in outer curvature

Illus 18 Cattle right horn cores, showing variations in outer curvature

Illus 19 Culling pattern of sheep/goats at Perth High Street (1975–77) medieval layers. After Payne (1973)

Illus 20 Three sheep skulls showing some horn core variations, with scur type below

Illus 21 Sheep skull with robust horn cores

Illus 22 Polycerate sheep skull

Illus 23 Jacob sheep

Illus 24 Goat horn cores showing variations in size related to sexual dimorphism

Illus 25 Female goat skull

Illus 26 Ankylosed cattle metatarsal and naviculo-cuboid tarsal; lateral view

Illus 27 Cattle skull fragment showing lesion on frontal bone

Illus 28 Diseased cattle metatarsals, posterior distal view (from left): possible ossified haematoma on shaft; osteoarthritis

Illus 29 Male and female sawn goat horn cores

Illus 30 Sawn cattle horn cores

Illus 31 Cattle carcasses split into equal sides of beef; 19th-century Perth butcher's shop

Illus 32 Rutherford's 1774 map of Perth

Illus 33 St Bartholomew, patron saint of the Perth Glover Incorporation, with the beaming knife used in his martyrdom; 16th century painted wooden panel taken from St John's Kirk

Illus 34 19th-century butchers at work in Mr Paton's shop, Perth

Illus 35 Cattle radii, innominate and humerus showing hack marks made by axes or cleavers

Illus 36 Cattle cervical vertebra (atlas), showing knife marks on ventral aspect

Illus 37 Domestic fowl furculae (chicken wishbones)

Illus 38 Greatest length of domestic fowl femora versus frequency; greatest length of domestic fowl tarsometatarsi versus frequency

Illus 39 Three domestic fowl tarsometatarsi, medial and posterior views

Illus 40 Domestic fowl tarsometatarsi, anterior view

Illus 41 Peacock (Scone Palace, Perthshire)

Illus 42 Oyster shells and animal bone from the site

Illus 43 Pearl mussel (*Margaritifera margaritifera*) from the Tay, containing pearl, 1960s

Illus 44 Wattle pathway preserved at the site

Illus 45 Building B4 Reconstruction (by Dave Munro)

Illus 46 Cattle radius showing gnaw marks made by dog or other carnivore on bone shaft

Illus 47 Reconstruction of medieval rubbish disposal

Illus 48 Latrine pit, with wattle hurdling used to strengthen trampled area, Kirk Close, Perth

Illus 49 Artist's impression of Perth High Street backlands

Illus 50 Worked bone. Casket mounts Cat Nos 2, 3, 10, 76

Illus 51 Worked bone. Combs Cat Nos 32, 49, 68, 72

Illus 52 Worked bone. Handles Cat Nos 45, 57. Playing piece Cat No 4. Die Cat No 51.

Illus 53 Worked bone. Pins/needles Cat Nos 9, 29, 38, 53, 56. Whorl Cat No 66. Tally stick/bobbin Cat No 59. Pin beater Cat No 77

Illus 54 Worked bone. Trial pieces Cat Nos 73, 81. Toggles Cat Nos 8, 61. Horn terminal Cat No 14. Skate Cat No 47. Handle Cat No 79. Teether Cat No 74

Illus 55 Stone whorls. Cat Nos 3, 4, 6, 14, 15, 18, 32

Illus 56 Stone whorls. Cat Nos 19, 20, 21, 22, 23, 24, 34

Illus 57 Hones. Cat Nos 35, 36, 37, 38

Illus 58 Mould for casting penannular brooches, brooch pins and ringlets. Cat No 39

Illus 59 Mould for a decorative mount (R) shown alongside a computerised model of the inverse (positive) surface (L). Cat No 40

Illus 60 Mould. Cat No 41

Illus 61 Mould (upper surface). Cat No 42

Illus 62 Mould (lower surface). Cat No 42

Illus 63 Mould. Cat No 43

Illus 64 Flint reused as strike-a-light (Cat No 47) and barbed-and-tanged arrowhead (Cat No 34) found in posthole of Building B18.

Illus 65 George Wharton Ian Hodgson, osteologist, 1970s (on left of photograph) contemplates the High Street assemblage

Tables

1 Number of cattle bones identified
2 Number of sheep/goat bones identified
3 Number of goat bones identified
4 Number of pig bones identified
5 Number of horse bones identified
6 Number of red and roe deer bones identified
7 Number of dog bones identified
8 Number of cat bones identified
9 Number of dog/fox bones identified
10 Number of hare bones identified
11 Total numbers of mammal bones identified
12 Minimum numbers of animals present, based on most frequently occurring bones
13 Minimum numbers of animals from selected sites in Scottish medieval burghs, estimated on the basis of the most numerous long bones (i.e. excluding horn cores and mandibles)
14 Minimum numbers of main meat producing mammals from selected Scottish medieval burghs, estimated on the basis of bones common to all of the sites
15 Percentages of food forming mammals from medieval sites in Perth, Elgin and Aberdeen, based on fragment count
16 Percentage of cattle assigned to age group on the basis of dental evidence
17 Frequencies of selected cattle bones having fused distal epiphyses and estimates of their ages
18 Frequencies of pig mandibles, classified by probable age
19 Frequencies of selected pig long bones, classified by probable age
20 Age assessment of horse maxillae and mandibles
21 Frequencies of selected canine long bones lacking epiphyses and their probable ages
22 Frequencies of selected feline long bones lacking epiphyses
23 Percentage contribution to meat yields by species, based on minimum numbers in 13
24 Percentage contribution to meat yield by species, excluding horse
25 Percentage contribution to meat yields based on Sheep Equivalent Units, based on minimum numbers in 13
26 Total numbers of bird bones identified
27 Total number of domestic fowl bones identified
28 Numbers of adult and immature domestic fowl bones
29 Total number of domestic goose/greylag bones identified
30 Numbers of adult and immature goose bones
31 Fish remains by species and bone
32 Fish bones collected by hand (arranged by species and period)
33 Fish bones collected by sieving (arranged by species and period)
34 Numbers of mollusc shells identified
35 Results of analysis of the feather remains
36 Details of botanical samples examined
37 Summary of plant remains
38 Numbers of carbonised cereal grains and florets, by species
39 Worked bone artefacts by Phase and type
40 Total number of bone artefacts by Period

Foreword

It was in Perth in the mid 1970s that we saw, for the first time in Scotland, just how rich the urban archaeological resource might be. Perth is still the jewel in our urban archaeological crown, unique amongst Scottish towns for the depth, importance and consistently high quality of its archaeological remains. On the High Street, a depth of four metres of deposits is not unusual: layer upon layer of floors, occupation levels, yards and rubbish pits, which together represent the remains of successive buildings – workshops, storehouses, byres and dwellings – their load-bearing timbers made of oak or ash, and their walls of birch wattle.

The Perth High Street 1975–77 excavation was extraordinarily rich in artefacts and environmental evidence, providing a remarkably detailed picture of domestic and commercial life within a 12th- to 13th-century Scottish burgh. The soil conditions were often waterlogged and large quantities of organic material survived: over 6,000 pieces of leather alone; a wide range of wooden artefacts, including a French wine barrel; and the textiles included silk and hair. Over 50,000 sherds of pottery were recovered – probably the largest assemblage from a single site anywhere in Scotland. Numerous excavations in Perth through the 1980s and 90s have continued to furnish a wealth of evidence and opened windows on the past in sometimes surprising ways.

And yet, when Nick Bogdan and his team began their work at Perth High Street in 1975, they could not have foreseen the riches they would unearth – or that it would become Nick's life's work. In many ways Nick was ahead of his time. He surveyed the standing buildings on the site in meticulous detail, long before it was generally realised that this was an important aspect of urban archaeological work. He pioneered the use of job creation schemes in Scotland, seeing the potential they offered in enabling large-scale excavations to take place, while also offering youngsters the opportunity for employment. He recognised the impact that the natural topography had on the history and growth of the burgh. His love of technology led him to embrace the use of computers in innovative ways long before this had become commonplace. He recognised early on that the results of his excavations warranted publication in a series of fascicules, which was not usual in Scotland in those days.

The Nick I knew was an entertaining companion, an unfailingly kind and considerate man, always enthusiastic, hugely knowledgeable in many areas, generous with both his time and knowledge, immensely loyal to his family and friends and, above all, a man fascinated by history and archaeology, and utterly dedicated to completion of the important work he started. In his latter years Nick found personal happiness when he embarked on a new project at the Bishop's Palace, Fetternear, with his partner Penny Dransart, and brought to it his customary scholarship and passion. But his commitment to Perth High Street never wavered. I never doubted that this project would be completed, and I have no doubt that Nick would have led its completion but for his untimely death at the age of 55.

It is a source of great sadness that Nick is not here to see these volumes in print. He would have been thrilled. He would also have been very aware of the great debt owed to all those volunteers, young people, archaeologists and specialists who worked with him, and those who have laboured long and hard in more recent years to bring the project to a successful conclusion.

I am delighted to welcome this fourth volume in the publication of Perth High Street 1975–77 archaeological excavations. The completion of this important project is not only a credit to everyone who has been involved, but also a fitting tribute to Nick's memory.

Olwyn Owen
Historic Scotland

Obituary
Nicholas Quentin Bogdan 18 June 1947 to 15 August 2002

The life story of Nicholas Q Bogdan is intimately entwined with that of the Perth High Street excavation. An energetic and forceful personality, Nick, as he was known to his digging team, came to prominence in Scottish archaeology as the director of these explorations in rescue archaeology in 1975, having previously excavated with Professor Nicholas Brooks in St Andrews. His academic career had begun at Gordonstoun in Moray, then took him to Queen's University of Belfast, where he read archaeology, thence to St Andrews where his postgraduate research on the origins of castles became part of a lifelong passion. Nick's enthusiasms crossed the boundaries of history, archaeology, architecture, genealogy and many other '-ologies' besides: he was not limited by mere geography and always looked beyond, keen to place medieval Scotland in its wider European setting.

He was involved in the formation of a number of archaeological bodies, among them the Scottish Castle Survey and the Scottish Episcopal Palaces Project. From 1976 until 1982 he was a founder member of the Tayside and Fife Archaeological Committee (TAFAC), the group which brought together those involved in and supporting archaeology in Tayside and Fife.

Nick, though with one foot firmly in the past, had an ability to spot trends which he could usefully exploit in his work and was therefore always an enthusiastic user of new technology. 'New' in the 1970s meant the use of computers which utilised punch cards; by the 1990s he had advanced so far as to set up his own archaeological website. Publication however always seemed to lie somewhere just out of reach and although several interim reports of his work at Perth High Street were intermittently produced, the final drawing together of the great work was forever 'in progress' or 'forthcoming'.

In later years, his major post-Perth project was at Fetternear Bishop's Palace, where with boundless enthusiasm and the help of his collaborator and partner Dr Penny Dransart, through the auspices of the University of Wales, Lampeter, he excavated and researched until his untimely and sudden death, of a heart attack, at the age of 55.

A newspaper obituary (*Guardian*, 28 August 2002) described Nick's 'cheerful disdain for administration'. Perhaps so, but it is despite this, and all the vicissitudes of fortune of the last three decades, that the present volume is now offered as a tribute to his memory.

The environmental remains

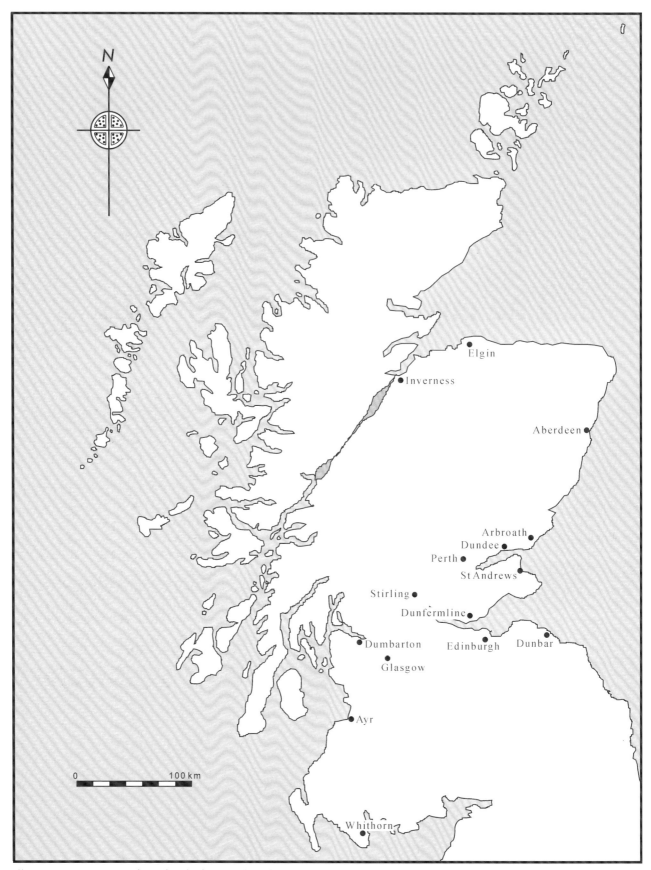

Illus 1 *Location map of Scotland, showing burghs where excavations of medieval sites mentioned in the text have taken place.*

The history of the environmental remains

Catherine Smith

When the excavation took place at the Marks and Spencer site on the High Street in Perth between 1975 and 1977, it could truly be described as ground-breaking. At the time there was an increasing awareness of Perth's potential for survival of significant archaeological deposits, and this excavation led to much future work in the town. The location of Perth and other Scottish sites mentioned in the text is shown in Illus 1. Subsequent major excavations in Perth referred to are shown in Illus 2.

Both during and after the course of the excavation the finds, artefactual and ecofactual, were dispersed to various specialists for detailed examination. At that time, the study of environmental archaeology was a relatively new discipline, and although experts certainly could be found, the subject was not the accepted part of the archaeological curriculum which it is at the present day.

Thus, for each different category of environmental remains from the excavation, each material type was separated and sent to the appropriate specialists

working in the field at that time. The large assemblage of mammal bone, for example, was sent to Duncan of Jordanstone College of Art in Dundee. Fish bones were sent to the Environmental Archaeology Unit at York, bird bones and mollusc shells to the National Museums, Edinburgh, and soil samples to Glasgow University.

On the closure of the Perth High Street Archaeological Excavation Committee's offices, several years after the excavation itself ended, the site records became dispersed. In March 1984, the bulk of the site archive was transferred to the offices of the Ancient Monuments Department, Melville Street, Edinburgh (now Historic Scotland). Subsequently, post-excavation activities were no longer closely co-ordinated and it became difficult to track the whereabouts of the environmental materials and relevant records. In the mid-1990s Historic Scotland agreed to back a renewed plan to publish the results of the excavation. Although much of the environmental material had been reported on, some detective work was required in order to find the most up-to-date records and reports, and in some cases the environmental

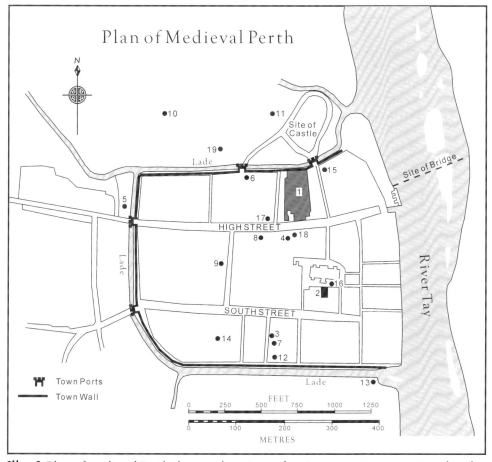

Illus 2 *Plan of medieval Perth showing locations of major excavations mentioned in the text.*

materials themselves. Due to the bulky nature of some of the environmental remains, particularly the soil samples, it had not proved possible to store all of the material in the intervening years. In the event, many of the soil samples had been collected by site staff inexperienced in working with environmental material. For these reasons, those soil samples which had not been processed by the mid-1980s were discarded. Even if they had been retained, deterioration of the macrofossil component would probably have occurred in the unprocessed material. Thus, the botanical report deals mainly with material recovered from the second season of excavation in 1977. The macrofossils were extracted at York from 1kg subsamples of soil by paraffin flotation, primarily for the purposes of extracting insect remains. Sadly those samples collected for the purposes of recovering entomological remains do not seem to have been kept and this work was subsequently abandoned.

Similarly, although the samples sent to York yielded fish remains, they had not been collected specifically for this purpose. There was however a substantial hand-excavated fish bone assemblage from which some useful conclusions could be drawn. The hand-excavated mammal bone assemblage was reported on at an early stage, and the records kept in good order. It was only necessary to re-examine some of the bone. For the bird bone, only those identification records from the first excavation season had survived, but as the bird bones themselves were still available for inspection, all of the bones were re-examined and a fresh report prepared.

Finally, all the reports were collected together and revised in the light of a further 20 years of excavation in the burgh of Perth, resulting in the completion of the first draft of the Environmental Fascicule in March 1996. Following the discovery of surviving feather and eggshell samples in 1997 a report was commissioned and added to the existing fascicule. A further hiatus unfortunately occurred on the untimely and sudden death of the site's director, Nicholas Bogdan, in August 2002. Following a meeting of the surviving contributors to the post-excavation of the site in Perth Museum in June 2004, Historic Scotland again declared its support for the project and work resumed on finalising the publication. A decision was taken to merge the nine fascicules originally planned by Nicholas Bogdan into four, thus this fascicule contains the environmental and miscellaneous finds reports (Fascicules 8 and 9 in the old publication scheme).

The first fascicule contains the stratigraphic and building reports and history of the site and the reader is referred to that volume for all information regarding the excavation itself. A further two fascicules containing the reports on the ceramic, metalwork, religious and wooden objects (Fascicule 2) and leather and textiles (Fascicule 3) are currently in progress. As David Bowler has noted in the epilogue to Fascicule 1, had the results of the Perth High Street excavation been published as originally intended in the early 1980s, they would have become a reference point for Scottish urban archaeology. In a curious way they have however always been there in the background, informing all subsequent work in the medieval burghs, and now themselves enlightened by 'the insights gained in more than a generation of work undertaken since' (Epilogue, Fascicule 1). It is with this understanding that the present volume should be read.

The current locations of the surviving environmental material are as follows. The bulk of the animal bone was originally deposited at the National Museum of Scotland (Natural History) by Dr Hodgson, c1980, and is currently located at the NMS Granton site. The dog and cat bones and a sample of the cattle bones are housed in Perth Museum and Art Gallery, George Street, Perth. The fish bones, feathers, bird egg shell fragments, intact eggs, hair samples, flotation residues and a small sample of the mollusc shells are also located at Perth Museum and Art Gallery.

The mammal bone

The late George W I Hodgson, Catherine Smith and Angela Jones

Introduction

The bulk of the mammal bone assemblage was identified by Dr G W I Hodgson and Angela Jones both during the excavation and and immediately after it took place. The first draft of the mammal report was written by Dr G W I Hodgson in 1979–80, with the assistance of Angela Jones. Subsequently, the data tables were compiled from 1980 onwards by Catherine Smith in the light of continuing revisions of the site phasing. Further identifications, text revisions and additions were undertaken from 1995–6 onwards by Catherine Smith, following the death of Dr Hodgson in 1986.

The material described consists of animal remains recovered during the 1975–77 excavations (OS NO 118923) under the direction of Nicholas Q Bogdan. The total assemblage of animal remains from a site is a sample of what is buried. The word sample is used in this context throughout this report. The samples under discussion were hand-excavated from primary deposits. In addition, eight samples, containing only a small number of bones, were retrieved from soil collected primarily in order to investigate for botanical remains. The archaeological features from which the bones were recovered dated mainly from the 12th–14th centuries. The material examined consisted of bone, tooth and antler fragments, although a few pieces of horn were also retrieved. The assemblage which they represent is a large one by Scottish standards and constitutes a useful reference of bone size ranges for domestic animals in a Scottish medieval context.

Methodology

Identification

The washed, labelled material was identified to particular bone and species by direct comparison with modern defleshed specimens (Illus 3). No attempt was made to identify, record or enumerate rib fragments or vertebrae other than the first two cervical (neck) vertebrae. In cases where there was uncertainty as to species the help of experts in other institutions was sought. Acknowledgement is made at the relevant place in the text.

Boessneck's (1964, 1–129) criteria were applied to the sheep and goat remains in order to try to distinguish them. These criteria may be applied only to certain long bones; often with eroded archaeological material it is impossible to make use of them (Illus 4, 5). The collection of comparative material which was used for reference included several of the rarer Scottish breeds

Illus 3 *Skeleton of young female Soay sheep used for comparison with medieval material*

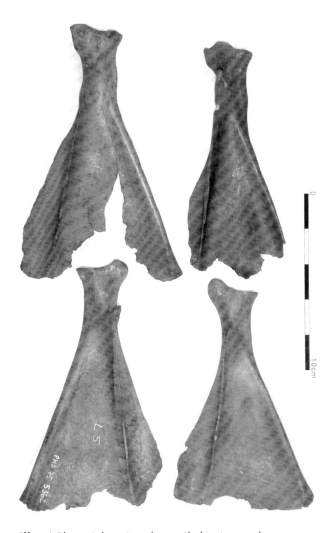

Illus 4 *Sheep (above) and goat (below) scapulae: note differences in morphology of scapula neck.*

of sheep but only a restricted range of domestic and
feral goat bones, perhaps tending to bias identification
of long bones towards sheep and away from goat. Since
most of the sheep and goat bones (with the major
exception of horn cores) could not be distinguished,
the relative abundance of the long bones of these two
species may not be accurately reflected and there may
be a bias towards sheep.

Identification of some canid long bones as fox is
tentative and some could have come from gracile dogs
rather than foxes.

Measurement

Measurements were taken in accordance with the
scheme recommended by von den Driesch (1976)
and are expressed in millimetres.

Nomenclature

Vernacular names are used when referring to domestic
animals (for example cattle, sheep, goat, etc) and, following the policy outlined by Armitage and Clutton-Brock
(1976, 1–2), no attempt is made to relate the animal
remains to distinct breeds found in Scotland at the
present day. Osteological names and terms are those
used by McFadyean (1884), Sissons (1964), Cornwall
(1974) and von den Driesch (1976).

Interpretation of the samples

The bone assemblages are the result of the interaction
of several agencies, as well as human activity, and are,
in consequence, biased samples of some of the animals
with which man interacted. In some cases the bones
originated from living areas, whilst others come from
refuse dumps. Bones from refuse areas (middens and
pits) predominate at this site, therefore the bones from
large animals may be better represented than those
from small animals (see Uerpmann 1973, 308 for
discussion). The refuse deposits seem to be a mixture
of domestic and industrial or commercial rubbish,
therefore it is unwise to use them solely as a guide to
diet (Alcock 1979 pers comm). The middens would be
exposed to depletion by dogs, cats and wild scavengers
such as foxes, rats, crows, ravens and buzzards (see
The bird bone).

The interpretation of the assemblage of bones from
medieval Scottish burghs is complicated by several
factors: the royal burghs and later, all burghs, had
a unique legal status which brought with it a double
commercial monopoly. Firstly, there was a monopoly
on the export of cattle hides, wool and woolfells.
Further, there was a monopoly against the agricultural
hinterland as regards the slaughter and selling of animals.
The nature of the legal status of the burghs, and of the
monopolies which they enjoyed, is explored in detail
later. Sufficient at this stage to note that the remains

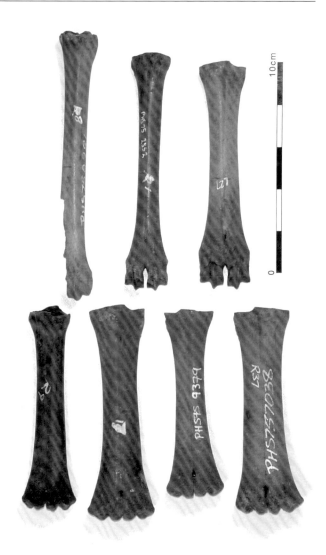

Illus 5 *Sheep (above) and goat (below) metatarsals and
metacarpals.*

of animals found in Scottish medieval burghs are not
necessarily those of animals eaten by the inhabitants.
Within the broad time period to which a sample may
be ascribed, national and burghal prosperity may have
dramatically altered, bringing about marked changes in
the standard of living of the people. These changes may
not be reflected by the sample as a whole. Standards
declined from the relatively prosperous times of the
12th century due to wars between Scotland and England. Perth was occupied by the English from 1296
to 1313 and used as a garrison town. Later, it was controlled by the adherents of Edward Balliol from 1332
and was only retaken for the Scots in 1339 (Bogdan
and Wordsworth 1978, 7).

In the 12th century Scottish burghs, the nobility and
artisans often lived 'cheek by jowl', thereby producing a
mixture of domestic refuse from rich and poor families.
Two unpaired gilt spurs from the site are described
as being of a type that would have been worn or earned
by a knight (Illus 6, 7, 8) (see Fascicule 2, The metalwork). Fragments of silk textiles attributed to the 12th–
13th centuries are associated with wealthy rather than
artisan households (see Fascicule 3, The textiles).

Illus 6 *Gilded copper alloy spur with animal head decoration, Context 5014, A11316.*

Illus 7 *Detail of underside of decorated spur.*

Both of these finds were found in close proximity to hundreds of cattle horn cores which are presumed to be commercial waste.

Behind the frontages of the burghal tofts there were often local industries, leading to a mixture of domestic and commercial waste. Finally, we have insufficient documentary evidence of the rules or customs concerned with the clearance of middens in Perth in the 12th–14th centuries.

Illus 8 *Copper alloy prick spur, Context 7299, A04–0551.*

Species present

The hand-excavated mammal remains represent the following species; cattle, goat, sheep, pig, horse, dog, cat, red deer (*Cervus elaphus*), roe deer (*Capreolus capreolus*), fox (*Vulpes vulpes*) and hare (*Lepus capensis*). In addition, three bones of small mammal were retrieved from the soil samples.

The mammalian remains are, for the most part, from domestic animals, which along with birds, fish, shellfish and crustaceans may well have been used as food. Dogs and cats may have been kept as working animals, for example as hunters, ratters, mousers, guards or to herd animals, as well as pets. Some of them may have lived as semi-wild (feral) animals loosely associated with the community and surviving mainly as scavengers. Olsen (1979 pers comm) has drawn attention to the fact that medieval towns had high ratios of dogs to men; thus a large dog population in a town would contribute towards the removal of individual bones of large animals as well as complete carcasses of small mammals from medieval middens, causing a bias both in the particular species reported and the relative frequencies of species to one another.

Relative frequency of species

Tables 1–11 show the numbers of bones identified as
to bone and particular species. (These tables exclude
twenty pieces of cattle horn sheath and an almost entire
foetal lamb). From these data the minimum number
of animals for each species present may be estimated,
thus allowing the relative frequency of the species to
be established. This information may lead to a better
understanding of the availability of certain meats and
of the dietary habits and preferences of the people.
Many workers have argued against the use of 'minimum
numbers of animals present' on the grounds that it may
be misleading, but on a large site it does give an indication of the proportion of animals represented. This site
seems to yield evidence of animals being slaughtered and
butchered at or near to it. Parts of these carcasses would,
presumably, be moved to other parts of the burgh, and,
if they turned up in subsequent excavations, the use of
'minimum numbers' could lead to an overestimate of
the total number of animals involved. The minimum
numbers of animals present are shown in Table 12.

Since those minimum numbers which were estimated
on the basis of the number of horn cores present may
have been inflated by the presence of horn cores imported
on to the site, these figures were re-estimated using long
bones only. These new minimum numbers are shown
in Table 13, along with estimates for samples of animal
bones recovered from other medieval sites in the burghs
of Aberdeen, Elgin and Perth (Hodgson and Jones 1979,
1982a, 1982b) where the relevant data were available.

On the basis of minimum numbers of animals, the
relative frequencies of cattle with respect to sheep which
were present contrast with those at St Ann's Lane, Perth,
and at Elgin High Street, and in six of the main deposits
from the medieval levels at High Street, Edinburgh reported on by Chaplin and Barnetson (1978, 234), where
goats were largely absent and sheep outnumbered cattle.
The higher numbers of cattle with respect to sheep at
Perth High Street may be due to commercial activity
in connection with the export of hides.

Alcock (1979 pers comm) doubts the validity of
such comparisons, on the grounds that like is not being
compared with like, that is, if for a given species the
same bone is not used to estimate minimum numbers
at each site. King (1978, 208) sought to demonstrate
that inter-site comparisons of frequencies of species,
based on several criteria, are still valid. To test the
point, the minimum numbers of animals present have
been estimated on the basis of selecting for each species
a bone which is common to all of the sites chosen.
These estimates are shown in Table 14. Alcock's
criticism seems to be sustained because the cattle:pig
ratios in Table 13 are, with one exception, much lower
than those in Table 14. On the basis of comparing the
same bone for a given species, the three sites within the
burgh of Perth have significantly higher cattle:pig ratios
than any of the sites in the other two burghs. This may
well reflect Perth's importance as a centre for the export
of hides.

Alternatives to the 'minimum number of animals
present' method of investigation are either to compare
the total number of bones present for each species or to
compare their weights. The weighing method was not
adopted because the bones from part of the site appear
to have been eroded in the soil while those from other
areas of the site are unaffected and weigh more heavily
in consequence. Comparisons of the percentages which
each species contributes to the total number of bones
recovered from a given site are not necessarily exact
because it is difficult to identify rib and vertebra
fragments as to species. Comparison between sites is
also made difficult because of lack of general agreement
on which species to include and whether loose teeth and
butchers' chips (small unidentified fragments) should
be counted. Some workers report only upon a sample
of the bones recovered from a site, thus adding to the
difficulties.

In spite of such problems, inter-site comparisons
have been made (for example Proudfoot 1961, 109–
15; Hodgson 1968, 135–9; Noddle 1975a, 250–260,
Hodgson 1980, 3–32) and these have shed some light
on preferences for certain meats and the availability
of certain species. For example, at seven out of eight
medieval sites in England and Wales located south of
the Wash but outside of London, Noddle (1975a, 251)
found cattle bones to be most numerous while sheep
were the second most numerous at four of these sites.
Armitage (1982) in reporting on five medieval sites
within the City of London, states that 'the meat in the
diet is mostly cattle and sheep'. Some northern English
medieval sites at Pontefract and Wharram Percy (Ryder
1961) and Tynemouth (Hodgson 1967) have however
produced evidence of sheep bones being more numerous
than those of cattle.

Noddle (1975a, 258) has extended inter-site
comparisons to include ten European medieval sites;
at two of them pig bones are the most numerous while
sheep and goat remains are in the majority at only a
single site. The scarcity of pig bones relative to those
of sheep/goat and cattle at British medieval sites is
striking. Noddle (ibid, 250) has sought to relate this
to the relative decline in woodland in which pigs were
kept but it is as likely that many of the medieval sites
excavated and reported on do not reflect the eating
pattern of the labouring people in rural areas. Often,
urban sites are those in which the inhabitants were
fairly wealthy or where the by-products of cattle,
sheep and goat would be fashioned and marketed and
therefore more liable to occur. In addition, Clutton-
Brock (1979, pers comm) has pointed out that the
numbers of pig bones give no indication of the quantity
of bacon and boned salt pork eaten.

It may be that because of the unique commercial
status of the Scottish burghs in relation to the marketing
of meat and export of hides, skins, wool and wool-fells
that a comparison of relative frequencies of animals
present for Scottish and English and European sites is
not justified. In a purely Scottish context, however an
inter-site comparison is useful.

Table 1 *Number of cattle bones identified.*

| | | number of fragments | | | |
		left	right	left/right	total
horn core		508	561	684	1753
skull				6	6
maxilla		236	222	80	538
mandible		270	234	270	774
atlas				140	140
axis				192	192
scapula		148	125	226	499
humerus	proximal	24	20	13	57
	distal	149	144	14	307
	shaft			20	20
	entire		1		1
radius	proximal	108	90	11	209
	distal	122	123		245
	shaft			26	26
	entire	1	2		3
ulna		107	105	1	213
metacarpal	proximal	126	150	22	298
	distal	263	193	40	496
	shaft			3	3
	entire	29	31		60
innominate		140	136	197	473
femur	proximal	64	54		118
	distal	72	72	27	171
	shaft			141	141
	entire	1	2		3
patella		18	13		31
tibia	proximal	83	79	16	178
	distal	151	168	31	350
	entire	1			1
astragalus		169	166		335
calcaneum		214	184		398
tarsal/carpal				335	335
metatarsal	proximal	118	140	5	263
	distal	242	212	54	508
	shaft			1	1
	entire	32	41		73
metapodial				107	107
1st phalange				1655	1655
2nd phalange				793	793
3rd phalange				798	798
total		3396	3268	5908	12572

note Tables 1–10 include all bones of medieval date, whether provenanced or unprovenanced

Table 2 *Number of sheep/goat bones identified.*

		number of fragments			
		left	right	left/right	total
horn core		30	26		56
skull				106	106
maxilla		146	149	3	298
mandible		371	376	24	771
atlas				70	70
axis				59	59
scapula		142	167	34	343
humerus	proximal	22	10		32
	distal	112	121		233
	shaft			7	7
	entire	1	1		2
radius	proximal	85	89		174
	distal	46	29		75
	shaft			25	25
	entire	15	16		31
ulna		32	45		77
metacarpal	proximal	119	130		249
	distal	11	5	22	38
	shaft			14	14
	entire	41	40		81
innominate		107	80	50	237
femur	proximal	24	17		41
	distal	54	48		102
	shaft			7	7
	entire	2	3		5
tibia	proximal	28	46		74
	distal	195	170	17	382
	shaft			37	37
	entire	2	1		3
astragalus		17	24		41
calcaneum		21	27		48
tarsal/carpal				12	12
metatarsal	proximal	107	125		232
	distal	11	12	28	51
	entire	41	49		90
metapodial		31	35	98	164
1st phalange				111	111
2nd phalange				9	9
3rd phalange				3	3
total		1813	1841	736	4390

note excludes skeleton of 1 foetal lamb

Table 3 *Number of goat bones identified.*

| | | number of fragments | | | |
		left	right	left/right	total
horn core		352	354	16	722
skull				7	7
axis				4	4
scapula		19	20		39
humerus	proximal	2	3		5
	distal	7	14		21
radius	proximal	10	4		14
	distal	2	4		6
metacarpal	entire	12	10		22
innominate		40	50		90
femur	proximal		1		1
	distal	1			1
tibia	proximal	6	2		8
astragalus		5	8		13
calcaneum		2	1		3
metatarsal	entire	1	1		2
metapodial				18	18
total		459	472	45	976

Table 4 *Number of pig bones identified.*

| | | number of fragments | | | |
		left	right	left/right	total
skull				14	14
maxilla		69	73	3	145
mandible		106	117	2	225
atlas				13	13
axis				10	10
scapula		38	37	2	77
humerus	proximal	1			1
	distal	66	61		127
	entire	1	1		2
radius	proximal	67	60		127
	distal	8	1	5	14
	entire	23	19		42
ulna		50	78		128
innominate		26	23	38	87
femur	proximal	9	16		25
	distal	4	17		21
	entire	4	2		6
tibia	proximal	7	6		13
	distal	45	63	2	110
	entire	28	41		69
fibula				29	29
astragalus		8	19		27
calcaneum		24	34		58
metapodial				218	218
1st phalange				35	35
2nd phalange				11	11
3rd phalange				2	2
total		584	668	384	1636

Table 5 *Number of horse bones identified.*

| | | number of fragments | | | |
		left	right	left/right	total
skull				1	1
maxilla		1			1
mandible		2	4		6
atlas				1	1
axis				4	4
scapula		2	6		8
humerus	proximal	8	3		11
	distal	2	9		11
	entire	2	2		4
radius	proximal	2	2		4
	distal	1	9		10
	entire	3	7		10
ulna		1			1
metacarpal	proximal	2	1		3
	entire	8	3		11
innominate			2		2
femur	distal	3			3
	entire		1		1
tibia	proximal		5		5
	distal	7	5		12
	entire	1	3		4
astragalus		3	6		9
calcaneum		2	3		5
metatarsal	proximal	1	2		3
	entire	6	4		10
splint				19	19
1st phalange				19	19
2nd phalange				15	15
3rd phalange				7	7
total		57	77	66	200

Table 6 *Number of red and roe deer bones identified.*

| | | number of fragments | | | |
		left	right	left/right	total
antler tine*				2	2
maxilla			1 roe		1
mandible			1		1
radius	distal	1			1
ulna			1		1
metacarpal	proximal	2			2
	entire	2	1		3
tibia	proximal	1	4		5
metatarsal	proximal	1	1		2
	distal	1			1
	entire		5		5
2nd phalange				1	1
total		8	14	3	25

note: unless stated otherwise, all bones are from red deer
*antler tines and offcuts listed in the worked bone catalogue are not included in this table

Table 7 *Number of dog bones identified.*

		left	right	left/right	total
				number of fragments	
skull				10	10
maxilla		7	5		12
mandible		12	8		20
atlas				3	3
axis				2	2
scapula		10	7		17
humerus	proximal		3		3
	distal	5	1		6
	entire	12	8		20
radius	proximal	1			1
	distal	1			1
	entire	6	4		10
ulna		2	3		5
metacarpal	i			2	2
	ii	1	3		4
	iii	3	3		6
	iv	3	2		5
	v	2	2		4
innominate		8	5		13
femur	proximal		1		1
	dist		1		1
	entire	6	11		17
tibia	proximal	2	1		3
	distal	4	1		5
	entire	11	6		17
fibula				2	2
astragalus			1		1
calcaneum				1	1
tarsal/carpal				1	1
metatarsal	ii	1			1
	iii			3	3
	iv	3	4		7
	v	3			3
1st phalange				5	5
2nd phalange				5	5
os penis				1	1
total		103	80	35	218

Table 8 *Number of cat bones identified.*

		number of fragments			
		left	right	left/right	total
skull				17	17
maxilla		3	2		5
mandible		16	13		29
atlas				6	6
axis				5	5
scapula		10	14		24
humerus	proximal	1			1
	distal	10	4		14
	shaft				
	entire	12	19		31
radius	entire	9	8		17
ulna		9	18		27
innominate		24	22		46
femur	proximal		4		4
	distal		1		1
	entire	29	27		56
tibia	proximal	2			2
	distal	6	1		7
	entire	23	24		47
fibula				5	5
astragalus		2	2		4
calcaneum		1	2		3
tarsal/carpal				12	12
metatarsal	entire			21	21
1st phalange				14	14
2nd phalange				13	13
3rd phalange				2	2
total		157	161	95	413

Table 9 *Number of dog/fox bones identified.*

		number of fragments			
		left	right	left/right	total
atlas				1	1
axis				1	1
scapula		2	1		3
humerus	entire	2	1		3
radius	entire	4	4		8
ulna		2	2		4
femur	entire	3	4		7
tibia	proximal	3			3
	distal	1			1
	entire	13	4		17
metapodial				3	3
1st/2nd phalange				5	5
total		30	16	10	56

Table 10 *Number of hare bones identified.*

| | | number of fragments | | | |
		left	right	left/right	total
maxilla		1	1		2
mandible			2		2
axis				1	1
scapula		1	2		3
humerus	distal	2			2
	entire		1		1
	distal	2			2
	entire	2	1		3
ulna		1			1
innominate		6	2		8
femur	entire	1			1
tibia	proximal	3			3
	entire	1			1
metatarsal				2	2
total		20	9	3	32

Table 11 *Total number of mammal bones identified.*

species	number of fragments
cattle	12,572
sheep/goat	4390
goat	976
pig	1636
horse	200
red deer*	25
roe deer	1
dog	218
cat	413
dog/fox	56
hare	32
small mammal	9
total	20,528

Table 12 *Minimum numbers of animals present, based on most frequently occurring bones.*

species	minimum number (MNI)	based on:
cattle	561	right horn core
	292	left distal and entire metacarpal
sheep/goat	197	left distal and entire tibia
goat	354	right horn core
	20	right scapula
pig	117	right mandible
horse	16	right distal and entire radius
red deer	5	right entire metatarsal
roe deer	1	right maxilla
dog	17	left entire and distal humerus
cat	31	right proximal and entire femur
dog/fox	16	left proximal and entire tibia
hare	6	left innominate

Table 13 *Minimum numbers of animals from selected sites in Scottish medieval burghs, estimated on the basis of the most numerous long bones (ie excluding horn cores and mandibles).*

	minimum numbers (MNI)					
site	cattle	sheep/goat	goat	pig	horse	red deer
Perth						
PHSAE	292	197	20	117	16	5
Canal Street I (Phase III)	5	3	1	1	1	
St Ann's Lane	17	21		9	1	
Meal Vennel (Phases 1-3)	15	8	6	4	1	1
Aberdeen						
Queen Street	16	9	6	12	1	1
42 St Paul Street	29	13	16	7	3	2
45-47 Gallowgate (Phases I-II)	7	6	1	2	1	1
53-59 Gallowgate (Phases I-III)	14	9	4	7	2	1
Gallowgate Middle School (Phase 2)	8	6	2	3	1	2
Elgin						
High Street	6	8	1	6	2	1

Table 14 *Minimum numbers of main meat producing mammals from selected Scottish medieval burghs, estimated on the basis of bones common to all of the sites.*

site	cattle (L distal metacarpal)	sheep/goat (L distal tibia)	pig (R distal humerus)
Perth			
PHSAE	292	197	62
Canal Street I (Phase III)	5	1	1
St Ann's Lane	13	4	2
Aberdeen			
Queen Street	8	4	6
42 St Paul Street	6	6	4
Elgin			
High Street	2	3	1

A comparison of the relative frequency of the main food forming animals based on the totals of bones identified for each species (excluding vertebrae other than the two neck vertebrae, ribs and loose teeth) is shown in Table 15.

These data indicate high rates of consumption of beef and mutton and low rates of consumption of pork and venison at all of the sites reviewed. It is interesting to compare fragment count data from this site with that from a site on the south side of Perth High Street, at 80–86 High Street (Smith 1997). Here, cattle numbers were strikingly lower when compared with the numbers of sheep/goats; indicating a possibility that there was a genuine preference for mutton on this site. However, this apparent contrast could be reflecting fluctuations in the hide and woolfell trade, since it is known from documentary sources that the level of trade did not remain constant throughout the medieval period (Lynch 1988, 269).

Size of animals

A summary of the size ranges of bones listed by species is included on the CD insert accompanying this volume.

Several authors have sought to compare the bone size ranges of selected bones of cattle and sheep from archaeological sites in an attempt to detect the possible effects of domestication, selective breeding and selective culling (Jewell 1962, 80–90; Hodgson 1968, 145–156). The parts of the bones for which size ranges have been compared are usually those which are well preserved, occur in relatively large numbers and which offer good measuring points. Such bones were often selected on these common-sense criteria and are those whose measurements yield data in which variance values are low. The difficulties inherent in comparing the relative frequencies of animals present at different sites have been discussed earlier. These same difficulties plus the fact that there is no overall agreement on which measurements to publish makes comparison of bone size ranges between sites difficult. In a Scottish context it is interesting to note that most of the measurements of animals from sites in Elgin (Hodgson and Jones, 1979), Edinburgh (Chaplin and Barnetson 1978), Inverness (Hodgson and Smith 1982), Inverkeithing (Hodgson and Smith 1983) and Aberdeen (Hodgson and Jones 1982b; Smith and Hodgson 1984; Smith and McCormick, 2001) fall within the size ranges of the Perth High Street material. For example, only six measurements of cattle bones and four of sheep from Elgin and Edinburgh extend the size ranges for Perth and these by only trivial amounts. Similarly, the vast majority of measurements taken from the medieval material from other sites excavated within the burgh of Perth, at St Ann's Lane (Hodgson and Jones 1982a), Kirk Close, South Methven Street, Canal Street II (Smith and Hodgson 1987, 199) 80–86 High Street, Meal Vennel, King Edward Street and Mill Street (Smith, 1997, Smith, 1996a; Smith, 1995a) also fall within the range of the large Perth High Street sample.

In a British context a comparison of the lengths and widths of cattle metacarpal and radii and of the lengths and widths of sheep metapodials (cannon bones) for the medieval levels at Perth, Southampton (Noddle 1975b, 339), Walton, Aylesbury (Noddle 1976, 278–282), King's Lynn (Noddle 1977, 386–396) and Baynard's Castle (Armitage 1978, pers comm) shows that at Perth there were cattle with leg bones which were narrower and shorter and sheep with leg bones which were narrower than any reported from the other sites. The lengths of sheep metapodials at Perth significantly extend the length ranges published for medieval sheep.

Some authors have preferred to compare the estimated heights of cattle at the withers rather than the actual bone sizes (Fock 1966, 73; Armitage 1978, 52). The latter suggests that multiplying the metacarpal length by a factor of 6.13 gives the most reliable estimate of withers height for oxen. Assuming that most of the non-juvenile metacarpals from this site came from castrates (see discussion of sex and characteristics of meat producing mammals, below), the range of withers heights is 95.6cm–113.4cm. This compares with a range of 104.3cm–151.1cm for oxen at Baynard's Castle, London and 106.8cm–112.7cm for a collection of Northumbrian Chillingham bulls. Sheep withers heights calculated using Teichert's (1975) factors ranged from 46.76cm–65.83cm.

Thus, at Perth we have evidence of cattle which were shorter in stature and more gracile than their English counterparts and of sheep which were much more 'spindly legged'. On the same basis of comparison the data for cattle and sheep from medieval Lund in modern-day Sweden (Bergquist and Lepiksaar 1957, 30–45) fall within the size ranges for Perth except that some of the cattle and sheep metacarpals and some of the sheep metatarsals from Lund are longer.

It is difficult to compare the bone size of pigs from different sites because pig bones are seldom found intact due to a number of factors including butchery and the culling of a high proportion of individuals while still osteologically immature. Few data relating to the size of mature pig bones are available from medieval sites. The size of pig metapodials is reported on from Baynard's Castle (Armitage 1978, pers comm) and Walton, Aylesbury (Noddle 1976, 282–3). The lower length limits for these bones are extended considerably by the Perth material. This suggests the presence in medieval Scotland of smaller, lighter boned pigs than those found in England.

Withers heights of pigs may be calculated from the length of the astragalus, after the method of Teichert (1969, quoted in von den Driesch and Boessneck, 1974). Thus withers heights at the site covered the range of 55.5cm to 82.3cm, based on a total of 24 astragali (Smith, 2000a). The maximum height estimation is only exceeded in Scottish animals by a withers height of 88.6cm obtained from a medieval pig astragalus from medieval Phase 14 at Castle Park, Dunbar (ibid).

Penny, presumably referring to the post-medieval period, refers to large droves of small Highland swine

Table 15 *Percentages of food forming mammals from medieval sites in Perth, Elgin and Aberdeen, based on fragment count.*

site	cattle	sheep/goat	goat	pig	horse	red/roe deer
Perth						
High Street (PHSAE)	63.5	22.2	4.9	8.3	1.0	0.1
80–86 High Street[1]	51.8	37.1	*	10.6	0.1	0.4
St Ann's Lane[2]	57.6	32.8	*	8.9	0.4	0.2
South Methven Street[3]	81.5	17.3	*	1.2		
Kirk Close[3]	76.1	18.7	*	4.8	0.2	0.1
Mill Street[4]	62.7	26.3	4.1	3.8	3.0	0.2
King Edward Street[4]	62.6	23.3	2.8	10.5	0.5	0.3
Kinnoull Street[4]	63.1	29.3	*	7.6		
Blackfriars House[4]	67.1	21.4	*	11.4		
Scott Street[5]	66.7	27.8	0.2	3.0	2.1	0.2
Canal Street I[6]	58.2	32.1	0.1	5.8	3.6	
Canal Street II[3]	67.7	27.1	*	3.4	1.8	
Canal Street III, Phases 1–5[7]	66.0	28.1	*	4.5	1.3	0.1
Meal Vennel, Phases 1–5[5]	69.7	20.6	2.0	6.4	1.0	0.3
Elgin						
High Street[8]	56.0	22.3	10.3	7.2	3.5	0.7
Aberdeen						
Queen Street[9]	58.1	24.9	1.8	13.8	0.2	1.2
42 St Paul Street[9]	69.1	17.2	2.2	8.4	1.6	1.5
45–75 Gallowgate[10]	63.0	27.6	1.0	7.1	0.8	0.6
45–47 Gallowgate[11]	61.3	25.6	0.9	10.2	0.7	1.4
Gallowgate Middle School, Phase 2[10]	54.9	32.1	4.5	7.6	0.2	0.7
16-18 Netherkirkgate Phases 1–4[10]	58.0	29.2	0.3	10.9	0.3	1.2
Rattray Castle[12]	49.9	34.2	*	11.1	1.9	2.9

notes   * indicates that sheep and goat are expressed as one figure

                 antler fragments which are cast or not seen to be attached to skulls are omitted

sources   1 Smith 1997 2 Hodgson and Jones 1982a 3 Smith and Hodgson 1987

                 4 Smith1995a   5 Smith 1996a   6 Hodgson & Jones 1984 7 Smith 1996b 8 Hodgson and Jones 1979 9 Hodgson and Jones 1982b 10 Smith and McCormick 2001 11 Smith and Hodgson 1984 12 McCormick nd

being driven to the Andersmass Fair (held on the feast day of St Andrew) at Perth and remarks that 'this small kind have entirely disappeared' (1836, 137) (Illus 9). This type of pig, shown in contemporary illustrations as a small, bristly backed, hairy animal with a long snout and curly tail, probably lingered on in some parts of the Northern Isles of Scotland until the early part of the 20th century, but is now entirely extinct (Smith, 2000a).

The horse remains from Perth range in size from those which compare almost exactly with bones from a modern Northumbrian pit pony to bones which approach the size of a modern small horse. Horses from other urban medieval sites in Scotland have been shown to have stood somewhat under 14:2 hands height and are thus classed as ponies in modern terms; for example, two animals from 80–86 High Street, Perth, one from Whitefriars, Perth and another from Castle Street, Inverness, showed very little variation in size, standing between approximately 13:1 and 13:2 hands height (Smith 1998).

According to John Major (*History*, 39) in his 16th-century History of Greater Britain, hundreds of unbroken horses were brought to Saint Johns (Perth) to be sold. He says of them 'they are of no great size, and are thus not fitted to carry a man in heavy armour to the wars, but a light-armed man may ride them at any speed where he will. More hardy horses of so small a size you shall no where find'. It seems that although small in stature the Perth horses were indeed ridden, as indicated by two unpaired spurs found on the site and thought to have belonged to a wealthy owner, perhaps a knight (Illus 6–8).

The horses from Perth may have been similar to the sturdy garrons of the Highlands, renowned for their activity and stamina (Grant 1961, 86). The ideal height for the garron was (and still is) considered to be about 14:1 hands high, and shortness of the cannon bone (metapodial) is a preferred feature (Fraser 1980, 85; 45). The medieval ponies of Scotland seem to have been very similar to this type.

Ten skulls of adult dogs were recovered; of these, nine were almost as long and wide as those of a modern adult fox-hound. The same skulls were also long and narrow in the muzzle. One dog skull was noticeably smaller than the others, had a rounded dome and lacked a sagittal crest; the specimen had its upper molars fully developed and was thus not a juvenile. This skull may represent a pet or lap dog (Illus 10, lower images). Thus there are apparently at least two different types of dog present. Clutton-Brock (1977, pers comm) and Harcourt (1974, 172–173) have cautioned against trying to relate the remains of animals from historic sites to distinct modern breeds. It was possible, however, to estimate shoulder heights for some of the intact long bones, using Harcourt's (1974) factors. Based on the humerus, there would appear to have been dogs at Perth High Street which ranged in height from approximately

Illus 9 *Conjectured appearance of the Scots sow, the unimproved pig prevalent in Scotland from the Iron Age to the Early Modern period. (Drawing by Maureen Rooney Mitchell)*

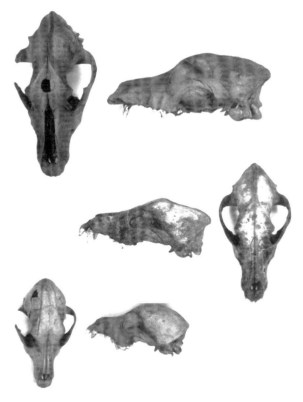

Illus 10 *Three dog skulls from PHSAE: frontal and lateral views.*

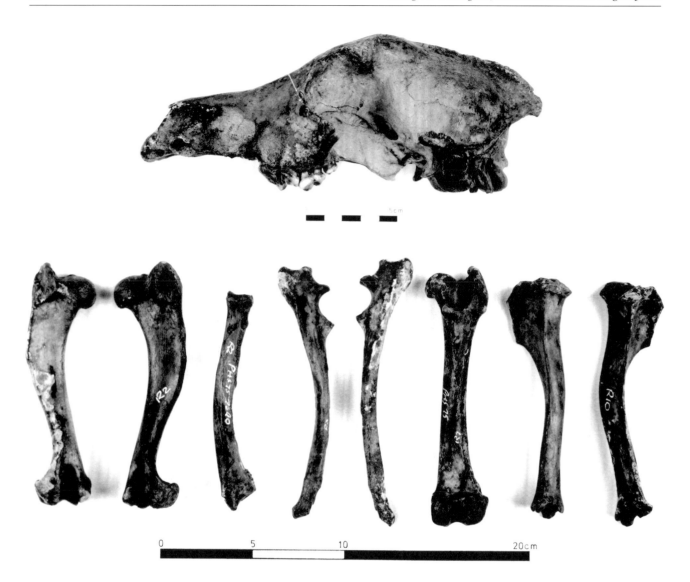

Illus 11 *Skull and long bones of bow-legged dog.*

23cm to 59cm. Dogs found at other medieval sites within the burgh of Perth have mainly been found to fall within these height ranges, as at 80–86 High Street, Perth (Smith, 1998). However one larger animal, with a height of 63.7cm estimated from the humerus, was found in a medieval context at Meal Vennel, although this example may have been unusually large (ibid). A substantially complete dog skeleton found in a cesspit at Mill Street and dating to the post-medieval period was of a very similar size and type to the medieval dogs from the High Street (Smith, 1995a).

Most of the canine bones from Perth High Street have dimensions which are indicative of working dogs (Illus 11) while a few indicate the presence of a smaller type of animal which may have been pets or lap dogs, although they could also have been ratters or even turnspits (Illus 12).

Seventeen cat skulls were found and examined (of which a selection is shown in Illus 13). None of these appears to have come from large wild cats (*Felis silvestris*) but it is impossible to state whether the feline remains came from truly domestic or feral animals.

Cat long bones from the site are typical of those from sites in medieval urban Scotland, being altogether more slender in their mid-shaft dimensions than modern day domestic animals (Illus 14) (Smith 1998, 873).

Red deer bones are few in number (Illus 15), possibly because venison was not legally available to the general public since the hunting and killing of deer was controlled by law. The antler fragments are poorly developed and the metapodials are much shorter and narrower than those reported from Northern sites in Roman times (Hodgson, 1977, 24), although it is important to note that they are still much larger than their modern day counterparts on the hills of Scotland (Illus 16). This diminution in size from the Roman to the medieval period may reflect either a change in nutritional status due to loss of preferred habitat as deafforestation progressed in Scotland, or it may be due to the best carcasses going direct to the aristocracy. Red deer of a similar size to those from this site have been found at the urban medieval sites at King Edward Street, Perth, and at Gallowgate Middle School, Aberdeen (Smith, 1995a; Smith and McCormick 2001).

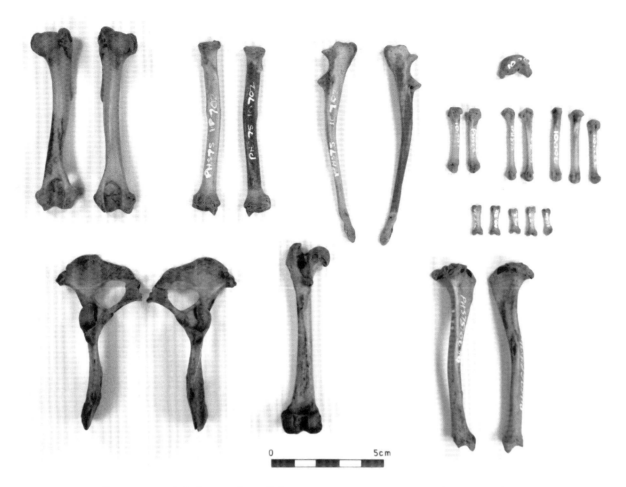

Illus 12 *Partial skeleton of small dog, Context 5019, A10702 and A10696, Phase IIa.*

Illus 13 *Cat skulls from Perth High Street.*

Illus 14 *Cat tibiae from Perth High Street.*

Illus 16 *Modern red deer stag (Camperdown Country Park, Dundee).*

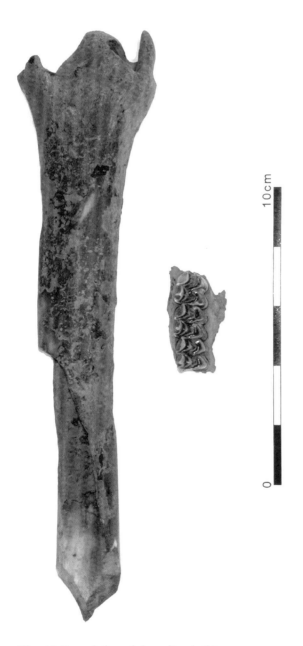

Illus 15 *From left: red deer distal tibia and roe deer maxilla.*

Sex and characteristics of meat producing animals

Cattle

Statistical methods of distinguishing the sexual status of cattle from their metapodials (Howard 1963, 91–4; Mennerich 1968, 132–156) seem to be of doubtful general value; the results derived from Scottish medieval material were inconclusive (see Hodgson 1980, 30–32).

Attempts to discern discrete groups which may be attributed to sexual status, by plotting the scatter of selected measurements derived from cattle horn cores, were also inconclusive (ibid). The scheme for identifying the sex of cattle by classifying adult horn cores, proposed by Armitage and Clutton-Brock (1976, 332), was more useful. On this basis, most of the horn cores from the site appear to have come from oxen or cows (Illus 17, 18). About 4% were attributable to bulls. On the evidence of a grant of grazing by Helen de Morville to the Cistercian monks of Melrose Abbey in the reign of William the Lion (1165–1214), the medieval stocking ratio of bulls to fertile cows was maintained at 1:40 (Barrow 1979, pers comm; *Melrose Liber*, no 82).

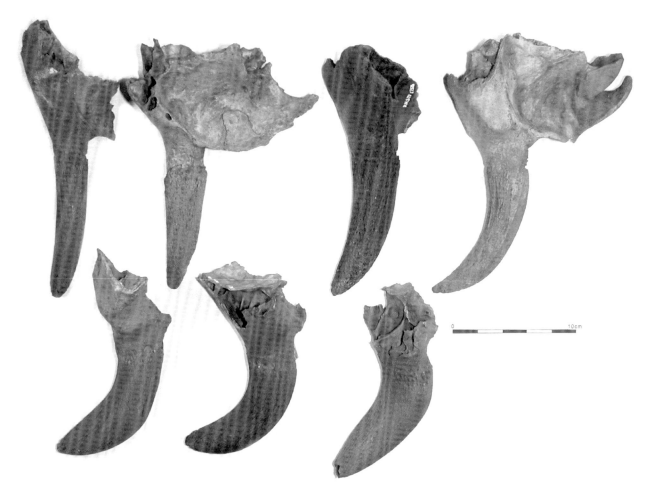

Illus 17 *Cattle left horn cores, showing variations in outer curvature.*

Illus 18 *Cattle right horn cores, showing variations in outer curvature.*

		A	B	C	D	E	F	G	H	I
%	DEATHS	2.2	6.9	14.6	29.2	20.7	16.9	6.4	3.0	0.1
%	SURVIVORS	97.8	90.9	76.3	47.1	26.4	9.5	3.1	0.1	0

n = 638

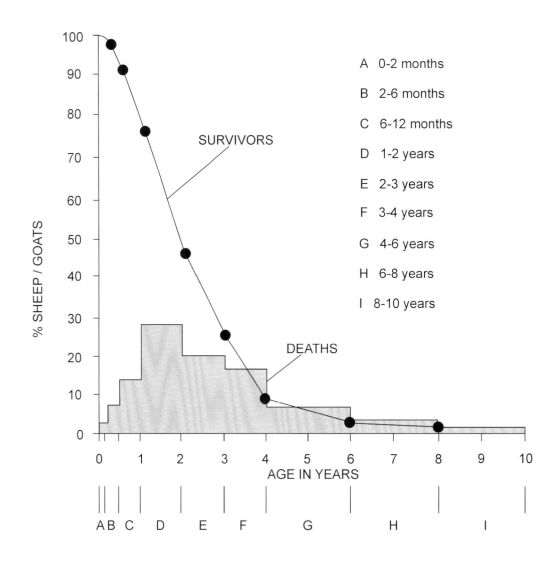

A 0-2 months

B 2-6 months

C 6-12 months

D 1-2 years

E 2-3 years

F 3-4 years

G 4-6 years

H 6-8 years

I 8-10 years

Illus 19 *Culling pattern of sheep/goats at Perth High Street (1975–77) medieval layers. (After Payne [1973])*

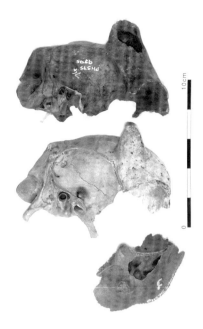

Illus 20 *Three sheep skulls showing some horn core variations, with scur type below.*

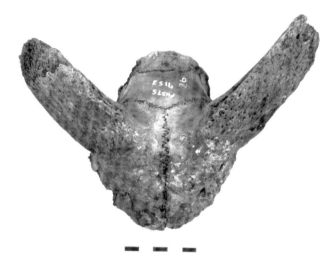

Illus 21 *Sheep skull with robust horn cores.*

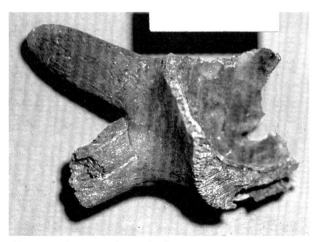

Illus 22 *Polycerate sheep skull.*

Illus 23 *Jacob sheep.*

Sheep

The sex of the sheep can be inferred from a culling curve (Illus 19) derived from a study of sheep/goat mandibles. The curve for Perth High Street is interpreted as evidence of sheep being raised to produce meat and woolfells. This implies that male lambs were reared as castrates or wedders to an age well beyond the lamb stage, until they reached the optimum for meat and woolfell production. Helen de Morville's grant of pasture to the monks of Melrose Abbey makes it clear that large flocks of wedders (castrated males) were raised well into maturity, that is, until the age of three to four years (Barrow 1979, pers comm). It seems that in medieval Scotland, male sheep were castrated, despite the assertion to the contrary of John Major in 1521 (*History*, 38).

The sheep from the site were small, spindly-legged animals, probably of a variety of breeds. Their horn cores ranged in size from mere swellings (scurs) to large robust structures (Illus 20, 21). Dr M L Ryder (pers comm) has remarked on the close resemblance of one skull to that of a modern 18 month old Shetland ram.

One specimen was a four-horned (polycerate) type (Illus 22), while all the others were either polled or two-horned. The four-horned varieties of sheep are geographically associated with the Western seaboard of Scotland (Ryder 1978, pers comm) and are represented by the Jacob (Illus 23) and St Kilda breeds today. The archaic breed of Highland sheep referred to by Grant (1961, 78) appears to have been four-horned in the 16th century. In an archaeological context, polycerate sheep have been reported at Roman sites on Hadrian's Wall (Hodgson 1977, 22). They have also been found in small numbers at medieval Scottish sites, in Edinburgh, at 16–18 Netherkirkgate, Aberdeen and Rattray Castle (Chaplin and Barnetson 1978; Smith and McCormick, 2001; Hamilton-Dyer et al 1993, 204.

Illus 24 *Goat horn cores showing variations in size related to sexual dimorphism.*

Goats

Two distinct types of goat horn cores have been recovered from the site (Illus 24). One group consists of
specimens which are massive in size, being both long
and having a large basal circumference, while the other
group is composed of specimens which are long but
smaller in basal circumference. It is assumed that the
former group represent males and castrates, while the
latter group represent females (Illus 25). Both types of
horn core are curved and untwisted; the bone is well
formed as if the animals had been well fed.

John Woolliams of the Animal Breeding Research
Organisation, Roslin, Midlothian, has established that
the differences between the two groups of goat horn
cores are statistically very significant. His colleague,
Dr M L Ryder, interprets these differences as being
due to difference in sex rather than of breed. Noddle
(1977, 397), using a different statistical treatment, has
demonstrated the presence of three groups of goat horn
cores from medieval material at King's Lynn, which she
attributes to females, male castrates and entire males.

Horses

Too few horse bones were recovered to allow for an
analysis of metrical data derived from them in regards
to the sex of the animals. Their small size has been
remarked upon. According to John Major (*History*,
39), it was the practice in 16th-century Scotland to geld
most male animals and there seems no reason to doubt
this. The Gaelic-derived name for the hardy Highland
ponies, 'garron', correctly describes a gelding, and

Illus 25 *Female goat skull.*

although the term is applied to all Highland ponies (Fraser 1980, 16), it provides further evidence for the practice of 'cutting' the animals.

Age of animals at death

Yealland and Higgs (1966, 140–142) have demonstrated that a knowledge of the age of death of domestic animals may lead to an understanding of the economy of a site. The killing of younger animals has been taken to indicate a plentiful supply of meat, a preference for younger, more tender meat or an inability or lack of incentive to raise young animals through adverse conditions such as drought in summer or cold in winter, when pasture and fodder might be in short supply. Noddle (1975b, 332) has argued that knowledge of the age of animals on slaughter is of less use in an urban setting than in a rural one. In the latter it tells us something of the standards of animal husbandry while in the former it may only reflect market pressures for meats and by-products. It is argued (see Economy of the burgh, below) that cattle and sheep at Perth High Street were not raised primarily for meat. During the lifetime of the animals, oxen would provide traction; horses, transport; sheep, wool and milk; and goats, milk, while at death they would provide meat and by-products. Some of these by-products may have commanded a greater market price in proportion to a single carcass than did the meat or fat which derived from it. The factors which influenced the age at which animals were slaughtered may have included: ability to husband animals; cost and availability of fodder in relation to financial return for meat and by-products; and fertility of female breeding stock. These factors would not necessarily remain constant but would vary with weather, political change, trade, economic climate and even with fashion.

Data have been published giving the ages at which teeth erupt and at which the articulatory ends of long bones (epiphyses) fuse (Silver 1969; Ewbank et al 1964, 424; Payne 1973, 299; Noddle 1974, 198–200). The ages of tooth eruption and epiphyseal fusion for modern domestic animals are usually younger than those quoted in historical sources. This may be due to the effects of improved animal nutrition and husbandry and the results of animal breeding. For these reasons

the later date ranges quoted by Silver (1969, 285ff) are used. However, a cautionary note may be sounded: because of the variability in timing of epiphyseal fusion between animals of the same biological age, Noddle (1984, 24) has advocated using great care when estimating chronological age by these means, and suggests that if dental and fusion evidence do not agree, the former should be given greater credence.

Cattle: evidence from tooth eruption

Cattle lower jaws (strictly speaking, half mandibles) were examined for the presence of deciduous molars and for the state of wear of the third permanent molar. According to Silver (1969, 296), the presence of the third deciduous molar (dm_3), and the first molar (M_1) being visible in the crypt of the jaw but not yet in wear, would indicate that the animal was less than nine months old. Silver (ibid), quoting a 19th-century source, suggests that the third permanent molar erupted between four and five years. Grigson (1974, 358) assumes that if the third accessory pillar (fifth cusp) of this tooth is in wear, the animal is about five years of age. The percentages of cattle in age groups based on these observations are shown in Table 16. These data show little evidence of the slaughter of calves for veal or calfskin production. Evidence from other sites within the burgh of Perth (for example Meal Vennel, Scott Street, Mill Street and King Edward Street) agrees well with the findings from the High Street, in that the great majority of the cattle were adult or immature/adult animals while calves were only rarely found.

Armitage (1978, 57) reports much higher percentages of juveniles from two sites at medieval Baynard's Castle, London. There, between 40–46% were juveniles and between 54–60% were adults. He argues that in medieval England there was no real incentive to rear fat cattle for food markets and that draught oxen were simply culled. In medieval Scotland the Crown and the merchant burgesses derived an income from the export of cattle hides. The animals concerned could only be slaughtered under strict burgh rules, thus we may be dealing with the remains of animals which were raised until the age of four to satisfy the needs of that export trade, rather than animals which were cropped at an optimum age or weight for their meat.

Table 16 *Percentage of cattle assigned to age group on the basis of dental evidence.*

	<9 months	9 months–4 years	4–5 years	>5 years	Total
n	14	26	26	150	216
%	6.5	12.0	12.0	69.4	99.9

note only 216 of the 774 cattle mandibles recorded were complete enough to be assessed

Cattle: epiphyseal fusion evidence

Selected long bones (radius, metacarpal, tibia and metatarsal) were examined to assess their age by determining the degree of fusion of their distal epiphyses (Silver 1969, 285–286). The frequencies of fused epiphyses and estimates of age are shown in Table 17. This evidence indicates that most cattle were successfully overwintered for two or more winters, and that 86% of the cattle survived beyond the age of three and a half years.

Table 17 *Frequencies of selected cattle bones having fused distal epiphyses and estimates of their ages.*

bone	number of distal epiphyses examined	%	age
radius	248	86.3	>3½ years
metacarpal	547	92.5	>2 years
tibia	319	90.0	>2 years
metatarsal	566	90.8	>2¼ years

Sheep and goats: evidence of tooth eruption and wear

Payne (1973) proposed a method of investigating the culling (or kill-off) patterns for sheep up to the age of ten years at slaughter. This technique of mandibular assessment was applied to 638 sheep and goat lower jaws dating to the 12th–14th centuries. Unfortunately, it was not possible to distinguish between sheep and goat mandibles, therefore both species are included in this analysis.

Illus 19 shows the cull pattern for the sheep at the site. It corresponds closely with the cull pattern obtained for a Roman site at Vindolanda in Northumberland (Hodgson 1977, 16) and that proposed for a closed flock of sheep on upland pasture in Britain in the 20th century (T Oliver 1977, pers comm). The results also compare favourably with culling patterns determined for other medieval sites in Perth, at Mill Street and King Edward Street (Smith, 1995a). It seems likely that the killing sequence would be:

i the slaughter of prime lamb and kids (probably tup hogs or uncastrated males) in the first year between weaning and first shearing

ii the killing of shearling tups in the second, third and fourth years along with barren ewes in the third and fourth years

iii the slaughter of breeding ewes and female goats between the fifth and seventh years as progressively they became barren, poor mothers or broken mouthed.

The old sheep (nine to ten years old) would almost certainly have been 'lead wedders', that is, male castrates allowed to live to an advanced age because of their ability to lead the flock to shelter and to herbage. We know little about the husbandry of medieval goats, but it seems likely that most of the males would have been castrated and that the goat equivalent of 'wedders' and 'lead wedders' would have existed.

The Perth High Street killing curve appears to indicate that the animals were being reared primarily for meat and wool-fells rather than for wool or milk. This is unexpected in view of the well established wool trade at Perth. However, data from a rural medieval site in Aberdeenshire, Rattray Castle, (McCormick nd) indicated that the majority (63%) of the sheep were killed between the ages of four to eight years. Rural communities in the hinterlands would appear to have sent their youngest animals to the burgh markets, while keeping the older animals in order to maintain wool production (Smith and McCormick, 2001). Older animals may not have been sent for sale at Perth, although their wool most certainly was.

Pig: evidence of tooth eruption

Silver (1969, 298) has published 18th-century data regarding the eruption ages of the teeth of domestic pig, but cautions that only a very general reliance can be placed on eruption dates as an indication of age. From these data it is possible to propose a four-stage scale to study the culling pattern of medieval pigs:

age	dental characteristics
<1 year	no molars erupted; deciduous teeth present
1.5–2 years	M2 erupted but M3 not yet visible
2–3 years	M2 in wear; M3 erupting but not in wear
>3 years	M3 in wear

The results appear in Table 18. On the basis of this dental evidence, 71% of the pigs survived into their third year and 23.5% survived three or more years, in contrast to the results noted at medieval Baynard's Castle, London, where Armitage (1978) reports higher percentages of young pigs (26.2–36.4%) being slaughtered in their first year and lower percentages (10.8–18.2%) of pigs surviving past the age of three years.

Table 18 *Frequencies of pig mandibles, classified by probable.*

number of mandibles	%	probable age
32	14.8	<1 year
31	14.3	1½ to 2 years
103	47.5	2-3 years
51	23.5	>3 years

Selected pig long bones were assessed as to age on the basis of the absence of certain epiphyses (Silver 1969, 283–286). The results are shown in Table 19. The osteological evidence derived from the fusion of distal epiphyses on certain long bones differs from that derived from mandibular evidence. This may be for the reasons discussed above, but may also be in part due to differing survival rates for bones of young animals, which are more fragile with respect to the denser bones of older ones; younger bones tend to be less resistant to decay and so would be lost to the archaeological record. However it is still surprising to find that many of the pigs survived to an apparent age of at least three years,

since once a pig has reached an optimum size, there is no economic advantage, other than in its capacity for breeding, in keeping it alive. Pigs, however, did appear to have been kept well into maturity at many other medieval sites in Scotland (for example Hodgson 1983, 14; Smith and Hodgson 1987, 198; Smith 2000a).

Horse

The incisor teeth of horses reveal valuable clues as to age (Silver 1969, 293). Seven specimens are reported on in Table 20. The animals ranged in age from five to eleven years old.

Table 19 *Frequencies of selected pig long bones, classified by probable age.*

bone	number examined	number lacking distal epiphyses	age inference
radius	65	60	92.3% younger than 3½ years old
tibia	144	99	68.8% younger than 2 years old
metapodial	109	72	66.1% younger than 2½ years old

Table 20 *Age assessment of horse maxillae and mandibles.*

specimen	accession/ context number	characteristics	estimated age
skull	A10446 C3835	incisors triangular; corner incisor hooked posteriorly	5–7 years
premaxilla	A3786 C2761	canines absent, corner incisor is triangular but lacks posterior hook	11 years
mandible	A4406 C1080	permanent corner incisor in wear, inner wall no longer level with jaw, canines blunt but star absent from incisors	5 years
L mandible	A3284 C3506	molars in similar state of wear as specimen A4406, therefore assumed to be of similar age	5 years
L mandible	A0749 C2001	molars in similar state of wear as specimen A4406, therefore assumed to be of similar age	5 years
R mandible	A02–1406 C7358	third molar in wear; but molars less worn than specimen A4406, therefore assumed to be younger	4½ half years
R mandible	A02–0112 & 0113 C7035	as specimen A02–1406	4 ½ years

Dog and cat

Dental evidence indicated that three of the canine mandibles came from puppies. Analyses of the frequencies of canine and feline long bones lacking epiphyses, with estimates of their probable ages, are given in Tables 21 and 22. On this evidence few puppies or young dogs died, while roughly equal numbers of kittens and adult cats died. This contrast possibly reflects the relative worth of the two species in medieval Perth. It may also provide an indication that young cats, or at least their skins, were a commodity in the fur trade (Smith 1998).

Red deer

Two out of six cervine metatarsals lacked distal epiphyses and probably come from young adults. Mature deer were also killed. There is no evidence for red deer calves having been killed.

Abnormal bones

Unfortunately, at the time of writing of the original animal bone report, few notes were made regarding abnormalities. A full re-examination of the bones was neither possible nor indeed desirable, given the vast quantity of bone which had been recovered and the rather chequered history of the material itself, some having doubtless been mislaid in the intervening years. However during the interval between the original report having been written and the deposition of the bulk of the material in the National Museums of Scotland annexe (then located at Newbattle), some additional observations were made on bones which were readily available for study. This material consisted mainly of the sheep/goat mandibles, the cattle tarsals and cattle first phalanges (from the first season of excavation) as well as a sample of the cattle bones in the keeping of the National Museums of Scotland.

Abnormal sheep/goat mandibles

All of the sheep/goat mandibles in which the cheek teeth still remained were re-examined for signs of dental disease. Eleven specimens (1.6%) were noted in which a degree of alveolar recession, indicating the presence of periodontal disease, had occurred. The most commonly affected area was located between the first and second molars (four cases), or between the third and fourth premolars (four cases). All of the sheep/goats in which this condition was observed were over the age of about two years in modern terms (that is over Payne's [1973] stage E), while five were over the age of about 6 years (that is Payne's stage H). The rate of periodontal disease at Perth High Street was slightly lower than at Meal Vennel, Perth, where about 2.4% of the population was affected.

Table 21 *Frequencies of selected canine long bones lacking epiphyses and their probable ages.*

	bones lacking epiphyses		
bone	proportion	%	age
humerus (proximal)	1/19	5.3	<15 months
femur (distal)	1/18	5.6	<18 months

Table 22 *Frequencies of selected feline long bones lacking epiphyses.*

	bones lacking epiphyses	
bone	proportion	%
humerus (distal)	4/45	8.9
radius (distal)	5/10	50.0
femur (distal)	29/54	53.7
tibia (proximal)	42/68	61.8

It is possible that dental disease such as this played a part in selecting which animals to cull. However, evidence of an economically important disease of sheep, broken mouth, was not found among the Perth High Street specimens (or for that matter, at any other site in Perth). This is not to say that this disease did not occur in the High Street material, indeed it is very likely that it did, since more than two-thirds of the sheep slaughtered in the UK at the present day are suffering from broken mouth (Henderson 1990, 580). However, the reason for the absence of evidence at the High Street and other sites is because the part of the jaw specifically affected by the disease is the oral end, which bears the incisor teeth. This part of the jaw is not well preserved under archaeological conditions. Animals suffering from broken mouth are unable to feed efficiently because the incisors become loose and drop out; the sheep thus become unthrifty and are usually weeded out from the flock. Modern veterinary repair may be effected by applying a splint around the incisors but there is no evidence that this remedy was available to medieval shepherds (Ewesplint, US Patent 4412818, 1983).

Slight congenital abnormalities (which are not harmful to the animals in life) were also observed. In one mandible, the fifth cusp (third pillar) of the third molar was reduced (C7079). This condition is found regularly in archaeological ruminant material (Andrews and Noddle 1975) and has been observed in cattle from Meal Vennel, Perth, and 53–59 Gallowgate, 16–18 Netherkirkgate and Gallowgate Middle School, Aberdeen.

A further sheep/goat mandible from the site also displayed what may have been a congenital abnormality, in that it lacked its second premolar (C5061; A12,260). Examination of the alveolar bone indicated no signs of resorption of the tooth socket, which would have been expected had the tooth ever been present. The condition of congenital absence of the second premolar has been reported by Andrews and Noddle (ibid) as occurring fairly frequently in archaeological material. It has also been observed in Scottish medieval cattle at 80–86 High Street, Perth and both sheep/goats and cattle at Canal Street III, Perth and 16–18 Netherkirkgate, Aberdeen.

Abnormal cattle phalanges

A 60% sample (consisting of 991 of the excavated 1,655 cattle first phalanges) was available for inspection for abnormalities. The most common abnormality in the material was the presence of more-or-less small depressions or lesions in the articular surfaces, of the type described by Baker and Brothwell (1980, 109–114). Type 1 depressions consisted of oval marks in the proximal and distal articulations, mainly orientated in an antero-posterior direction, while Type 2 consisted of narrow slits of variable length between the facets (ibid). Of the sampled phalanges, 240 bones, or 24.3%, were affected by depressions of these two types. At King Edward Street, Perth, 29% of the cattle phalanges were thus affected, and at Kinnoull Street, 30%. Similar abnormalities have been observed at medieval urban sites in Aberdeen, for example at 16–18 Netherkirkgate, Gallowgate Middle School and 53–59 Gallowgate. They are probably non-pathological in origin and would have conferred no ill effects on the affected animals.

However, other anomalies observed in the High Street phalanges were probably pathological: the most extreme cases probably represented the results of changes caused by osteoarthritis. Baker and Brothwell (1980, 115) consider that at least three out of the following list of four changes must be observed in order to confirm a diagnosis of osteoarthritis:

i grooving of the articular surface of the bone

ii eburnation or 'polishing' of the bone

iii extension of the articular surface by new bone formation

iv exostoses around the periphery of the bone

Given these criteria, it was thought that osteoarthritis had been present in eight of the cattle first phalanges from the site, corresponding to 0.8% of the sample. A further 23 phalanges showed evidence of exostoses or extended articular facets, which may have been due to osteoarthritis, but may have had some other aetiology.

Two phalanges were affected by bony proliferations on their anterior shafts rather than the articular surfaces, which may have corresponded to the disease 'ring bone', a term more commonly used with respect to horses (ibid, 120). Ring bones are thought to be caused by concussion of the animal's foot against hard surfaces, or to faulty conformation of the limbs and thus may well have been an occupational hazard of draught oxen also. Diseases such as osteoarthritis and ring bone, if severe, would have caused lameness, and animals suffering from these conditions would be more likely to be selected for culling than healthy beasts.

Abnormal cattle tarsals

All of the cattle naviculo-cuboid and lateral cuneiform tarsals from the 1975 season of excavation were available for observation. In cattle, these tarsals form the hock joint of the hind limb and are often the site of an arthropathy known as spavin, in which exostoses typically form around the inner, lower aspect of the joint (Baker and Brothwell 1980, 117). A substantial number of the cattle naviculo-cuboids displayed a variety of bony changes, some of which were probably the manifestations of spavin (Illus 26). The symptoms most commonly seen in the material included combinations of the following:

i lipping or bony exostoses

ii porosity or increased vascularisation, appearing as circular pits, usually at the anterior edge of the bone, near its articulation with the lateral cuneiform, and occasionally having a honeycomb appearance

Illus 26 *Ankylosed cattle metatarsal and naviculo-cuboid tarsal, lateral view.*

iii interarticular lesions, particularly on the distal surface

iv fusion of the naviculo-cuboid with the lateral cuneiform, to the extent that the junction between the two bones becomes obliterated. While it is conceivable that in some cases such fusion may be congenital, in the presence of the above symptoms it seems more likely to be pathological

v complete fusion of the proximal metatarsal with the naviculo-cuboid and lateral cuneiform

One hundred and fourteen cattle naviculo-cuboids were observed. Of these, 25 showed some combination of the above symptoms, with the worst affected showing at least three different symptoms, in other words, 21.9% of the total were diseased. Two of these tarsals also exhibited grooving and eburnation as well as exostoses, and so could be more properly considered to be symptomatic of osteoarthritis, but the remainder were thought to represent animals suffering from spavin to a greater or lesser degree.

Of the lateral cuneiform tarsals examined (12 examples), nine showed some degree of abnormality ranging from small interarticular lesions (which may have been, like those seen in the cattle phalanges, non-pathological) to deeper, more extensive interarticular lesions and associated lipping. The proximal articulations of these small tarsals, that is, the junction with the distal aspect of the naviculo-cuboid, were affected in four out of twelve cases (33.3%) while the number affected distally, at the articulation with the metatarsal, was seven out of twelve cases (58.3%).

Similarly affected tarsals have been found at other medieval sites in Perth, for example at Meal Vennel, Mill Street, King Edward Street and Scott Street and at Ayr, Harbour Street (Smith, unpublished). The frequency of occurrence of fusion of the lateral cuneiform with the naviculo-cuboid was highest at Meal Vennel, where 11 out of 55 cases were noted (20%) as compared with Perth High Street where only seven out of 114 tarsals showed complete fusion (6.1%).

The exact cause of spavin is not known, but a variety of factors have been cited, such as heavy work on hard surfaces and faulty conformation of the leg. Affected animals may exhibit only a slight degree of lameness and if allowed a period of rest, in which time the joint may ankylose (as in the six examples above), the animal will still be useful for slow work (Baker and Brothwell 1980, 119). It is likely, then, that some plough oxen, as represented by these diseased tarsals, were present in the High Street material, as well as at other sites in Perth.

A number of cattle metatarsals displayed arthritic changes which may also have been related to hard work. Four of these could be classified as being osteoarthritic (C7024; C7326; C2404, A3204; C6021, A02 0454).

Other abnormal bones: evidence of trauma

Several cattle bones showed signs of traumatic damage, for example, the lateral processes of two vertebrae displayed evidence of healed fractures (C7335; C7185). A cattle skull fragment bore evidence of what was probably a healed, depressed fracture, in which a roughened circular depression on the right frontal bone, near the base of the horn core, corresponded with a bulge on the internal, cranial surface (Illus 27). This damage may well be evidence of rough handling of the animal, or even the result of a failed attempt at pole-axeing, but could also represent the end result of aggression between animals known to bear substantial horns.

A smooth swelling on the medial portion of a cattle metatarsal shaft (C7140, A02–0733) was probably an ossified haematoma (Illus 28). Such modification to the bone can occur following a blunt impact to the bone (ibid, 83) such as may have followed a kick from another beast, for example on a plough team.

Illus 27 *Cattle skull fragment showing lesion on frontal bone.*

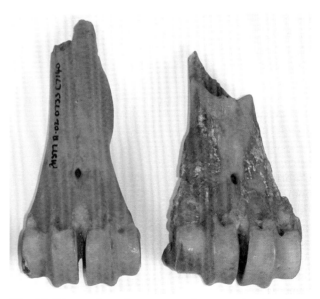

Illus 28 *Diseased cattle metatarsals, posterior distal view (from left): possible ossified haematoma on shaft; osteoarthritis.*

Abnormal pig bones

Two bones of pig, a right scapula and left tibia, showed changes which were probably due to osteomyelitis (C9051, A02–0355; C9095, A02–0204). The glenoid of the scapula (the articulation with the humerus) was surrounded by a heavy band of exostoses. This new bone growth was perforated by three large sinuses, through which it could be seen that necrosis, (destruction of the original bone) of the neck of the scapula had taken place. In the tibia, there was massive expansion of the shaft above the distal end of the bone. The new bone growth was mainly rough and porous, although there were also some denser areas present. A line in the new bone formation may represent a break in the bone, perhaps a pathological fracture which often accompanies osteomyelitis. Such infection is often haematogenous (blood-borne) and commonly affects the radius, ulna and tibia (ibid, 64). Both of these pigs must have been very lame indeed.

Abnormal dog and cat bones

All of the dog and cat bones were available for study and were re-examined for abnormalities. The dental health of the dogs was generally good. Only one case of ante-mortem tooth loss was detected, a left mandible in which the alveolus (root hole) for the second premolar had been filled in with new bone (C2166, A4640). Two other cases of missing teeth were probably congenital in origin, since there was no apparent roughening of the alveolar bone; these teeth had failed to develop and had never been present. These were a right maxilla with absent first premolar and a right mandible with a missing third molar (C0547, A7522; C0206, A1737). Both the first premolar and the lower third molar are insignificant teeth in dogs and their absence is relatively common both in archaeological and modern material. Other congenital dental anomalies observed were examples of tooth crowding, resulting in rotation of the teeth in the lower jaw (C2166, A4640; C3696, A7690; u/s). The dog long bones were mainly free from visible disease, with the exception of a skeleton of a very small individual (C5019, A10702 and A10696) (Illus 12). The long bones, vertebrae and ribs of this tiny animal showed various symptoms of osteoarthritis, including lipping, grooving and eburnation of articular surfaces, particularly in the spine. There was also localised osteoporosis, most noticeable in the lower fore limbs. Unfortunately the skull and teeth of the animal were not retrieved, but it was very likely that it had been elderly. This, together with the small size of the animal, and its obvious osteoarthritis, make it tempting to suggest that it may have been a cossetted pet rather than a working dog. Indeed, its disposal in a pit rather than on an open midden may reflect its worth to its owner (Pit 5259) (Smith, 1998).

As with the dogs, cat dental health was good, perhaps because of the young age at which many of the cats had died. Tooth crowding, of the first molar against the fourth premolar, was however observed in five mandibles.

A few long bones of cat demonstrated the results of trauma. A radius, associated with a partial skeleton, was probably fractured (C2714, A2125) while three tibiae displayed bony lumps on the posterior aspect of the shaft which probably indicate a response to traumatic damage of the musculature and periosteum (C2419, A3149; C3597, A6822; u/s). Such injuries perhaps reflect the precarious existence of cats within the medieval burgh.

In addition, there were several instances of exostoses and/or eburnation in the joints of long bones, particularly in a misshapen femur head, indicating a defective hip joint (C2430, A3961).

Distribution of bones over the site

Various archaeological features such as middens, buildings, pits and paths were identified at the site (see Fascicule 1). The distribution of mammal and bird bones over the site was studied with respect to these groupings, the data being included on the CD insert accompanying this volume.

The frequency of occurrence of different parts of the skeleton of cattle and sheep/goat was compared for selected context groups. Data Tables 3.1.1–3.2.34 (see CD insert) show the numbers and percentages of cattle and sheep/goat bones which would be expected if a whole animal carcass was recovered, compared with actual numbers and percentages found. The context groups chosen were middens from which at least 50 cattle bones had been recovered as well as all buildings on the site. Other features which contained fewer than 50 identified bones in total were not further analysed, since the sample numbers were considered too small to be statistically reliable.

When the frequency of occurrence of cattle horn cores (Illus 17, 18) is examined, it is obvious that although there are fluctuations with time, it is always higher than expected. The pattern appears to be one of high frequencies in the early phases, for example 18.4% in midden M2.1b (Phase Ic) where the total number of cattle bones (n) was 54, increasing with time throughout Period II (late 12th century), then dropping by Phase IVb (4.5%; n=200). In Period V (14th century), there are notable differences in the contents of the middens. Although midden M8a (Phase Va,Vaa) contained only 4.7% cattle horn cores, the overall sample was large (n=889). This relatively low horn core frequency contrasts with the situation in M4a (Phase Vaa–Vc) as well as in M3a (Phase Vb–Vc) where the horn core frequencies were 30.7% (n=199) and 40.4% (n=193) respectively. In some instances, the frequencies of mandibles are almost equal to, or exceed that of horn cores, which perhaps indicates that the horn cores were still attached to skulls when they arrived on site.

In the case of goat horn cores, frequencies also fluctuate with time. They were particularly plentiful in midden M4a (Phase Vaa–Vc), where 32.9% of the sheep/goat bones (n=79) were identified as goat horn cores, and in M3a (Phase Vc; 33.8%, n=71). It has already been noted that cattle horn cores were also plentiful in M4a and M3a. The frequencies of sheep/goat mandibles are also consistently higher than expected. However, as sheep and goats could not be distinguished, it cannot be determined whether whole goat heads, or even carcasses, rather than detached horn cores, were imported to the site.

As regards other skeletal elements of cattle, sheep and goats, it is apparent that although all parts of the carcass were well represented at the site, lower meat yielding bones from the lower limbs (metapodials and phalanges) were plentiful in all periods. This trend is particularly noticeable in midden M8a (Phase Va,Vaa) from which large quantities of phalanges were recovered, accounting for just over 31% of the total cattle bones from this feature (cattle n= 889). It is possible to account for the presence of these numerous toe bones in several ways: they may have been brought to the site attached to cattle hides; they may have been the detritus of butchery; or they may have been the remains of industrial processes such as hoof-boiling in order to make glue or neatsfoot oil.

Animals in the economy of the burgh

Duncan (1974, 30–50) has drawn a profile of Perth in the century from 1130 to 1230 and has emphasised its relationship with the nation, the surrounding countryside, and the trading and manufacturing industries within its boundaries. In tracing the burgh's development from a settlement of the eleventh century where ships came up the Tay to unload, to its status as the second town in Scotland, Duncan attributes some of the impetus for this change to royal patronage and a small active business community. The activities of these merchant burgesses were mainly concerned with the manufacture of cloth and leather goods, the import of wine and grain and export of wool, hides, skins and salmon.

Before interpreting the meaning of the osteological evidence it is necessary to understand the legal status of the royal burghs as regards the marketing of cattle, sheep and their products, and to understand the laws governing the killing of game (that is, deer, wild boar and hare) in medieval Scotland, and how these evolved.

Legal status of the burghs

Dickinson (1961) has examined the role of the burgh in the mercantile revolution which led to the change from a self-supporting agricultural Scottish economy to an organised trading economy. During this change the agricultural products of wool, woolfells (sheepskins with wool attached), skins and hides were exchanged for manufactured goods, for luxuries and for raw materials in which Scotland was deficient. This trading

was in the hands of the burgesses of the new burghs which had been deliberately created by the king.

The trading privileges enjoyed by the burghs have been discussed by Keith (1913, 454–71), Ballard (1916, 16–29), Grant (1930, 383) and Dickinson (1961, 112). These privileges were enshrined in the charters granted to the burghs. Innes (1868, XXXV), in discussing the oldest burgh charters in Scotland, which date from the reign of William the Lion (1165–1214), advances other charter evidence to show that they point 'plainly to a previous burghal organisation'. Specifically a writ of David I dated 1124x1127 refers to a toft in the burgh of Perth, (Barrow 1999, no 19) yet the earliest extant burghal charter is that granted by William the Lion to Perth in 1209 (RRS, ii, no 467; Duncan 1974, 41). This latter charter shows the double nature of the monopoly involved. Firstly, it involved a monopoly of trade against the agricultural hinterland of the Sheriffdom of Perth and secondly, it was a monopoly against foreign merchants concerned with exports and imports. Grant (1930, 358–406) has discussed the effects of this double monopoly on the economic life of Scotland. Later, in the reign of David II (1329–1371) the privileges as regards foreign trade were summarised and made applicable to all the burghs of Scotland. In short, the charters granted to the burghs (and therefore to the burgesses) the power to control all exports and imports and to control the selling of agricultural and craftsmen's produce from the surrounding countryside by allowing such produce to be sold only at legal fairs within the burghs.

The new status of being a burgh was largely a legal concept in that the burgesses enjoyed special laws and privileges, and that the laws of the burghs were different from the law of the land. In return for these privileges the king received useful revenue in hard cash (Dickinson 1961, 112–13). Barrow (RRS, i, 52) has reviewed the sources of revenue available to Malcolm IV (1153–1165). Included in these are tribute or cain in cash or kind, enjoyed by the king by virtue of his regality, and customs duties. The same author cites an example of a charter attributed to David I which refers to his cain at Perth and which is further evidence of a burghal organisation before William the Lion's charter to Perth (ibid, 54; APS, i, 358; Barrow 1999, no 127).

Laws governing the hunting and killing of game

Gilbert (1975) has traced the origin and evolution of hunting reserves in medieval Scotland and has examined the interaction of their development and the economic activities of the common people. Historically, prior to the 12th century, Scottish kings had favourite hunting areas rather than actual hunting reserves.

The principle of Roman law that game was *res nullius*, that is, that it belonged to whoever killed it, regardless of where or on whose land it was killed, was probably current in Scotland before the 12th century, although it was not universally accepted. In the 1130s David I established forests as hunting reserves in

Scotland. The king created Royal Forests, probably by proclamation, and Baronial Forests by the process of free forest grant. Legally, the king had the right to reserve all greater game to himself but this was never seriously enforced and did not, in Gilbert's view, limit the operation of *res nullius*. A subject with free forest grant could only have a forest (reserve) on his own land and then only by royal grant. The owner of a forest legally controlled everything on or above the ground.

A body of forest law developed: this may first have been written down by the mid-14th century and is reflected by several later sources (*APS*, i, 749, 652; Skene 1609). This body of law incorporated many of the rights exercised and regulations imposed on royal and baronial forests. The reservation of game by the creation of royal forests or by the grant of free forest referred to greater game, later known as venison, and which consisted of red deer, roe deer and wild boar. Lesser game was reserved by the grant of free warren, and this applied to fox, rabbit, marten, wild cat and hare.

Gilbert (1975) argues that the right given to anyone to hunt anywhere (*APS*, i, 652, c31, *Quoniam attachiamenta*) refers only to freemen hunting outside reserves (forests and warrens) and applies only to lesser game. He correlates the increase in the proportion of the population having the right to hunt in the 14th century as due to a decline in serfdom, with increased interest on the part of landowners of that time in creating reserves. Such reserves, deer parks and rabbit warrens, in which game could be more easily controlled and preserved, were created on the basis of property rights rather than that of royal grant. It appears, therefore, that the hunting activities of the common people were affected by a limitation of the principle of *res nullius* and by a reduction in the number of places in which they could hunt. In some areas this situation may have been reached long before the act of 1621 (*APS*, iv, 629, c31) which resulted in landowners being the only people with the right to hunt from that date. The erosion of the rights of the common people to hunt game and the lack of opportunities for them to do so may explain in part the relative absence of the remains of wild boar and deer in the Perth High Street assemblage. There is also the possibility that in the lowlands of Scotland the increased economic activity near the burghs in the 13th and 14th centuries destroyed the natural woodland habitat of game and created a shortage (Gilbert 1979, pers comm). Depletion of game stocks would give additional incentive to landowners to create deer parks where the animals could be conserved.

Evidence of animal based industries

By-products from common animals which would have been in demand in medieval Scotland would include hides and skins either for export as such, or for production of leather goods and parchment for home consumption; wool and hair for textiles, grease and tallow to make candles, tapers, soap and lubricants; dairy products from the milk of sheep, goats and cows; offal, blood, and bone as food for people and dogs and cats; gut and sinew; bone, antler, hoof and horn for ornaments, keepsakes and personal and household goods; goose feathers to make flights for the bolts of cross-bows; dogs' dung for use in bating or puering leather prior to the actual tanning process (Forbes 1966, 4).

The evidence of animal based industries at Perth is sixfold:

i the large number of horn cores present

ii the large amount of animal hair present

iii carcass analysis reveals the presence of a high proportion of low meat yielding bones

iv the customs accounts

v the evidence of maps and place names

vi the presence of tools and artefacts believed to be associated with skinning and tanning

Evidence of the horn cores

The large numbers of cattle (1,753) and goat (722) horn cores and the almost complete absence of the skulls from which they came is indicative of commercial waste from a horner's industry (Illus 29, 30). Armitage and Clutton-Brock (1976, 329) have reviewed the many uses to which horn was put in European towns before the industrial revolution and have thereby demonstrated its value as a commodity. They argue that ox horn was probably preferred to cow simply because it was larger and that the discarded horn cores can appear either among general urban refuse or more rarely as a single collection of industrial waste. The horn cores of cattle and goat at Perth High Street seem to have been dumped amongst general town refuse. At only one other site in Perth has such a relatively high proportion of cattle horn cores been discovered; at South Methven Street 53% of the cattle bones from the town ditch were in fact horn cores and are presumed to be industrial waste (Smith and Hodgson 1987, 197).

The large number of goat horn cores present at sites in Perth (Illus 24, 29) is in sharp contrast to that found at the excavations of medieval levels at High Street, Edinburgh (Chaplin and Barnetson 1978, 234), Elgin (Hodgson and Jones, 1979) and Aberdeen (Hodgson and Jones, 1982b). Prummel (1979, 1983) has reported large numbers of cattle and goat horn cores from the early medieval port of Dorestad and the mid medieval town of Den Bosch in the Netherlands. In both cases there is a relative absence of the post-cranial bones of the two species as is the case at Perth High Street. The same author speculates that the preponderance of horn cores compared with other bones may be due to the importation of loose horns or to the practice of sending hides to a tannery with horns still attached to

Illus 29 *Male and female sawn goat horn cores.*

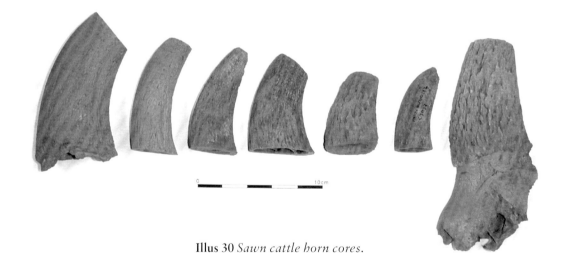

Illus 30 *Sawn cattle horn cores.*

them. None of the Perth goat horn cores display the rectangular holes reported by Prummel (1983) and Noddle (1977, 397), although one example has been pierced through by a transverse perforation (The worked bone; Cat No 78, A0238).

The cattle horn cores from Perth High Street are curious in that several of them have been sawn through, mainly at the base, although a few have been sawn twice, once at the base and again near the tip (Illus 30). This contrasts with the situation at a medieval horner's shop at York where the cattle horn cores were found still mainly attached to the skull (Ryder 1977 pers comm). Sawn cattle horn cores have also been found at other sites in Perth, for example at Kirk Close (Smith and Hodgson 1987, 197) as well as Aberdeen (Smith and McCormick 2001) and it is believed that such care in removing the horns is further evidence of their use in horning, rather than trading the hides with the horns attached.

Evidence of the hair

Ryder (1977, pers comm) has suggested that the large amount of animal hair found at Perth High Street is indicative of the presence of a skinner's workshop nearby. Hair from horse, pig, ox and goat is reported from the site, along with textiles made from wool and goat hair (see The textiles).

Evidence of the carcass analysis

Chaplin (1971) drew attention to the need to study the relative frequencies of bones of high meat value and those of low meat value as a means of distinguishing bones deriving from domestic refuse from those which formed commercial debris. Chaplin and Barnetson (1978, 230) have interpreted the presence on the same site of equivalent numbers of high and low meat yielding bones to indicate that the slaughter, carcass dressing, butchering and consumption of meat occurred on or near the area excavated. This appears to have been the case in the medieval levels of the High Street and Tron Kirk sites in Edinburgh which they reported on. Anatomical distribution analysis has been applied to medieval sites at Aylesbury, Southampton and King's Lynn by Noddle (1975b, 322; 1976, 271–6; 1977, 385) although she has cautioned against too numerical an interpretation on the grounds that certain bones and parts of bones survive cooking and burial in soil better than others.

The situation at Perth High Street is difficult to interpret, probably because the bone remains may be a mixture of both domestic refuse and commercial waste. The femur and humerus are bones of high meat yield representing the leg and shoulder joints respectively while the metacarpal and metatarsal bones are of low meat yield. (Tables 1 and 2 show the frequency of these bones for cattle and sheep; see also CD insert: Animal bone data for carcass analyses of bones found in middens and buildings). If the frequencies

of the left distal ends of cattle femora and humeri are compared, it can be seen that low meat yield bones outnumber high meat yield bones by between two and three to one (metatarsal:femur = 274/73 = 3.75, and metacarpal:humerus = 292/149 = 1.96). These ratios indicate that commercially valuable meat joints were moved from the site after slaughtering, carcass dressing, and butchering; in other words, there was commercial marketing of beef. Alternatively the relative abundance of low meat yielding metapodials may be due to industrial processes associated with animal by-products. The theory that joints of meat were dispersed from the site is apparently contradicted by the large numbers of shoulder blades and pelvic fragments that are present. These bones are associated with heavy musculature and therefore with meat but the explanation of their presence may lie in the fact that the blade of the shoulder joint and the aitch-bone of the haunch were boned out by medieval butchers before the joints were sold. Unfortunately, the surviving records of the Flesher Incorporation at Perth do not start until 1603 and even these late records shed little light on butchery practice, being more concerned with the Fleshers' properties within the town.

The low numbers of cattle toe bones, astragali and calcanea are difficult to reconcile with the large numbers of metapodials; both types of bone being in the low meat yield category. Possibly the low numbers of toe bones (phalanges) is due to the production of 'neatsfoot' oil. Along with the phalanges, the whole hoof was used to produce this oil, which was employed as a lubricant for leather. Horns and hooves were distilled to produce liquor of ammonia and sal ammoniac (Jackman 1978, pers comm).

An alternative explanation for the relative lack of cattle phalanges may be that the hides were sold by weight with the feet on. Noddle (1977, 381) cites evidence of this practice in medieval Germany and suggests that the comparative rarity of cattle toe bones at a medieval site in King's Lynn is due to it. There was a thriving export trade in hides at Perth and trade links existed with the Baltic, the Low Countries and with Germany. However, documentary evidence from the Exchequer Rolls indicates that hides were sold according to size, quality and number, being reckoned in dacres and lasts (ten hides to the last, twenty lasts to the dacre; Guy 1986, 64) rather than by weight. There would therefore be no reason to include either the feet or horns as a 'make-weight'.

The preponderance of low meat yielding bones at Perth High Street may be construed as evidence that we are dealing with poorer people, perhaps craftsmen rather than merchant burgesses, and that the high meat yield joints were sold to people from a better-off part of the burgh. If this is so, and the evidence for it is slender, it is not to argue that there was a lower level of nutrition because lower prestige meats such as spare rib, offal and marrow bone for stock have high nutritional values. The cattle sized vertebrae are frequently split longitudinally indicating that sides of beef were dealt with rather than whole carcasses. This splitting of carcasses into sides may have been a preliminary to the butchering into joints discussed above. Illus 31 shows split carcasses in a19th-century butcher's shop.

A similar comparison of sheep/goat long bones of high and low meat yields is not possible because of difficulties in distinguishing between distal metacarpals and distal metatarsals. A comparison of the numbers of proximal ends of the humerus, femur and metapodials would be invalid because the heads of sheep humeri and femora are small and easily eroded and so can be lost to the archaeological record. Chaplin and Barnetson (1978, pers comm) found it convenient to use mandibles (jaw bones) as being indices of 'low meat yield cuts' but this may not be appropriate here for several reasons: firstly it was not possible to distinguish sheep from goat mandibles; secondly in times of high meat prices in Britain in the modern period, the muscles associated with jawbones have been carefully cut out by butchers for use in making mince and sausage meat and thirdly if the mandibles were discarded while still attached to the skull, a different, industrial aspect of the economy, rather than a domestic one, may be represented. If however the sheep/goat jaw bones are indeed treated as an index of low meat yield, there is *prima facie* evidence of the removal of shoulders and legs of mutton from the site, that is, of commercial retail of mutton.

An analysis of the skeletal remains of pig has not been attempted because bones from young animals are readily eroded by cooking and by burial in soil.

Illus 31 *Cattle carcasses split into equal sides of beef; 19th century Perth butcher's shop (copyright Perth Museum and Art Gallery)*

Evidence of the Customs Accounts

The customs duties were of two kinds, the toll or *parva custuma* paid on produce which was brought for sale at the burgh market either from the country or abroad and included harbour duties on ships arriving in port, and the great customs or export dues paid on wool, woolfells, skins and hides which were traded overseas (Dickinson 1961, 114). The *parva custuma* or petty custom was regulated by two codes, *Assisa de tolloneis* and *Custume portuum*, and was levied by the provosts of the burghs, whereas the great custom was collected for the king by special officials or *custumarii*. The 19th-century editors of the Exchequer Rolls have argued that Scotland enjoyed virtual free trade in imports until the end of the 16th century and that the rates of custom specified from time to time in the *Assisa de Tolloneis* (see APS, i, 668, Appendix iii, for example) are burghal taxes trifling in amount compared with the great custom on the same articles (*ERS* i, p xcix).

The accounts of the *custumarii* are recorded in the Exchequer Rolls only from 1327, but the references in a charter of David I's reign to cain (levied on ships and merchants bringing imports to Scotland) is evidence that royal revenues were derived from trade much earlier than this (Barrow 1999, no 127). Sometimes these accounts reveal the actual rate of custom to be levied on each article at that time (*ERS*, i, pp xcix).

These great customs formed a substantial part of royal revenue and it was therefore in the interest of the crown to encourage export (Mackinnon 1920, 88). In times of national economic crisis, for example, the raising of the ransom for King David II, the royal revenue was increased by trebling and later quadrupling the rate of duty to be levied. Webster (1975, 169) points out that the revenue recorded in the Customs accounts depends exactly on the amount of customable material passing through the ports and that these records may therefore be used as economic evidence of trade patterns. Grant (1930, 353) has used this evidence to estimate the relative importance of the various burghs in relation to the export of certain commodities and showed that by 1379 Perth and Dundee were fourth equal in importance as regards the export of hides.

During the late 14th–early 15th centuries, wool and woolfells together accounted for over 90% of customs receipts, and during this period (1327–1431), Perth exported an average of about 2.6 tonnes per year, the national average for the whole of Scotland being about 52 tonnes (Stevenson and Torrie 1988, 191).

Evidence of maps and place names

Rutherford's map of the 'Town of Perth' dated 1774 gives further indirect support for the contention that

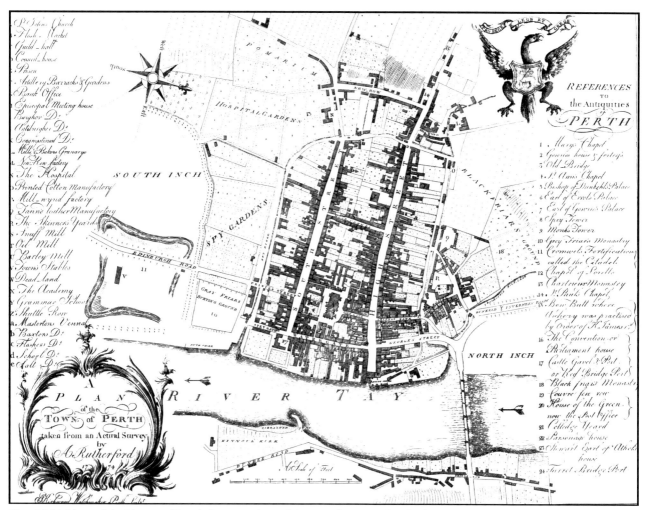

Illus 32 'A Plan of the Town of Perth from an Actual Survey' by A Rutherford, 1774.

there was a well developed commercial meat trade in Perth (Illus 32). Place names within close proximity to the site include Fleshers' Market and Fleshers' Vennel while other names in the town are Skinners' Yard and Skinner Gate. A legend on the map reads 'Tanned Leather Manufactory'.

Evidence of tools and artefacts

Several tools recovered from the site have been identified as scrapers which may have been used in the preparation of hides and skins. Reference to 'bemys knyffis', dating to 1550, is made in the Perth Guildry Book (Stavert 1993, 207). This is taken to mean beaming knives (also known as scudding knives), which are specialised tools with curved blades used to remove hair, epidermis

Illus 33 *St Bartholomew, patron saint of the Perth Glover Incorporation, with the beaming knife used in his martyrdom; 16th-century painted wooden panel taken from St John's Kirk. (Copyright Perth Museum and Art Gallery)*

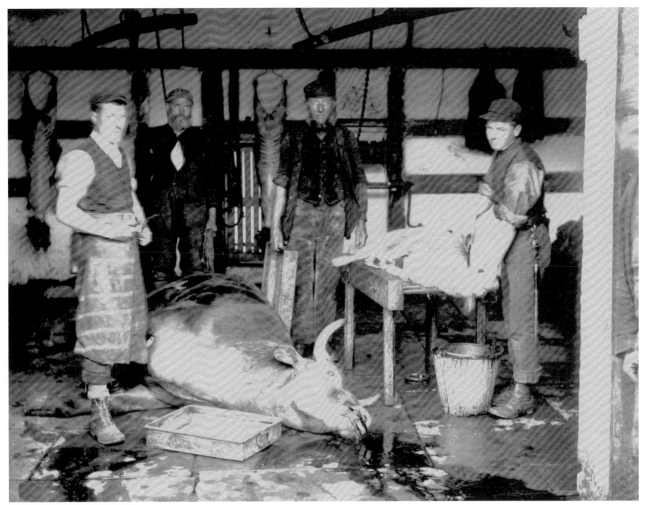

Illus 34 *19th century butchers at work in Mr Paton's shop, Perth. (Copyright Perth Museum and Art Gallery)*

Illus 35 *Cattle radii, innominate and humerus showing hack marks made by axes or cleavers.*

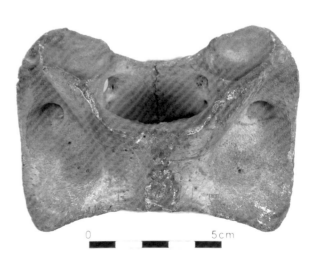

Illus 36 *Cattle cervical vertebra (atlas), showing knife marks on ventral aspect.*

and any adhering subcutaneous flesh and fat from the skins (Serjeantson 1989, 133–5); an example is shown in a 16th-century panel depicting the martyrdom of St Bartholomew, patron saint of the Perth Glover Incorporation (Illus 33).

Direct evidence of the types of tools used also came from the bones themselves; saws were used only infrequently at Perth High Street, as has been found to be the case at other medieval urban sites in Scotland, and were generally reserved for removing valuable parts of the carcass such as horns or antlers. Heavy butchery, as until recently (Illus 34) was usually performed using axes or cleavers, as shown by chop marks on the bones (Illus 35), while meat was removed from the bone by means of metal knives, which have left traces in the form of fine cuts (Illus 36).

Some of the dog and cat bones from Perth High Street showed evidence of fine knife cuts which were probably inflicted during skinning (CD Insert: Animal bone data). There is evidence from other sites within the town that skinning took place; for example, at Meal Vennel, a pit contained the skeletons of three dogs and a cat. One of these dog skeletons showed evidence of knife cuts (on the tibia) and it is likely that all four of these animals had been skinned (Smith 1996a; Smith 1998). At Whitefriars, Perth, cut canine bones have been recovered from both pre- and post-Reformation contexts (Smith 1989, mf 13:F2). Similarly, at 53–59 Gallowgate, Aberdeen, one butchered dog bone was found amongst the contents of a tan pit (Smith and McCormick 2001).

Some documentary evidence exists to show that dog skins were imported into England from Scotland in the 17th century, along with skins of wild cat, domestic cat, otter, hare, rabbit, polecat, fox and deer (PRO Customs 3 Vol 1, 48; Smout 1963, 218). More particularly, in the records of the Merchant Guildry of Perth, an entry for the year 1552 details a list of skins which include 'hertis hird hidis, lamb skynnis, gatis, cunyng skynnis (and) cattis', in other words, deer, lamb, goat, rabbit and cat (Stavert 1993, 216).

Meat supply and contribution of meat to the diet

The relative frequencies of food forming species may by themselves give a misleading impression of the extent to which different meats were available or were preferred. Several authors have drawn attention to the need to consider carcass weights or the yields of meat from the carcasses of different species (Yealland and Higgs 1966; Chaplin 1971). Such estimates will depend on the ages at which the animals were slaughtered. Obviously a young lamb will normally yield less than an older sheep of the same breed, therefore the ages at which the animals were slaughtered have to be considered. Young animals may not have been killed merely to supply a market demand for the tender meat of lamb, veal or piglet, but may have been culled when young because of an inability to overwinter them successfully or because of a lack of financial incentive to do so. At Perth and

other burghs concerned with the export of hides and skins, meat was a secondary product, and the animals were probably raised until they were at an optimum as regards hide quality rather than meat production. Evidence has been considered which indicates that at Perth the animal remains are a mixture of animal based industry and food production, therefore it may be misleading to interpret these remains in terms of meat yield (Alcock pers comm). However, because hides had to be brought to market along with the carcass from which they came (which in the majority of cases, probably meant on the hoof) (APS, ii, 543) we can assume that the meat was indeed eaten, probably within the burgh itself.

Estimates of carcass weights of domestic animals vary according to time and author but accepting Yealland and Higgs' (1966, 140) estimates of cow 900 lbs, horse 800 lbs, sheep 125 lbs and pig 200 lbs for a medieval site in England, and assuming that goats had carcass weights similar to those of sheep, it is possible to arrive at some estimate of the relative contribution of each species to the meat supply of the site, based on the minimum numbers present. (Estimates of minimum numbers are presented in Table 13.) The estimates used are based on long bones rather than on horn cores, since if horn cores were imported into Perth without the carcasses which grew them, the calculation of meat yield would be distorted. The contribution of species to meat yield is shown in Table 23.

There is little direct evidence as to the actual live or carcass weights of the animals concerned. The need to estimate more accurately the meat yield of animal species at archaeological sites has been reviewed (Smith 1975, 99) while Noddle (1973, 377–89) has tried to devise a method for cattle by extrapolating from observed relationships between bone size and carcass weight in modern cattle. Chaplin (1971, 134) proposed a scheme to overcome the absence of carcass weights by assigning to each species a sheep equivalent (SE) value in terms of dressed carcass weights. If we apply these SE values, (cattle=12 SE, pig=2 SE, goat=1 SE) and make the assumption that the dressed carcass weight of a sheep was 25 lbs, then the relative contributions of each species to the diet may be estimated (see Table 25).

It appears therefore that beef was the major source of meat at Perth, this being supplemented by mutton and to a lesser extent, pork, along with venison, hare, rabbit, poultry, game birds, fish, and shellfish. There is a possibility that other animals such as horses were eaten in medieval Scotland, although some writers dispute this; for example, Armitage (1978, 33) argues that it was not eaten in late medieval England, while Clason (1967, 60) advances evidence to suggest the Christian church opposed its consumption. Certainly there had been a Papal ban on the eating of horsemeat in the early 8th century (Harris 1986, 96), but it is unlikely that this was still current in Scotland in the 12th to 14th centuries. The evidence of chopped horse bones at other sites in Perth, such as Meal Vennel

Table 23 *Percentage contribution to meat yields by species, based on minimum numbers shown in Table 13.*

site	% contribution to meat yield				
	cattle	sheep/goat	goat	pig	horse
Perth					
PHSAE	80.6	7.6	0.8	7.2	3.9
St Ann's Lane	74.5	12.8		8.8	3.9
Canal Street I	75.0	6.3	2.1	3.3	13.3
Meal Vennel	80.1	5.9	4.5	4.7	4.7
Aberdeen					
Queen Street	73.9	5.8	3.9	12.3	4.1
42 St Paul Street	77.9	4.8	6.0	4.2	7.2
45–47 Gallowgate	75.2	9.0	1.5	4.8	9.6
53–59 Gallowgate	73.1	6.5	2.9	8.1	9.3
Gallowgate Middle School	75.0	7.8	2.6	6.3	8.3
Elgin					
High Street	57.9	10.7	1.3	12.9	17.2

Table 24 *Percentage contribution to meat yield by species, excluding horse.*

Site	% contribution to meat yield, excluding horse			
	cattle	sheep/goat	goat	pig
Perth				
PHSAE	83.8	7.8	0.8	7.5
St Ann's Lane	77.6	13.4		9.1
Canal Street I	86.5	7.2	2.4	3.8
Meal Vennel	84.1	6.2	4.7	5.0
Aberdeen				
Queen Street	77.1	6.0	4.0	12.9
42 St Paul Street	83.9	5.2	6.4	4.5
45–47 Gallowgate	83.2	9.9	1.7	5.3
53–59 Gallowgate	80.6	7.2	3.2	9.0
Gallowgate Middle School	81.8	8.5	2.8	6.8
Elgin				
High Street	69.9	12.9	1.6	15.5

Table 25 *Percentage contribution to meat yields based on Sheep Equivalent Units, based on minimum numbers shown in Table 13.*

site	% contribution to meat yield			
	cattle	sheep/goat	goat	pig
Perth				
PHSAE	88.6	5.0	0.5	5.9
St Ann's Lane	84.0	8.6		7.4
Canal Street I	90.0	4.5	1.5	3.0
Meal Vennel	89.1	4.0	3.0	4.0
Aberdeen				
Queen Street	83.1	3.9	2.6	10.4
42 St Paul Street	89.0	3.3	4.1	3.6
45–47 Gallowgate	88.4	6.3	1.1	4.2
53–59 Gallowgate	86.2	4.6	2.1	7.2
Gallowgate Middle School	87.3	5.5	1.8	5.5
Elgin				
High Street	77.4	8.6	1.1	12.9

and Mill Street, as well as at sites in the burghs of Inverkeithing, Inverness and Aberdeen, (Hodgson and Smith 1983; Hodgson and Smith 1982; Smith 1998) presents a strong case for consumption of the meat, although it is possible that this could have been prepared as food for dogs rather than as for humans. Since it is not always clear as to whether horse flesh was eaten by humans (rather than dogs) in the medieval period, the relative contribution of the main domestic mammalian species, excluding horse, is presented in Table 24.

Whether dogs themselves were eaten is similarly uncertain, since cut marks on some of the bones may indicate skinning rather than consumption for food; however when the burgh of Perth was besieged, or during periods of food shortage and dearth, the incentive to do so must have been great. During famine conditions in early 17th-century England, dogs, cats and horses were all resorted to as a source of food (Thomas 1983, 116). The sentimentality which surrounds animals regarded as pets at the present day would not have prevailed in such conditions (Smith 1998, Smith 2006).

Discussion

It is worth reflecting that we have no accurate method of assessing the size of the human population of the Scottish burghs in early times. Russell's (1948, 358) study of British medieval populations cites comparison of

rents paid to the king in 1327. On this basis Perth was third in importance to Berwick and Aberdeen but it will be realised that several of the border burghs would be out of the reckoning because of the wars with the English (Edward III did not acknowledge Robert Bruce as King of Scotland until 1328). Froissart reported in 1385 that Edinburgh consisted of only some 400 dwellings (1867, ii, 314). However, a text by an unknown author who travelled to Scotland with Edward I in 1296, refers to 'Saynt Johns' (Perth) as being 'a metely goode toune' (Hume Brown 1978, 4). Estienne Perlin in 1551–2 describes the Scottish seaports, which would include Perth, as being 'petites villes et bourgardes' (ibid, 75).

Whichever criterion is used to assess the size of the population of the Scottish medieval burghs, they appear to have been small even before the plague pandemic of the mid 14th century, known as the Black Death (Tyler 1882), and consisted of a probable maximum of 1,500 to 2,000 people.

The dilemma posed by the animal remains described in this report is why, during the 12th–14th centuries, should so few people at Perth be associated with the remains of so many cattle, sheep and goats? The answer most probably lies in part, in the fact that cattle were raised to satisfy an export trade in hides in which the king and the merchant burgesses had a pecuniary interest. By the same reasoning the sheep remains can be explained as being the waste produced by the export of woolfells and the remnants of meals. The ages of the animals on slaughter may reflect something of the rival claims of the enterprises of a thriving retail meat trade and its considerable by-products industry although it may be preferable to consider the hides, wool and woolfells as the primary products, while meat itself is the by-product.

The substantial quantity of goat remains present at Perth in a 12th–14th–century context is more difficult to understand. Later in the 17th century there was a massive export trade in goat and kid skins from animals reared mainly in the Highlands, as shown, for example by the Mar and Kellie estate papers relating to customs returns for all Scottish ports. In the three years between 1611 and 1614, 1,226 kid skins and 16,321 goat skins were exported (*HMC*, Mar and Kellie, 71). This large scale production of goats grew up in spite of repeated attempts to discriminate against goats by legislation over the centuries (Skene 1609, 18, c.5; Innes 1868, i, 179). Goats, having a hard palate, are able to eat almost any kind of vegetation and because of this became a major cause of denudation of the Scottish forests – hence the need to discriminate against them. It is not possible to estimate the size of this export trade at various ports in mid-medieval times from the Exchequer Rolls for no great custom was levied on the goatskins at this time, although the rate of the petty custom is listed from time to time (*APS*, i, 668, Appendix ii, *Assisa de tolloneis*). It is tempting to explain the medieval goat remains found at Perth simply as being the beginnings of this export trade, despite the lack of documentary evidence for it; but the explanation may lie in the production of cheap meat for home consumption.

Grant (1930) has discussed the dilemma facing the central government; that of having to ensure that the people had food and other necessaries at reasonable prices while at the same time having to sustain an export trade of raw materials which was both the basis of Scotland's commerce and a source of royal revenue. Even in the relatively prosperous times of the 12th century, attempts were made to establish a natural system of fixing food prices so that the cost of living was fairly stable (*APS*, i, 675–9; see also discussion of this legislation by Innes in the preface of the same volume). Later, after 1292, in an economy progressively ruined by the cost of wars and the ravages of invasion, inflation was rife. Concern by the central government for the meat and commodity supplies for the home market is reflected in the banning of the export of hide and skins in 1483, 1555 and 1561 (*APS*, ii, 166, *APS*, ii, 496; Burton 1877), the introduction of compulsory meatless market-days in 1584 (*APS*, iii, 353, Item 12), and the prohibition of the export of sheep and nolt (cattle) in 1592 (*APS*, iii, 577, c. 11).

Whether the shortages of meat stemmed entirely from inflation or were due in part to the rival demands of the hide export trade or were sometimes due to the chance coincidence of bad winters and disease among livestock (Lawrie 1910, iii, 15) is difficult to assess but very real shortages there undoubtedly were. The records of the Privy Council make repeated references to 'the greit derth' and to 'exorbitant prices' (see Burton, 1877, 94; 114; 200–1). It is difficult to understand why there should be a meat shortage at a time of large scale production of cattle hides. Paradoxically a demand for hides would not necessarily have produced a glut of cheap meat. In practice, because of the monopoly the merchant burgesses exerted over the beef and mutton producers in the hinterland, the animals would have been raised to an optimum for hide production and not for meat. The time of slaughter of animals would thus largely be at the dictate of the export trade rather than the market forces of supply and demand for meat and may have been linked to the arrival and departures of ships as well as to seasons thus causing an erratic supply of meat resulting in gluts and shortages. Perhaps rising inflation and the ravages of war caused beef to be priced out of the market for many poor people.

It seems reasonable to suppose therefore that goats, which are easier to nourish than cattle or sheep because they can eat rough pasture, and which are quick to grow and easy to tend, would fill this gap in the meat market. Penny (1836) reports 'before the plantations huge flocks of goats were brought down from the Highlands to Perth to be sold at a tryst'. These animals were apparently used to supply the home market for he states that the flesh was much prized as hams while the skins were used to make saddles, side packs and soldiers knapsacks. If Penny's use of the word plantations refers to the 'Planting Act' of 1457 (*APS*, ii, 51, c. 27) which sought to encourage the planting of hedges for shelter or broom for cattle fodder it may be that he is referring to large scale goat production in a medieval context. However, Barrow (1979 pers comm) doubts whether Penny can be referring to the Planting Act of 1457 and suggests that he is referring to more recent 'improvement' plantations of the 18th and early 19th centuries. If this is so it remains to be established that the goat horn cores described from medieval Perth were from animals which were eaten locally.

As well as being a source of cheap meat, goats also produce milk for human consumption. Goats' milk came to be perceived as more 'healthy' than cows' milk since it is less frequently affected by bovine tuberculosis and was eventually considered to be itself a cure for consumption (Campbell 1965, 183–4; Smith forthcoming).

The bird bone

Catherine Smith and A S Clarke

Introduction

The bird bones from the first season of excavation, 1975–76, were identified by Dr A S Clarke of the former Royal Scottish Museum, Edinburgh. Those from the subsequent season (1977) were identified by C Smith who also made anatomical measurements after the scheme of von den Driesch (1976) on the bird bones from both seasons and supplied the text of this report. Reference was made to the comparative skeletal collections of the National Museums Scotland, Edinburgh; Perth Museum and Art Gallery and Dundee Art Galleries and Museums.

Species present

The bird assemblage was dominated by the bones of domestic fowl (*Gallus gallus*) (Illus 37). Geese were present to a much lesser extent, although it was not possible to determine their true status, whether domesticated or wild greylag (*Anser anser*), their bones being impossible to distinguish morphologically. A few bones of pinkfooted goose (*Anser brachyrhynchus*) were, however, found. Ducks were not numerous, rather surprisingly, given the proximity of the site to the River Tay. Mallard/domestic duck (*Anas platyrhynchos*), wigeon (*Anas penelope*), shoveler (*Anas clypeata*), goosander (*Mergus merganser*) and probable eider (*Somateria mollissima*) were found in small numbers. Whooper swan (*Cygnus cygnus*) also occurred, while other water birds were heron (*Ardea cinerea*), crane (*Grus grus*) and red-throated diver (*Gavia stellata*). Other edible wild species were black grouse (*Lyrurus tetrix*) and ptarmigan (*Lagopus mutus*). One bone of peafowl (*Pavo cristatus*) must have come

Illus 37 *Domestic fowl furculae (chicken wishbones).*

from a domesticated bird. Finally, species which may have been scavengers around the burgh middens were buzzard (*Buteo buteo*), raven (*Corvus corax*) and carrion crow/rook (*Corvus corone/frugilegus*). A few bones of eagles, both golden (*Aquila chrysaetos*) and white-tailed sea eagle (*Haliaetus albicilla*) also occurred.

The number of bones recorded from each species is shown in Table 26.

Species accounts

Domestic fowl and peafowl

By far the most numerous avian species at the site appeared to be the domestic fowl (*Gallus gallus*), although care had to be taken in identification in order to avoid confusion with related wild galliform species such as red grouse and pheasant (see Table 27). Anatomical measurements of the bones revealed that at least some of the birds must have approached the size of modern farmyard breeds, while at the bottom of the size range were individuals most closely resembling bantams. However the sex of the birds, rather than their breed, may have been responsible for this wide size range, males presumably having been larger than females of the same breed. The situation is further complicated by the possible occurrence of capons. A true capon is a castrated male in which the gonads have been inactivated either by surgical removal or burning with a hot iron, a somewhat barbaric procedure which has been carried out in past centuries, often with fatal results (West 1982, 255) or as in more recent times by means of a hormone implant in the bird's neck, a process made illegal in Britain in the late 20th century (Twinch 1985, 8). In either case, the reasoning behind the procedure would have been to produce a bird with a meat distribution more characteristic of the female than the male, with, in particular, plumper breast meat.

Simply removing the external indicator of maleness, the bony spur which is found projecting from the bone of the lower leg (that is, on the tarso-metatarsus) also seems to have been believed to produce capons, and although this would not render a cock bird sterile, it may have had the result of making it less likely to fight.

In order to try to separate the bird remains by sex, frequency histograms were plotted for the femur and tarso-metatarsus, plotting greatest length (GL) of each bone against the numbers of bones present (juvenile bones were omitted; Illus 38). Results for

Table 26 *Total numbers of bird bones identified.*

common name	species	number of bones
red-throated diver	*Gavia stellata*	2
grey heron	*Ardea cinerea*	10
stork (?white)	*Ciconia ciconia*	1
whooper swan	*Cygnus cygnus*	1
pinkfooted goose	*Anser brachyrhynchus*	14
greylag/domestic goose	*A. anser*	337
wigeon	*Anas penelope*	1
mallard/domestic duck	*A. platyrhynchos*	19
shoveler	*A. clypeata*	1
eider	*Somateria mollissima*	1
goosander	*Mergus merganser*	1
small duck *sp*		1
buzzard	*Buteo buteo*	2
golden eagle	*Aquila chrysaetos*	3
white-tailed sea eagle	*Haliaetus albicilla*	2
eagle *sp*		1
domestic fowl	*Gallus gallus*	798
black grouse	*Lyrurus tetrix*	6
ptarmigan	*Lagopus mutus*	2
peafowl	*Pavo cristatus*	1
crane	*Grus grus*	2
crow/rook	*Corvus corone/frugilegus*	7
raven	*C. corax*	80
indeterminate species		3
total		**1295**

the femora seem to indicate a bimodal distribution, two peaks being present. The peak in total numbers at a greatest length of between about 69–71mm is most likely to represent females. Those which peak at approximately 10mm longer are probably from males, although it is possible that capons may also have been present. Similarly, in the frequency distribution for the tarso-metatarsus, two groupings seem to occur, hens appearing on the left of Illus 38, while cocks and capons are on the right. The presence or absence of bony spurs on the tarso-metatarsi was also noted. However although it is normally the male birds which bear these outgrowths, West (1982) has shown that capons (in this case meaning male birds from which the gonads have been removed in order to improve their rate of meat production), as well as hens with defective ovaries, are capable of producing impressive spurs. In the case of the Perth High Street tarso-metatarsi, all those bones which bore spurs tended to occur to the right of the distribution diagram, indicating that they were indeed males or capons.

Certainly all three sexes are mentioned in documents relating to the Cistercian Abbey of Coupar Angus, dating from the middle of the 16th century (*Coupar*

Table 27 *Total number of domestic fowl bones identified.*

	number of domestic fowl bones
skull	7
mandible	1
furcula	9
coracoid	57
scapula	8
sternum	41
humerus	133
radius	28
ulna	67
carpo-metacarpus	5
innominate	55
femur	143
tibio-tarsus	155
tarso-metatarsus	85
lumbar vertebrae	3
rib (cf fowl)	1
total	798

Table 28 *Numbers of adult and immature domestic fowl bones identified.*

	number of bones		
bone	adult	immature	total
coracoid	38	6	44
scapula	7		7
humerus	113	20	133
radius	24	3	27
ulna	57	9	66
carpo-metacarpus	4	1	5
femur	119	13	142
tibio-tarsus	149	3	152
tarso-metatarsus	62	20	82
total	573	75	648
%	88.4%	11.6%	100%

Angus Rental). Rentals due to the abbey included for example 'ane dusane [dozen] of pultre and ane dusane of capones' or 'sax [six] pultre cok and hen' where the term 'pultre' (poultry) seems to have meant either female birds only, or any bird other than a 'capone'. Whether these were truly castrated birds or merely those with the spurs removed remains obscure.

One tarso-metatarsus from the site bore a large spur which appeared to have been sawn, at least 7.5mm of its length still remaining (C2770, Phase Vdd; Illus 39, 40). This modification would not have occurred as a result of normal butchery and may have resulted from a deliberate attempt to caponise the bird by the external method of removal of the spurs, although as noted above this would have had no effect on its growth. West (1982, 258, Plate 2) illustrates a strikingly similar example from a late 18th- or early 19th-century context at Greyfriars, Oxford, which she believes to have come from a fighting cock. The spurs of such birds were sawn off and replaced with much more lethal steel attachments and it is likely that this was the reason for spur removal at the High Street.

Another tarso-metatarsal, in which there may have been interference with the spur, showed evidence of swelling and pitting of the shaft of the bone as well as the production of a small osteophyte (or bony outgrowth) just proximal to the spur. These changes may have been caused by reaction to an infection introduced into the bone via a failed attempt to remove the spur either for the purposes of caponisation or cock fighting (C3738, Phase Ie). Assessment of the ages at which the birds died or were killed revealed that most of the domestic fowl (88.4%) had passed the age of six months, this being the age by which the epiphyses of the long bones have ossified (Silver 1969, 300) (see Table 28). The presence of so many older birds implies that egg production was of greater importance than the provision of young, tender meat, although it is very possible that porous, fragile bones of younger birds did not survive so well as those of older ones. Egg shell fragments were indeed found at the site, as well as three remarkably well preserved complete eggs which were thought to be from domestic fowl (further investigation would have resulted in damage to the specimens and so was not attempted).

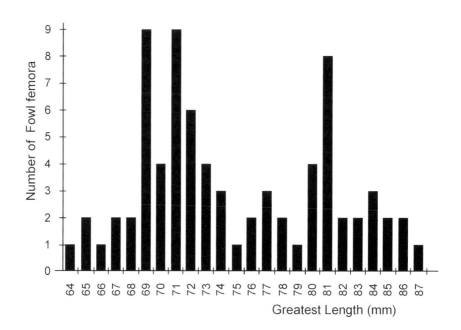

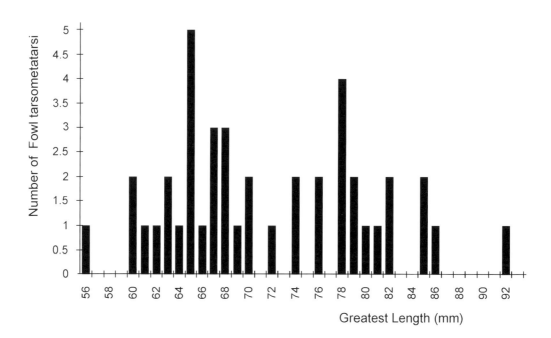

Illus 38 *(above) Greatest length of domestic fowl femora versus frequency.*
(below) Greatest length of domestic fowl tarsometatarsi versus frequency.

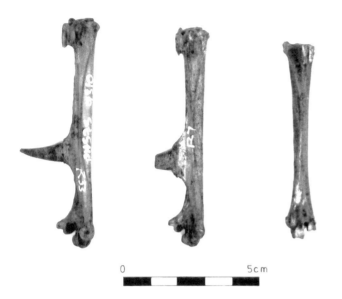

Illus 39 *Three domestic fowl tarsometatarsi, medial and posterior views.*

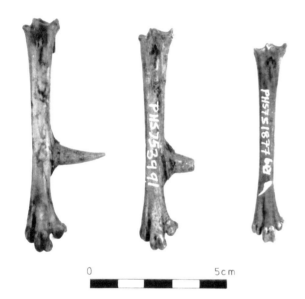

Illus 40 *Domestic fowl tarsometatarsi, anterior view.*

Illus 41 *Peacock (Scone Palace, Perthshire).*

Since only a single bone of peafowl (*Pavo cristatus*), a sternum or breastbone, was found, this species cannot be said to have been eaten every day. Its place has probably always been on the banqueting table where it was served only on special occasions; for example, at the wedding feast of Henry IV of England, 'pokokkys' were consumed during a vast second course, which also included cranes and bitterns (Pullar 1972, 92). Peacock was typically served roasted, then replaced inside its own skin, resplendent with ornate tail feathers, before serving (Illus 41). For this reason, the male bird was preferred since the female's plumage is unremarkable; in the book of accounts of the Percy family, the Northumberland Household Book, it is stipulated that only 'pacokes' and not 'payhennys' are to be bought on the occasion of principal feastdays such as Christmas (Percy 1905).

Geese

Greylag/domestic goose

Determining whether the geese from the site were true wild greylags or their domesticated descendants was, in all but a few cases, impossible. The bones were morphologically indistinguishable from greylag (*Anser anser*), and in many cases were identical in size to the wild type, only a very few reaching the size of a modern domestic goose used for comparison. The surrounding environment of medieval Perth would have provided ample opportunity for wildfowling, particularly on the flat (and in the medieval period, undrained and boggy) Carse lands. In winter time, wild grey geese can still be seen grazing at the present day, although probably not in the density of former times. Baxter and Rintoul (1953, 365), the great authorities on the status of birds in Scotland, have noted that 'draining the marshes undoubtedly made wild geese less plentiful than they were in the old days; there are notes to this effect in a good many of the old writings', although they also observe that the species referred to has not been differentiated in early documents. Wild geese are listed in the rentals of Coupar Angus Abbey in 1541 and 1547 as one of the types of bird to be caught by the 'craft of fowlarie' by the appointed fowler, John Sowter of Mylnhorn, the price to be paid by the cellarer for 'ilk wild guiss, tuay schillingis' (*Coupar Angus Rental*, ii, 13). Elsewhere, wild geese are referred to as 'geis siluistres' and are always distinguished from the domesticated variety which are described as 'tame', 'fatted' or 'fed' (ibid, xix).

That many of the geese from the site must have been of the 'tame' kind is suggested by the numbers of their bones, which although by no means so numerous as those of domestic fowl, are still far more plentiful than those of other edible wild birds such as ducks (see Table 29). Analysis of age at death revealed that the majority of the geese (96. 0%) were mature when killed, as Table 30 shows. The value of the older birds must have lain in their capability to produce eggs, feathers (quills for

Table 29 *Total number of domestic goose/greylag bones identified.*

bone	number identified
skull	1
mandible	1
quadrate	1
furcula	8
coracoid	23
scapula	4
sternum	19
humerus	55
radius	56
ulna	31
carpo-metacarpus	49
innominate	11
femur	17
tibio-tarsus	31
tarso-metatarsus	28
phalange (wing)	2
total	337

Table 30 *Numbers of adult and immature goose bones identified.*

	number of bones		
bone	adult	immature	total
coracoid	23		23
scapula	4		4
humerus	40	4	44
radius	53	2	55
ulna	28	1	29
carpo-metacarpus	48	1	49
femur	16	1	17
tibio-tarsus	25		25
tarso-metatarsus	24	2	26
total	261	11	272
%	96.0%	4.0%	100.0%

arrows and pens), goose grease for lubrication and medicinal purposes and substantial amounts of meat as opposed to the lower meat yield and downier feathers of younger birds.

Other goose species

Although no definite evidence of the bean goose (*Anser fabalis*) was found at the site, it is possible that some of the smaller specimens identified as its close relative, the greylag, could have come from this species. At the present time, the bean goose is described as a 'less than annual visitor' to the area and as a rarity even in the first half of the twentieth century (Burnett 1993, 12; Harvie-Brown 1906, 223). However it is believed to have been much more abundant on Tayside in the past and may have been overlooked in the assemblage.

Another goose species which was however found at the site was the pinkfooted goose (*A brachyrhynchus*) although its positive identification proved difficult due to similarities to wild greylag. Although an abundant and increasing winter visitor at the present day (Thom 1986, 96–8) the very few bones recovered from the excavation may indicate that it was not always so numerous.

Ducks

As with the difficulty in separating the greylag from the domestic goose, so with the mallard (*Anas platyrhynchos*) and its descendant the domestic duck. Only a small number of duck bones was recovered from the site in any case and these were referable to true mallard, none of them approaching the large size of the modern domestic variety. It would seem that domestic ducks came very late to Scotland, or that they remained very similar to the wild progenitor for a considerable period of time.

Currently the River Tay at Perth abounds with mallard, which breed in close proximity to the town and could easily have been netted or snared, thus it is somewhat surprising that there was so little evidence for their exploitation. Perhaps they may have been considered too troublesome to catch when there were numerous domestic fowl available, within the town itself. Indeed the price paid to the fowler of Coupar Angus was only fourpence for each 'duik', rather less than that allowed for larger birds (*Coupar Angus Rental*, ii, 13).

Duck species other than mallard were poorly represented at the site, but in view of their smaller size, it is not surprising that bones of species such as wigeon (*A. penelope*) and shoveler (*A. clypeata*) were found only rarely. Goosander (*Mergus merganser*), which can still be seen regularly on the Tay at Perth, was represented by only one bone. Eider (*Somateria mollissima*) overwinter in great rafts at the mouth of the Tay, and have in recent years been noted in numbers as great as 20,000 birds. Breeding in Tayside at the present day has however been restricted to Montrose Basin (Burnett 1993). Since sea ducks are trapped most easily during the breeding season, when they are forced on to dry land, it is probable that the Perth specimen was caught some distance away from the town on coastal mudflats or dunes at the river mouth.

Swans

Only one bone of whooper swan (*Cygnus cygnus*) was found. Surprisingly, mute swan (*C. olor*) was absent, although today it is common on the Tay all year round, while the whooper swan visits only in winter. There is little doubt as to the edibility of swans, although we are recommended that to enjoy this bird to the full, 'the young cygnet is best' (Smith nd, 194). The price to be paid to the fowler of Coupar Angus Abbey for one swan was five shillings, not surprising, given the amount of meat it could yield, whereas a goose was only worth two shillings (*Coupar Angus Rental*, ii, 13).

Other edible species

Other birds which could have been eaten, and probably were, included red-throated diver (*Gavia stellata*), grey heron (*Ardea cinerea*), stork (*Ciconia ciconia*) and crane (*Grus grus*) as well as the relations of the domestic fowl, the black grouse (*Lyrurus tetrix*) and ptarmigan (*Lagopus mutus*). There is no doubt as to the edibility of grouse, both the red and black species, although as regards the former, younger birds are preferred for the table than older ones, being less tough, while the black grouse (also known as black game) is not considered such good eating as the red, tending to be hard, dry and flavourless if not well hung (Smith nd 39, 105).

Reference is made to the crane in the Rental Book of Coupar Angus Abbey, bringing in the same price as a swan, five shillings (*Coupar Angus Rental*, ii, 13). However it may always have been something of a speciality dish; for example, 'cranys' feature in the Northumberland Household Book (Percy 1905) as a bird to be bought in only for Christmas and other principal feasts. This status may have been conferred on the bird by its comparative rarity as much as its large size. At the present day it occurs in Scotland only as a vagrant and has not bred in Britain since about 1600 (Thom 1986, 166). Crane bones, including a few from juveniles, have also been recovered from medieval archaeological sites in Aberdeen, implying that the bird did once breed in the north-east of Scotland (Hamilton-Dyer 1993 and 1994; Hamilton-Dyer et al

2001, 279–80). But the meat of the crane did not appeal to all tastes. A 16th-century document described this bird as being 'hard of digestion, and maketh yll juice, but beyng hanged up longe in the ayre, he is the lesse unwholesome' (Elyot's *Castel of helth*, quoted in Simon 1983, 548).

The status of the heron, however, is less doubtful. This species breeds locally and is still common along the banks of the Tay and, although it is not mentioned specifically by the compiler of the Coupar Angus Rentals, it is likely that it was not differentiated from the 'cran' to which it bears a superficial resemblance. The name 'crane' was, in many areas, transferred to the heron after the former bird became less widely distributed (Lockwood 1984, 48). Herons (preferably young birds) were also among the fowls served to the Earls of Northumberland at holiday times (Percy 1905). Care is recommended in handling and cooking this species, however, since if the bones are broken, it is best to discard the bird since, 'it will only prove a disappointment, due to the fishy fluid escaping from the broken bones tainting the meat' (Smith nd, 123). The 16th-century writers all advised the drinking of plenty of good strong wine with such 'weather-sore' birds as the heron, presumably to disguise the taste (Simon 1983, 572).

The red-throated diver, although breeding only in small numbers in modern-day Perthshire (Thom 1986, 68) was probably more widely distributed in the past. Its presence at the site is probably an indicator of the type of undrained land which would contain the small moorland lochans which are this species' preferred breeding grounds.

Birds of prey and scavengers

A few bones of golden eagle (*Aquila chrysaetos*) and probable white-tailed sea eagle (*Haliaetus albicilla*) were found at the site. The latter species, also known as the earne, occurred commonly in Scotland in the past, and could be found in Perthshire until the early part of the 20th century (Love 1983, 116) when driven to extinction by gamekeepers and shepherds intent on preserving wild game and lambs. Golden eagles were also considered to be vermin and persecuted in the same way, as were buzzards, which were named as 'foulys of reif' in an act of James II of 1457 (Baxter and Rintoul 1953, 301), 'reif' having the meaning of robbery or spoliation. Bones of buzzards have also been found elsewhere in medieval Perth, at Meal Vennel and Canal Street (Smith 1996a and 1996b).

Raven (*Corvus corax*) bones were relatively numerous, indicating rich pickings from the open middens of the burgh, which presumably also attracted carrion crows and buzzards as well as mammalian scavengers such as dogs. Raven bones have also been retrieved at King Edward Street, Perth (Smith 1995a, 989) and medieval Aberdeen (Hamilton-Dyer et al 2001, 279). Corvids were probably persecuted since they are believed to peck the eyes of sickly lambs.

The gardener engaged by the Abbey of Coupar Angus was enjoined to promise that he would 'nocht let ane craw big within the bundis, eftir his power' (that is, build within the grounds), presumably meaning that any nests would be destroyed in order to protect valuable livestock (*Coupar Angus Rental*, ii, 208).

Distribution of bird bones over the site

Details of the numbers of bird bones from each species found in context groups such as middens, buildings, pits and paths are shown in the CD insert. A study of the distribution of bird bones found in middens shows that some of the birds which scavenged on the rubbish of the town also became part of the middens when they died. In midden M14b(b), Phase Ie, for example, 31 raven bones from a minimum number of four individuals were recovered from Context 3622. This midden also contained bones of eagle and buzzard, and taken together with the unusually high number of raven bones may be interpreted as deliberate pest control.

Midden M1.4d (Phase IVb,IVc) contained 46 fowl bones, representing at least five different birds, most of which were found in Pit 2566. A pit in midden M3e (Pit 2111, Phase Vdd>) contained 37 fowl bones, including a skull, representing at least four individuals, as well as an intact egg. These pit fills may indicate deliberate disposal of whole birds, perhaps as a result of disease.

Discussion

The avian assemblage from the site has provided a large data bank of measurements of domestic fowl and goose, unmatched by any subsequent excavation within the burgh and thus of great value for comparison with future urban sites in Scotland. Domestic fowl were considered to vary in size from birds as small as bantams to those which approached the size of larger modern breeds. This finding compared remarkably well with data from contemporary sites in Britain and Europe (Brothwell and West pers comm). Similarly, due to the large size of the sample, a greater number of wild bird species was seen to be exploited at the High Street than has proved to be the case at other sites in Perth.

However notable similarities have also been found with more recently excavated sites within the burgh. For example, the proportion of domestic fowl to goose has consistently been found to be very similar to that at the High Street. The observation that wild bird species are always in the minority in the assemblage, compared to the domestic species, has also been made for sites throughout the burgh as well as elsewhere in medieval Scotland, for example, in Aberdeen, and in England, at 16–22 Coppergate, York (O'Connor 1989, 193).

The wild species found at the site are an indicator of the changing environment of Perth from the medieval period to the present day. Cranes are no longer to be found along the waterways of the Tay, the boggy ground and wet meadows which are the birds' preferred breeding habitat having long been drained and reclaimed for agriculture. Similarly, the breeding habitat of the red-throated diver has presumably also decreased because of drainage and change of land use, and although this species can still be found in winter in the outer Tay Estuary its breeding success within the Perthshire area has been limited to sites such as Loch Rannoch, at some distance from the town of Perth itself (Perthshire Bird Report 1976–8, 13).

Buzzards and ravens have ceased to circle the once open middens of the burgh, their niche in the modern townscape having been taken by herring gulls, wheeling over the municipal coups of Scotland. Crows, however are still common, despite the local persecution by farmers and gamekeepers which has until very recently greatly reduced the modern buzzard population.

The study of the bird bones has in a small way given a tantalising glimpse of life in the medieval burgh, ranging from the evidence of everyday diet provided by the numerous fowl and goose bones, to the food of special occasions and holidays when peacocks, cranes and herons would have been enjoyed. Wildfowling on the banks of the Tay, probably with nets and snares, would have been engaged in, although possibly by professional wildfowlers such as those employed by Coupar Angus Abbey. The pastimes, too, of the people of the town, as well as their day to day existence, have been revealed; that spectacles such as cockfights were barbarous and often fatal to the participating birds is indisputable; that they took place in late medieval Perth, only slightly less so.

The fish bone

Andrew K G Jones

Introduction and methods

The highly organic, waterlogged early 12th- to later 14th-century deposits of central Perth provided a favourable environment for the survival of fish remains of many kinds. Fragile scale fragments, otoliths, and cranial bones from small fish were recovered, in addition to vertebral centra and robust head bones of large gadid (cod family) fish. Table 31 shows which elements were present for the recorded taxa. (For a discussion of the kinds of fish remains which can be encountered in archaeological deposits, see Wheeler 1978). The majority of the fish bones from the site were unabraded and were dark brown in colour, typical of those recovered from urban waterlogged deposits.

Two procedures were used to recover fish remains. A group of approximately 1,500 identifiable large bones was hand collected by excavators sorting trowelled soil during both the 1975–6 and 1977 seasons. A second group of 219 identified bones was collected from the dry residues of approximately 40 one kilogram soil samples sieved on 300micron meshed sieves. Fish bones were identified by comparing archaeological specimens with modern reference skeletons in the collection at the Environmental Archaeology Unit, University of York. Nomenclature follows Wheeler (1969).

It is well understood that hand collected assemblages of fish remains are subject to considerable bias favouring

Table 31 *Fish remains by species and bone.*

bone	SEL	HER	SAL	SME	EEL	SAI	COD	HAD	LIN	PLE	HAL
articular							+		+	*	
ceratohyal							+		+		
cleithrum							+	+	+		+
dentary			+			+	+*		+		
denticle	*										
hyomandibular		*			*		+		+		
maxilla		*					+	*	+	*	
opercular		*						*		*	
otic bulla		*									
otolith							+*	+			
parasphenoid							+		+		
post temporal							+	*	+		
preopercular							+				
premaxilla						+	+*	*	+		
pterygiophore										+	
quadrate							+	*		*	
rib			*								
supracleithrum							+			*	
vertebral centrum (vc)	*	*	+*	*	*	+	+*	*	+*	*	+
vomer							+			*	

notes/key

+	bone recovered by hand excavation
*	bone recovered from sieved samples

SEL	Selachii (cartilaginous fishes)
HER	herring (*Clupea harengus* L.)
SAL	Salmonid (probably *Salmo salar* L.)
SME	smelt (*Osmerus eperlanus* L.)
EEL	eel (*Anguilla anguilla* L.)
SAI	saithe (*Pollachius virens* L.)

COD	cod (*Gadus morhua* L.)/Gadid
HAD	haddock (*Melanogrammus aeglefinus* L.)
LIN	ling (*Molva molva*)
PLE	Pleuronectid (Flatfish/plaice/flounder)
HAL	halibut (*Hippoglossus hippoglossus* L.)

the large bones of large fish (Jones 1982). The hand collected material was identified rapidly. All the vertebrae, the small number of otoliths and readily recognisable head bones (principally dentaries, pre-maxillae, articulars, quadrates, hyomandibulars and maxillae) were identified. Less easily determined bones (for example cranial bones) were not studied in detail. Large numbers of fin rays, branchiostegal rays, ribs and small fragments were not determined. The unidentified material was composed almost exclusively of bones from large gadid fish; it probably comprised only the remains of fish which were represented by vertebrae or other elements.

An attempt was made to identify as much of the sieved bone as possible. Many remains were assigned to species but some elements could only be identified to genus or family. A considerable number of fin rays, branchials and other relatively featureless bones were left unidentified.

Notes on the identifications

The remains of cartilaginous (selachian) fish were of three kinds: mineralised cores of vertebral centra, teeth and denticles similar in form to rose thorns. All were assigned to the ray family, Rajidae, although it is possible that the teeth may have come from some other kind of cartilaginous fish.

Salmonid (salmon family) vertebrae were all large (>7mm diameter) and were considered to be from salmon *Salmo salar* L., rather than trout, *S. trutta* L. Salmon dentaries and large salmonid rib fragments were also present.

Some of the cod family vertebrae proved particularly difficult to identify. Centra from cod, *Gadus morhua* L., and saithe, *Pollachius virens* L., were not always assigned to species and were frequently placed in the family Gadidae. Ling vertebral centra were assigned to the genus *Molva* but not to species.

A flatfish maxilla was identified as plaice, *Pleuronectes platessa* L.; however, a number of other small flatfish bones, including vertebral centra, while consistent with plaice, may have come from flounder, *Platichthys flesus* L. Halibut, *Hippoglossus hippoglossus* L., a member of the flatfish family Pleuronectidae, was recognised by its distinctively large vertebral centra and cleithra fragments.

Results

Tables 32 and 33 indicate that the assemblage collected by hand comprised a different species composition to that recovered by sieving. The hand collected assemblage was dominated by cod (80%), while ling occurred in many layers. Saithe, haddock *Melanogrammus aeglefinus* L., flatfish (both ?plaice and halibut) and salmon were also present, but were

represented only by small numbers of bones. By contrast, the sieved assemblage was dominated by herring, *Clupea harengus* L. (54%). The sieved sample contained all the species collected by hand except saithe and halibut and in addition included remains of cartilaginous fish, Rajidae, smelt (sparling) *Osmerus eperlanus* L. and eel *Anguilla anguilla* L.

All of the site phases produced large gadid head bones and vertebrae indicating that whole, and therefore probably locally caught, fresh fish were imported on to the site. The distribution of skeletal elements of large gadid fish on archaeological excavations has been used by Wilkinson (1979, 75) to suggest that some of the cod imported to Exeter arrived dried, as 'split fish'. Large gadids are usually decapitated and gutted as the first stage of processing, thus an archaeological assemblage composed of large gadid vertebral centra, with no head bones, may be interpreted as the remains of dried fish.

Of particular interest in the hand collected material was a large number of cod upper and lower jaws (pre-maxillae and dentaries respectively). These were measured at points described by Wheeler and Jones (1976). Using these measurements and the procedure outlined (ibid) it was possible to estimate the modal size of the large cod brought on to the site and to give some idea of the maximum size of fish eaten. The cod were mainly 110cm long, with a maximum length of 130cm. Using the cod jaw bone measurement data, it was possible to compare the bones collected by hand at the site with those recovered by hand at Great Yarmouth (Wheeler and Jones 1976). Although the results from the hand collected bone sample show that cod ranging from 50–130cm in length were present, the modal length of the Perth cod was 20cm larger than those recovered by hand at Great Yarmouth. It would however be unwise to assume that the hand collected cod bones reflect the total population of cod brought on to the site. Only three measurable cod jaw bones were present in the sieved sample and all were from small fish, c35–45cm total length, indicating that many small cod were also present in the deposits, but were overlooked during hand excavation. Only cod bones were sufficiently abundant to allow comparison with other published data. The haddock, ling, saithe, halibut and salmonid bones were all from medium to large animals (approximately 75cm total length or larger). The first anal pterygiophores of flatfish were from fish smaller than 50cm. The sieved assemblage, on the other hand, was dominated by small and medium sized fish. Only ling, cod and salmonid remains were from fish larger than 75cm. (It is not possible to estimate the size of the cartilaginous fish with the same accuracy but it seems likely that these too were about 100cm long).

Thus, contrasting, but mutually complimentary, pictures emerge from the analysis of the hand collected and sieved fish bones. However, both assemblages were composed largely of marine species, with a small number of migratory fish.

Table 32 *Fish bones collected by hand (arranged by species and period).*

number of contexts	period	SAL	SAI	COD	HAD	LIN	FLA	total
21	I	1*		20*				21
				9	1			10
7	I–II			4*	1*			5
				4	1			5
40	II		23*	80*		7*		110
			1	28	2	3		34
12	II–III			36*		2*		38
				1		3		4
3	II–IV			3*				3
				1				1
20	III	1*	5*	38*		1*		45
		2		28	2	2		34
5	III–IV			23*		3*		26
						1		1
104	IV	1*	3*	246*		33*	1*	284
			5	80	3	8	1	97
23	IV–V		2*	30*		10*		42
				9		3		12
102	V		19*	283*		62*	1*	365
			2	122	4	18	2	148
5	V–VI			78*		27*		105
				16		1		17
3	VI			1				1
				3				3
4	Area 5			5*		1*		6
				2		1		3
1	Area 6			1				1
7	u/s		1*	32*		17*		50
		2	1	16		1		20
	total vertebral centra (vc)	3	53	879		164	2	1101
	total other bones	4	9	320	11	43	3	390
	grand total	7	62	1199	11	207	5	1491

note * indicates number of vertebral centra (vc)

Table 33 *Fish bones collected by sieving (arranged by species and period).*

number of contexts	period	SEL	HER	SAL	SME	EEL	COD	HAD	LIN	PLE	total
1	II		2*								2
					1			1			2
1	III		2*								2
26	IV		57*		2*	1*	5*	5*	1*	17*	88
		3	3	1				4		3	14
12	V	1*	45*		1*	3*	3*	4*		23*	80
			3	2		1	4	4	1	4	19
2	u/s		7*			1*				3*	11
					1					1	2
	total vc	1	113		3	5	8	9	1	43	183
	total other	3	6	5		1	5	8	1	7	36
	grand total	4	119	5	3	6	13	17	2	50	219

abbreviations as Table 32; u/s = unstratified

Discussion

Differences both in species composition and size of the fish collected by hand and by sieving are marked. These differences demonstrate how recovery techniques can influence what is learnt from an excavation. A number of authors have shown how assemblages of fish collected by hand are dominated by large-boned species, while sieved samples produce a more representative group of bones (for example Wheeler and Jones 1976). Problems of recovery can be readily tackled by the institution of carefully conceived sieving programmes. Other biases are less easily assessed. Fish do not all contain the same number of bones and these bones are not equally resistant to mechanical and chemical damage under burial conditions. These aspects must be borne in mind when considering any archaeological fish bone assemblage. Nevertheless, it is clear that the townsfolk of Perth exploited a considerable variety of fish in their diet, and it is likely that the overall picture presented by the two assemblages reflects the main trends in fish consumption. Clearly marine fish were the most frequently eaten. Remains of exclusively freshwater fish (for example pike and roach) were absent from the assemblages, while bones of migratory species (salmon, eel and smelt) were not present in very large numbers.

Marine fish, mainly herring and gadids, appear to have played a more important role in feeding the medieval population of Perth than locally available migratory species. This indicates that the demand for fish was probably greater than the river's capacity to supply food. The Tay is navigable and tidal as far upriver as Perth and the importation of fresh marine fish caught in the North Sea (and possibly of preserved fish caught and prepared at some distance from the site) would have been relatively easy. Migratory and estuarine species could have been taken locally. It is impossible to be certain of the fishing methods used by the ancient fishermen, but it is clear that several different techniques must have been employed to catch the range of fish found at the site. Most of the marine fish were probably caught using hook and line; several fish hooks were recovered from the site (see Fascicule 2, The metalwork). Large cod, ling, saithe, haddock, plaice and halibut are traditionally taken on handlines in Scotland although trawling is now widespread. Such fish were probably fairly readily taken from the east coast of Scotland. Herring, by contrast, almost never take hooks and are usually caught using floating nets. Unfortunately, there is no evidence to indicate whether the herring were brought to the site as fresh fish or if they were imported preserved in barrels or smoked. The history of the Scottish herring fishery dates back to at least 1410. At this time William, Count of Holland, was assisting the Dutch to make reprisals against the Scots for having ill-treated Dutch fishermen who had attempted to catch herring in Scottish waters. By 1423 there was a considerable export trade in herring and duties were imposed by James I (Samuel 1918, 86). It thus seems likely that herring were caught by Scottish fishermen throughout the medieval period.

As for locally available migratory species, a number of different kinds of net and trap may have been set in the Tay to catch eel, smelt and salmon.

Unfortunately, it is impossible to use these results to compare the roles of large gadids and smaller marine species (small cod and herring) as components of human diet because it is not possible to determine how well the assemblages compare with the actual quantities of food fish consumed or traded on the site. However, it is apparent that during the 12th century a large number of different kinds of fishes were brought to Perth, adding to the variety of food available to the townsfolk. In addition, it is reasonable to conclude that supplying fish to the town was an important aspect of the medieval economy.

The human bone

I H M Smart and R B Longmore

One fragment of human bone was recovered during the excavation (A11043; Context 5085–3; Phase (Id–)IIb–IId; Rigs V and VI). This was the lower facial region of a skull, consisting of both maxillae, left zygomatic bone and the lower parts of both palatine bones. The specimen was hard and unfriable, the surface stained a medium brown colour with darker patches and was of slightly polished appearance. In its general condition of preservation this specimen was similar to many of the animal bones which were found at the site. Most of the median wall and orbital surface of both maxillae were missing, exposing the interior of the sinus. A vestige of the premaxillary suture could be distinguished on the right side near the mid line.

The surviving parts of the maxillae contained sixteen tooth sockets. On the right side, three molars and the second premolar were present, along with the roots of the first premolar and the lateral incisor. On the left side, the first and second molars were present as well as the stumps of the two incisors and second premolar. The remaining sockets were empty. The margins of the empty sockets and those occupied by tooth stumps were sharply defined with no evidence of bone resorption, indicating that the loss and breakage of the teeth occurred post-mortem. The teeth, although patchily stained, showed no signs of caries or dental calculus. A small amount of wear was present, maximal on the first molars where dentine was just visible in the centre of the mesio-buccal and mesio-palatal cusps. There was no evidence of mesial drift beyond a small worn facet on the anterior surface of the surviving left first molar. Transverse ridging on the enamel surface was also an indication of minimal wear.

The presence of a completely erupted third molar indicates a minimal age of 18 years at death. The slight amount of wear on the teeth, the minimal mesial drift and the vestige of unfused premaxillary suture suggest early rather than late adulthood, perhaps 20–25 years. No strong indication of the sex of the individual was present, or of any pathological conditions. The three bones, that is, the two maxillae and left zygomatic bone, were not separated from the skull by fracturing but were dislocated along the suture lines where they articulated with the missing parts of the skeleton.

Table 34 *Numbers of mollusc shells identified.*

common name	species	number of shells
oyster	*Ostrea edulis*	6393
mussel	*Mytilus edulis*	3158
limpet	*Patella* cf *vulgata*	29
freshwater pearl mussel	*Margaritifera margaritifera*	314
buckie/whelk	*Buccinum undatum*	21
cockle	*Cerastoderma* cf *edule*	27
periwinkle/wulk	*Littorina littorea*	276
dog whelk	*Nucella lapillus*	10
Iceland cyprina	*Arctica islandica*	4
trough shell	*Spisula solida*	2
screw shell	*Turritella communis*	1
top shell	*Gibbula cineraria*	1
scallop	*Pecten maximus*	2

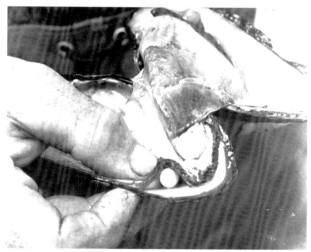

Illus 43 *Pearl mussel* (Margaritifera margaritifera) *from the Tay, containing pearl, 1960s. (Copyright Perth Museum and Art Gallery)*

Illus 42 *Oyster shells and animal bone from the site. (Copyright Perth Museum and Art Gallery)*

The mollusca

The late David Heppel, Catherine Smith and David McKay

Notes on the identification

The molluscan material was initially sorted and listed
by William Finlayson and Kathleen McSweeney and
identified by David Heppel at the Department of
Natural History, National Museums Scotland, then
known as the Royal Scottish Museum, Edinburgh.

For all bivalve species, that is, shells composed
of two halves called 'valves', it is the number of
single valves, not complete shells, which have been
counted, and which appear in Table 34. In the case
of fragmented mussel shells, only the hinges of the
valves were counted; if no hinge was present, the
presence of mussel fragments was noted but not
enumerated. Thus, by counting both valves separately,
the relative abundance of the bivalves has been over-
estimated by a factor of two compared to the univalves.
It should also be noted that marine bivalve shells vary
considerably in their resistance to mechanical damage:
scallops and oysters are the most resistant, while
cockles and mussels are the least.

Species present

Marine bivalves which were identified at the site were
oyster (*Ostrea edulis*) (Illus 42), mussel (*Mytilus edulis*),
cockle (*Cerastoderma edule*), trough shell (*Spisula
solida*), Iceland cyprina (*Arctica islandica*) and scallop
(*Pecten maximus*). Other marine mollusca recovered
were limpet (*Patella* sp), whelk or buckie (*Buccinum
undatum*), periwinkle (*Littorina littorea*), dog whelk
(*Nucella lapillus*), screw shell (*Turritella communis*)
and top shell (*Gibbula cineraria*).

The most commonly occurring marine species,
found in relatively large numbers at the site, are all
edible, and must have been deliberately collected,
while those species occurring in small numbers in only
a few contexts, such as top shell, screw shell and dog
whelk, may have been deposited accidentally by other
means. Only one freshwater species, the pearl mussel
(*Margaritifera margaritifera*) was recorded at the site.

Discussion

Of the marine species, all except the screw shell,
Iceland cyprina and scallop are associated with
intertidal or immediately subtidal waters. Scallops
could be collected on the west coast of Scotland at one
time, but there are no such records for the east coast.
All the species recovered from the excavation require
almost fully salt water for survival and therefore could

not have occurred naturally at Perth. Although small
mussels can be collected from most rocky shores, large
mussels are obtained from beds in semi-sheltered areas.
In order to accommodate the development of ports,
many changes have been made to sheltered coastal
areas on the east coast of Scotland, with detrimental
effects on the mussel beds. At the present day, the
nearest large concentrations of mussels occur at
Tayport, the Montrose Basin and in the Eden estuary.
Mussels were widely collected as food for humans, as
well as for baiting hand- and set- lines used to catch
cod and haddock. Rights to collect mussels have been
jealously guarded in the past: a charter of James VI in
1612 confirms the privileges of the royal burgh of Tain
on the Dornoch Firth, granting sole rights over the
collection of mussels: *concharum petram conchasque
lie mussi-scape et mussillis in conspectu dicti burgi
et territorii ejus nuncupat. Sanct-Duthois-scape* (the
rock of the mussels and the mussels, the 'mussi-scape'
and 'mussillis', in sight of the said burgh [of Tain] and
its territory called Sanct-Duthois-scape) (*RMS*, vii,
no 768). The rights conferred by this charter govern
access to this fishery up to the present day and are
administered through the former burgh of Tain's
Common Good Fund.

Perth is some 24km (15 miles) from the open sea,
a distance equivalent to some two or three hours
each way travelling by boat. It is thus unlikely that
Perth would have been the base for a fishing fleet, and
therefore improbable that mussels would have been
transported to Perth for use as bait. It seems more likely
that they were intended as food for humans.

Whereas mussels may still be collected from the
Firth of Tay at the present day, oysters are absent.
However, it is notable that very rarely has an archaeological investigation been carried out in the medieval
burghs of Dundee, Perth and Arbroath which has not
recovered oyster shells. Although a sizeable proportion
of these oysters were probably imported from the
Forth, which supported a thriving oyster fishery up
until the 19th century (Yonge 1960, 156), it is possible
that some derived from now extinct local beds in the
Tay. Fossil oysters are found in the upper layers of the
Arctic clay deposits, formed during the period of the
last glaciation, at Inchcoonans near Errol in the Carse
of Gowrie (Walker 1961, 52; Davidson 1932, 60). There
is no evidence as to the date at which oysters became
extinct in the Tay, but archaeological evidence from
coastal burghs on the Firth may be construed to imply
that they continued to survive until the medieval period.
Their final extinction may have been due, at least in

part, to over-fishing, as shown by the example of the Forth oyster beds. These were at one time extremely bountiful, and in the 18th century supported a fishery based in Prestonpans, Cockenzie and Newhaven (Yonge 1960, 157). In the late 16th century the beds yielded, according to Fynes Morison, 'plentifully . . .(among other fish) store of oysters and shel fishes' (Hume Brown 1978, 85). A sense of the rate at which the Forth beds were depleted is indicated by the record of exports from the port of Leith: in the year 1666, 721,000 casks went out through the port, yet in 1690, the number had fallen to 10,000 (Mowat nd, 219). In the latter quarter of the 18th century, the intensity of the fishing increased leading to a serious decline in the oyster beds. Although temporary measures were taken to restrict fishing in the early part of the 19th century, the decline continued until the fishery was eventually abandoned around 1920 (Millar 1961, 10–11).

Both mussels and oysters can survive for several days after collection, especially in periods of cooler weather, and it is more likely that in the medieval period they would have been eaten in the winter months.

As regards the relative abundance of mussels and oysters, mussels live in the intertidal area and may be easily collected from the shore at low tide. However, in the historic period, the available evidence indicates that the oyster beds in the Firth of Forth were all located below low water mark, and their exploitation would have required the use of boats and the development of rakes and dredges to recover them. This may account for the higher relative abundance of mussels in the earlier phases of the excavation, since they could perhaps have been obtained with less effort.

Cockles are also widely eaten, but although they currently occur on the east coast of Scotland, are nowhere present in abundance. The small number of cockle shells found probably reflects this natural scarcity rather than any dietary preference.

Periwinkles and limpets are also widely eaten. As a food, periwinkles are more highly valued than limpets, which tend to be eaten mainly in times of food shortage, and this would account for their relative abundances at the site. Top shells and dog whelks occur in areas where periwinkles are abundant, and may have been collected with them from the shore. Iceland cyprina and screw shell, however, are only rarely found on the shore since their natural habitat is in deep water. It is probable that these species were brought to Perth as a by-product of fishing operations, either as a by-catch on fishing vessels, or in the stomach contents of some of the larger target species such as cod. Accidental importation on to the site in building sand intended for use in mortar is also possible. It is also worthy of note that human beings the world over appear to be fascinated by the variety of form of seashells and their deliberate collection cannot be ruled out.

Early evidence of exploitation of shellfish in the Tay estuary comes from a 'kitchen midden' of Mesolithic date, located about 2km from the burgh of Dundee, in the Stannergate. This midden, along with a number of cist burials which overlay it, was discovered during extensions to Dundee Harbour in the 19th century, and the finder noted the shells were 'principally' those of mussels, periwinkles (known locally as 'wulks'), whelks (known locally as 'buckies'), cockles and limpets. Oysters are not mentioned in this list, although this does not necessarily mean they were absent, given the circumstances of the hurried recording which it was necessary to make before the site was destroyed (Mathewson 1879, 303–7).

Two specimens of the scallop, *Pecten maximus*, found at the site, were of interest. Although this is an edible species and occurs abundantly in the waters off the east coast of Scotland, all currently known beds are in deep water at some distance from the coast. Occasional scallops may have been caught as a by-catch in the line fishery, but no commercial scallop fishery is known prior to the 1980s. Modern dredges towed by clam-boats on the west coast of Scotland consist of a triangular iron frame with a toothed crossbar used for raking the shells out of the seabed (Martin 1995, 52).

Both of the scallop shells from the site were found to have been deliberately bored through, the more complete specimen (A07–0574; Context 7296–7; M9a; Phase IVc,IVcc; Rig VII) having two holes, while the smaller example (A5190; Context 2462A–3; M1.4c; Phase IIIa–IVcc; Rigs V and VI) showed evidence of having been treated in a similar way. It is possible that these shells were pilgrims' badges obtained at Santiago de Compostela in Spain. This may account for the pink colouration observed in these shells, a feature not normally found in British specimens. A similarly bored scallop shell interpreted as a pilgrim's badge has also been noted at a site in Va in Sweden (Stockholm, Statens Historika Museum no. 23785, Spencer pers comm). Further evidence from Scotland of the use of scallop shells as a religious symbol has been found at the medieval burial site on the Isle of May, where the body of a young man was excavated still containing a shell placed in the mouth. Presumably the body was that of a pilgrim who had made the journey to the shrine of Saint James the Great at Compostela (James and Yeoman 2008, 180–1 and Illus 5.24).

Besides the marine species, one freshwater mollusc was also fairly abundant, the pearl mussel *Margaritifera margaritifera* (Illus 43). This species, too, is edible, and has been used by the cod and ling fishermen of the Ythan estuary in Aberdeenshire for baiting lines, but it is also the source of freshwater pearls (Goodwin 1985, 28). In recent times the pearl mussel has become much less abundant and in danger of extinction due to over-fishing and has since 1991 been protected under the Wildlife and Countryside Act 1981 (Statutory Instruments 1991/367 and 1998/878).

The feathers

Ruby Cerón-Carrasco

Introduction

Feather fragments recovered from 15 contexts at the site (1975–6 and 1977 seasons) form the subject of this report, commissioned in 1997. Not all of the feathers stated to have been found during the excavation were found at the time of writing. Of the feathers submitted for analysis, some were still embedded in the original soil. On examination in 1997 it was found that some of their original features had been lost and as a result it was possible in some cases only to identify the order or the family group present.

Methods

The feather remains from the site were recovered by a conservator and were examined under an Instant Light Binocular Microscope using a magnification of between 40 and 450. Comparative reference material was used for identification where possible as well as reference keys (Chandler 1916; Day 1965).

Feathers are formed by a shaft, a vane, rachiis, barbs and barbules. Under the microscope a complex mesh of a vane feather can reveal how each barb of the vane is in effect a miniature feather. Identification was based on the analysis of the rachii, barb and barbule structures of the feathers where these had survived.

Results

Table 35 summarises the results of the analysis of the feather remains from the site. Most of the feather remains appear to have been deposited whole and most were remains of pennae (outer flight and contour feathers) which give shape to the birds and provide insulation. Most were broken fragments due mainly to taphonomic conditions and post-excavation decay.

Context 2246 contained a fragment of shaft from a primary flight feather. This was unidentifiable. Context 2385 contained a primary flight feather, of which 20% survived. This has been assigned to the family Galliformes, which includes domestic fowl.

Context 2462C contained remains of a covert (contour feather), 60% of which survived. This has been assigned to the order Passeriformes, family Corvidae (crows, ravens).

Context 2611 contained a fragment of possible primary flight feather or tail feather, 20% of which survived. Examination of the structure of the basal portion of the barb determined that this probably belonged to a species of the order Anseriformes, family Anatidae (ducks, geese and swans).

Context 7235 contained fragments of a covert feather (small contour), 20% of which survived. The analysis of the structure of a basal portion of the barb and the structure of barbules determined that these belong to the mallard (*Anas platyrhynchos*).

Context 7310 contained a fragment of covert feather (small contour) of which only 5% survived. Analysis of the structure of the barbules determined that this belongs to a species of the order Anseriformes, possibly of the Anatidae family (ducks, geese and swans).

Context 7323 contained fragments of covert feather (small contour), only 10% of which survived, and a fragment of primary flight feather, 20% of which survived. Examination of barbule structure of the covert feather fragments determined that these belong to a species from the order Anseriformes, family Anatidae (ducks, geese and swans). Examination of the basal structure of the flight feather's barb and barbules determined that this belongs to the order Anseriformes, family Anatidae, possibly greylag goose (cf *Anser anser*).

Context 7342 contained fragments of covert feather (small contour), 10% of which survived, and a fragment of primary flight feather, 20% of which survived. Barbule structure of the covert feather fragments determined that these belong to a species of the family Galliformes. Examination of the basal structure of the flight feather's barbs determined that this possibly belongs to the greylag goose (cf *Anser anser*). On first inspection of this specimen, the conservator advised that the feather may have represented an arrow flight (A Clydesdale pers comm). However on further cleaning and examination, it was decided that these were in fact unworked feathers. On closer inspection, it became clear that the shaft of this feather had become mineralised and it appears to have split following its natural pattern; this had given the appearance of having a wooden shaft and hence led to the early opinion that this was an arrow flight. This proved not to be the case. It is, however, noteworthy to add that greylag goose wing feathers have traditionally been used as arrow flights (Pope 1974, 66).

Context 7343 contained fragments of a primary flight feather, 20% of which survived. Very few barbules survived but these determined the feather belongs to a species of the order Anseriformes, Anatidae family (ducks, geese and swans).

Context 2562 contained a flight feather (secondary or tertiary). Although 90% of the feather survived, it

Table 35 *Results of analysis of the feather remains.*

context	main feature	feature	phase	description	identification
2385	M10		IId-IIg	primary (flight feather) 20% survived	Order Galliformes cf *Gallus gallus*
2611	M1.2	Pit 2468	<IIg(IIh)	primary (flight feather) or tail feather 20% survived	Order Anseriformes Family Anatidae
2462C	M1.3		IIi	covert feather (small contour) 60% survived	Order Passeriformes Family Corvidae
2246	M1.4a(a)		IIIa-IIIc	shaft fragment from primary (flight feather)	unidentified
9443	P8.1b/B19 (Phase 2b)	South Room, Occ (1a)	IIIc	covert feather (small contour) x 3 fragments 10% survived	Order Anseriformes Family Anatidae
9439	B19 (Phase 2b)	North Room, Floor (2b)	IIIc	semi-plume 90% survived.	Order Anseriformes
9439	B19 (Phase 2b)	North Room, Floor (2b)	IIIc	fragment covert feather (small contour) 10% survived	Family Anatidae
9444	B19 (Phase 2b)	North Room, Occ (2b)	IIIc	covert feather(s) – several fragments	Order Passeriformes Family Corvidae
9413	B19 (Phase 2b)	North Room, Occ (3)	IIIc	covert feather (small contour) 40% survived	Order Anseriformes Family Anatidae *Anas platyrhynchos*
9404	M15		IIId	covert feather (small contour) 40% survived	Order Anseriformes Family Anatidae
2562	B2	Floor/ Foundation (1)	IVa,IVaa	secondary/tertiary feather (flight feather) 90% survived	Order Anseriformes Family Anatidae cf *Cygnus Cygnus*
7342	MC126	Pit 7402	IVaa,IVb	primary (flight feather) 20% survived.	Order Anseriformes
7342	MC126	Pit 7402	IVaa,IVb	covert feather fragments (small contour) 10% survived	Order Galliformes
7310	B18 (Phase 1/2)		IVaa,IVb	covert feather (small contour) 5% survived	Order Anseriformes Family Anatidae
7323	B18 (Phase 2a)	External (1), Pit 7314	IVb	covert feather fragments x 2 (small contour) 10% survived.	Order Anseriformes
7323	B18 (Phase 2a)	External (1), Pit 7314	IVb	primary (flight feather) 20% survived	Family Anatidae cf *Anser anser*
7343	B18 (Phase 2a)	External (1), Pit 7314	IVb	primary flight feather x 6 fragments 20% survived	Order Anseriformes Family Anatidae

Table 35 *(continued)*

context	main feature	feature	phase	description	identification
7235	B18 (Phase 2b)	North Room & Hall - Floor 2	IVb	covert feather (small contour) x 2 fragments 20% survived	mallard *Anas platyrhynchos*

was quite mineralised and very few features could be distinguished under the microscope. Examination of a few surviving barbules determined that this feather may belong to a species of the order Anseriformes, family Anatidae, possibly to whooper swan (cf *Cygnus cygnus*) and probably to a cygnet.

Context 9404 contained a fragment of a covert feather (small contour), of which 40% survived. Examination of the basal structure of the barbs determined that this belongs to a species of the order Anseriformes, family Anatidae.

Context 9413 contained fragments of covert feather (small contour), of which 40% survived. Examination of the barbules determined that these probably belong to the mallard or wild duck (cf *Anas platyrhynchos*).

Context 9439 contained the remains of a semi-plume, 90% of which survived, and a fragment of covert feather (small contour), 10% of which survived. Examination of the barbule structures of the semi-plume determined that this belongs to a species from the order Anseriformes, family Anatidae. Examination of the covert feather fragment's basal structure of the barb determined that this possibly belongs to the mallard or wild duck (cf *Anas platyrhynchos*).

Context 9443 contained fragments of covert feather fragments (small contour), 10% of which survived. Examination of the barbule structure determined that these belong to a species from the order Anseriformes, family Anatidae.

Context 9444 contained fragments of covert feathers (small contour), 10% of which survived. Examination of the barbule structure determined that these belong to a species of the order Anseriformes, family Anatidae.

Discussion

The families and species identified among the feather remains from the site were also present in the bird bone assemblage (see The bird bone). Therefore it is possible that there is some relationship between the bones and the feather remains.

The recovery of Galliformes feathers may represent the presence of domestic fowl, *Gallus gallus*, which in the bird bone assemblage was present with variable size ranges. This has been explained in terms of possible egg production and the possible breeding of birds for the purpose of cock fighting (see The bird bone).

Feather remains from the Anseriformes, family Anatidae, were also recovered, of which mallard or wild duck (*Anas platyrhynchos*), greylag goose (*Anser anser*) and whooper swan (*Cygnus cygnus*) were the species tentatively identified. As these species were all present in the bone assemblage, there may be a relationship.

The presence of feather remains of Passeriformes, family Corvidae, (crows and ravens), may be explained in terms of the scavenging nature of these species. Raven bones were relatively numerous in the bird bone assemblage.

The feather remains from the site appear to have derived from either natural loss or as a result of waste from processing of bird carcasses. Although there seems to be no indication of other uses for these feather remains, this may be due mainly to the poor conditions of their preservation. It would be difficult to observe deliberate cut marks under such conditions.

Table 36 *Details of botanical samples examined.*

context	context group	phase	extraction method	context description
6048	M9b(b)	IVc,IVcc	PF	** moist organic soil in Pit 6132
6078	M9b(b)	IVc,IVcc	PF	moist peaty clay soil with much dung
6100	M9b(b)	IVc,IVcc	PF	dungy material
6104	M9b(b)	IVc,IVcc	PF	dung with wood fragments (possibly same as 6078)
6131	M9b(b)	IVc,IVcc	WS 100 cm³	** well preserved organic debris, with straw and many woodchips; fill of Pit 6127
7125	B53 (Phase 2), North Room, Occ(7c)	Vbb	PF	clayey loam
7129	B53 (Phase 1)	Vb	PF	clayey soil with straw, fill of T7152
7168	M8a	Va,Vaa	PFR	clayey soil with much organic material
7169	M1.5b	Vaa	1. PF 2. bot	organic clayey soil
7175	M8a	Va,Vaa	PF	*fibrous material filling Pit 7183
7205	M8a	Va,Vaa	PF	clayey soil with patches of mortar, fill of T7206
7213	M8a	Va,Vaa	PF	loose silty soil with some fibrous material, filling MF7212
7218	M9a	IVc,IVcc	PF	dungy soil with some woodchips, ash patches and areas of burning
7223	M9a	IVc,IVcc	PF	charcoal and dungy soil, filling hearth H7224
7225	M9a	IVc,IVcc	PF	sand with woodchips
7234	M9a	IVc,IVcc	1. PF 2. WS 100 cm³	** dung with much straw, some peat and seeds, much moss; fill of Pit 7230
7320	B18 (Phase 1/2)	IVaa,IVb	bot	mixed clayey soil and sand with many woodchips
7323	B18 (Phase 2a)	IVb	WS 100 cm³	**dung in Pit 7314
9137	B18 (Phase 1/2)	IVaa,IVb	PF	compact dung layer
9153	B18 (Phase 1/2)	IVaa,IVb	1. PF 2. WS 100 cm³	dung with many woodchips and some ash and sand
9235	B18 (Phase 1/2)	IVaa,IVb	1. PF 2. WS 100 cm³	compact brown soil

The botanical remains

Mhairi Fraser and Catherine Smith

Methods

The plant material dealt with here comes largely from the second season of excavation at the site (1977). A total of 31 biological samples from Areas 7, 9 and 10 were examined for their plant macrofossil content. The macrofossils were extracted by J A W Lock from 1kg subsamples of soil by paraffin flotation. Plant remains were recovered from both the flot and the residue, with the exception of four samples from which only the residue was examined. Small sub-samples of 100cm^3 of soil (300cm^3 in one case) from a number of contexts were also examined by wet-sieving to ensure recovery of all remains. In addition hand-picked botanical samples were examined.

Extracted plant remains were sorted and identified by comparison with modern reference material. Nomenclature of plants follows Clapham, Tutin and Warburg (1962) for angiosperms and Smith, A (1978) for bryophytes.

Table 36 lists the samples taken, with brief notes on their archaeological contexts.

Table 36 *(continued)*

context	context group	phase	extraction method	context description
9240	P8.2b	IVb	PF	patch of peaty soil in pathway
9251	B18 (Phase 1/2)	IVaa,IVb	PFR	clay, partially burnt; lining for hearth H9244
9261	B18 (Phase 1b)	IVa,IVaa	1. PFR 2. bot	grey ash; destruction layer
9273	B18 (Phase 1/2)	IVaa,IVb	PF	organic soil filling posthole PH9270
9275	B18 (Phase 1/2)	IVaa,IVb	PF	*sandy soil with some woodchips filling Pit 9276
9277	B18 (Phase 1/2)	IVaa,IVb	PF	organic soil with lenses of ash
9279	B18 (Phase 1/2)	IVaa,IVb	PF	ash with lenses of black organic material
9280	B18 (Phase 1b)	IVa,IVaa	PF	dung, mortar and soil filling posthole PH9242
9282	B18 (Phase 1/2)	IVaa,IVb	PFR	loam and woodchips
9285	B18 (Phase 1/2)	IVaa,IVb	PF	dung with ash and woodchips
9302	B18 (Phase 1/2)	IVaa,IVb	PF	*dungy soil with woodchips, filling Pit 9301
9317	B18 (Phase 1/2)	IVaa,IVb	PF	*dung with patches of ash and sand, filling Pit 9301
9325	B18 (Phase 1/2)	IVaa,IVb	PF	ash with lens of dung

notes/key

PF	paraffin flotation		bot	botanical sample
PFR	paraffin flotation; residue only examined for plant remains		*	sample from a pit
WS	wet sieved		**	sample from a possible cess pit

Dating of the botanical samples

Dendrochronological studies of timbers from the site and studies of imported pottery have shown that most of the deposits from which the samples came date to within the period c1120 to c1370. Timber from a pit under Building 18 gave a felling date of after 1139 (no bark was present), while timber from inside the building gave a felling date range of 1172–1208 (Fascicule 1, Appendix 5). Sherds of Rouen pottery dating to around the mid 13th century were found associated with the same building.

Description of plant assemblages recovered from the contexts examined

Most of the plant material in the deposits was preserved under anaerobic conditions due to waterlogging which effectively excludes the oxygen necessary for decomposition by aerobic organisms in the soil. However the majority of cereal grains, a few legume seeds and a small number of seeds of weeds, heathland and wetland plants were carbonised.

The samples were remarkably rich in terms of number of species (see Table 37). A total of 147 taxa were recorded, including 24 bryophytes (mosses and liverworts). Of this total, however, only 26 were considered as 'plants useful to man', the great majority being weeds and plants of wet places and heathland. Of the potentially useful plants, some, such as bramble and hazel, probably grew wild nearby. The waterlogged conditions of the site were favourable to the preservation of seeds of wild plants, many of which are weedy species producing large quantities of persistent seeds. Remains of plants of economic importance such as cereal grains and flax seeds were present only in small quantities. Even fig seeds, often abundant in medieval cess pits, for example at Elgin and Aberdeen (Fraser 1981), were extremely scarce. Of the cereals, carbonised grains of oats were the most frequent while barley, wheat and rye were also present.

Cereal debris, in the form of grain fragments of wheat, oats and barley, was present in cess pits, for example, in Contexts 6131 (Pit 6127), 7234 (Pit 7230) and 7323 (Pit 7314). The paraffin-floated samples produced only tiny quantities of cereal debris indicating that such small fragments are generally not retrieved using this processing method. Eggs of the roundworm parasite, *Trichuris*, were found on wheat fragments in the sample from Context 7323 (Pit 7314; Building 18 (Phase 2a); Phase IVb). Legume seed coat fragments were present in the three contexts mentioned but the species were not determined. Large robust mosses were particularly abundant in Context 7234 (Pit 7230; M9a; Phase IVc,IVcc) and were possibly used as 'toilet paper' or for stuffing and packing, indicating that the feature may have been used as a latrine or cess pit.

Many of the samples come from layers of dung and in these, seeds of weed species are particularly frequent. It is not always simple to distinguish between human and animal dung although evidence of cereal debris will usually indicate the former. Seeds of many wild plants may have been consumed by animals and humans alike. Many of the weeds are common species of arable land and waste ground. Some of these weeds may have been growing on the site, for example, nettles and docks, while others, such as cornflower and stinking mayweed, were probably brought to the site perhaps in association with crops or in animal dung. Petals and calyces of clover species and grass grains may indicate the presence of fodder. Grass grains are generally poorly represented in the samples. Many grasses possess transient seed banks which are present only during the summer (Thomson and Grime 1979) and thus the likelihood of incorporation in the deposits is reduced. The meadow grasses (*Poa* spp), whose grains were fairly frequent in the wet-sieved samples, produce a quantity of 'seeds', a proportion of which fail to germinate directly; some of these are incorporated into a persistent seed bank (ibid). This, combined with their relative ease of identification, may account for their apparently greater frequency at the site. The commonest weed seeds recovered were pale persicaria, redshank, fat hen, sheep's sorrel, hemp-nettle, corn spurrey, chickweed and nettle. These were all very frequent in waterlogged samples from archaeological contexts and, though some may have been gathered in times of scarcity, it is likely that most have no economic significance.

Heathland plants were frequent in most of the samples, in particular, shoots of heather and achenes of tormentil. Heather probably had a variety of uses including bedding and thatching.

A great variety of wetland plants was present in the samples. Most of these probably grew close by on wet ground bordering the Tay, although some, such as bogbean and bristle club-rush, were probably brought in to the site. The river was liable to flood, as it did for example in 1209 when the castle and bridge were swept away, thus helping to produce the waterlogged conditions in which plant remains are preserved. Nuts of sedges were very frequent. Along with rushes, whose seeds were also common, sedges may have been gathered for use as floor covering, although no direct evidence of this was found on the site. A few fruits of meadowsweet were also found. The sweet-scented flowers and leaves were also formerly used for floor covering. According to Gerard (1597) 'the leaves and flowers far excell all other strowing herbes ... for the smell thereof maketh the hart merrie, delighteth the senses'.

Egg cases of the freshwater invertebrates, *Daphnia* and *Plumatella*, were common in some samples. Since the Tay is tidal as far upstream as Perth, the habitat of these creatures is more likely to have been the lade, ditches and streams flowing into the main river.

Table 37 *Summary of plant remains.*

Key to abundance

+ 1–5 fossils
* 6–15 fossils
** 16–100 fossils
*** Over 100 fossils

Plants useful to man

species	common name	type	abundance	number of contexts in which fossil occurs
Avena sativa L.	oats	floret	**	19
		grain	***	29
		grain fragment	**	4
Hordeum vulgare L.	bere barley	rachis internode	*	2
		grain	**	15
		grain fragment	**	1
Secale cereale L.	rye	grain	*	7
Triticum aestivum s.l.	wheat	grain	*	9
		grain fragment	***	6
Cereals – unidentified		grain	+	4
Brassica campestris L.	turnip	seed	**}	
B. cf *campestris*		seed	*}	}30
Brassica sp		seed	**}	
Corylus avellana L.	hazel	nut shell	***	29
Ficus carica L.	fig	seed	*	8
Fragaria vesca L.	wild strawberry	achene	*	6
Hyoscyamus niger L.	henbane	seed	*	6
Juglans regia L.	walnut	stone (walnut)	+	1
Linum usitatissimum L.	flax	seed	**	10
Malus silvestris s.l.	apple	seed	+	2
Papaver somniferum L.	opium poppy	seed	+	2
Prunus avium (L.)	gean, wild cherry	stone	**	1
P. domestica ssp *institia* (L.) C.K.	bullace	stone	+	1

Table 37 *(continued)*

species	common name	type	abundance	number of contexts in which fossil occurs
Quercus sp	oak	acorn	+	1
Reseda luteola L.	weld, dyer's Rocket	seed	**	9
Rosa canina agg	dog rose	achene	+	3
Rubus chamaemorus L.	cloudberry	seed	+	1
Rubus fruticosus agg	bramble	seed	*	5
Rubus idaeus L.	raspberry	seed	+	1
Sambucus nigra L.	elder	seed	*	7
Sorbus aucuparia L.	rowan	seed	*	3
Vaccinium myrtillus L.	blaeberry	seed	**	8
Polytrichum commune Hedw.		moss rope	+	1

Plants of waste places and arable land

species	common name	type	abundance	number of contexts in which fossil occurs
Achillea millefolium L.	yarrow	achene	*	7
Agrostemma githago L.	corn cockle	seed	**	14
Anthemis cotula L.	stinking mayweed	achene	**	8
Avena fatua L.	wild oat	floret	*	4
Bromus mollis agg	lop-grass	grain	+	2
Capsella bursa-pastoris (L.) Medic.	shepherd's purse	seed	**	4
Cerastium fontanum Baumg.	mouse-ear chickweed	seed	**	15
Chenopodium album L.	fat hen	seed	***	32
Chrysanthemum segetum L.	corn marigold	achene	*	6
Cirsium arvense (L.) Scop.	creeping thistle	achene	+	2
Cirsium vulgare (Savi) Ten.	spear thistle	achene	+	2
Euphorbia helioscopia L.	sun spurge	seed	+	3
Galeopsis tetrahit agg	hemp-nettle	nutlet	***	29
Hypochaeris radicata L.	cat's ear	achene	+	1
Juncus bufonius L.	toad rush	seed	**	11
Lapsana communis L.	nipplewort	achene	***	24
Leontodon autumnalis L.	autumnal hawkbit	achene	**	13
Myosotis arvensis (L.) Hill	forget-me-not	nutlet	**	12
Odontites verna (Bell.) Dum.	red rattle, bartsia	seed	+	1
Papaver dubium L.	long-headed poppy	seed	*	5

Table 37 *(continued)*

species	common name	type	abundance	number of contexts in which fossil occurs
Plantago lanceolata L.	ribwort plantain	seed	+	3
P. major L.	great plantain	seed	+	1
Poa annua L.	annual meadow grass	grain	*	3
P. trivialis L.	meadow grass	grain	**	8
Polygonum aviculare L.	knotgrass	fruit	***	25
P. convolvus L.	black bindweed	fruit	**	24
P. lapathifolium L.	pale persicaria	fruit	***	32
P. persicaria L.	redshank	fruit	***	31
Prunella vulgaris L.	self heal	nutlet	***	27
Ranunculus repens L.	creeping buttercup	achene	***	31
Raphanus raphanistrum L.	wild radish	fruit segment and seed	**	16
		fruit segment	**	6
		seed	*	5
Rhinanthus sp	yellow-rattle	seed	*	1
Rumex acetosa L.	sorrel	fruit	+	1
Rumex acetosella agg	sheep's sorrel	fruit	***	29
R.cf conglomeratus Murr.	sharp dock	fruit	+	2
R. crispus L.	curled dock	fruit	+	2
Rumex sp		fruit	***	27
Scleranthus annuus L.	annual knawel	fruit	+	1
Senecio cf *vulgaris* L.	groundsel	achene	+	2
Silene sp (*Melandrium* Roehl.)	campion	seed	*	5
Sinapis arvensis L.	charlock	seed	*	5
Sonchus asper (L.) Hill	prickly sow-thistle	achene	*	8
S. oleraceus L.	sow-thistle	achene	*	5
Spergula arvensis L.	corn spurrey	seed	***	32
Stachys cf *sylvatica* L.	hedge woundwort	nutlet	+	1
Stellaria media (L.) Vill.	chickweed	seed	***	30
Thlaspi arvense L.	field pennycress	seed	*	7
Torilis japonica (Houtt.) D.C.	upright hedge-parsley	fruit	*	7
Trifolium pratense L.	red clover	calyx	+	1
T. repens L.	white clover	petal	**	2

Table 37 *(continued)*

species	common name	type	abundance	number of contexts in which fossil occurs
Tripleurospermum inodorum L. Schultz-Bip.	scentless mayweed	achene	*	6
Urtica dioica L.	stinging nettle	achene	***	23
U. urens L.	small nettle	achene	**	12
Vicia cf *cracca* L.	tufted vetch	seed	+	1
Vicia sp		seed	+	3
Viola sp Subgenus *Melanium*	pansy	seed	**	17
Compositae		achene	+	2
Graminae		achene	+	2
Labiatae		nutlet	+	1
Umbelliferae		nutlet	+	4
undetermined seeds			**	18

Heathland plants

species	common name	type	abundance	number of contexts in which fossil occurs
Calluna vulgaris (L.) Hull	heather	flower/ fruit	***	24
		seed	**	11
		shoot	***	21
		leaf	**	7
Erica cinerea L.	bell heather	seed	**	13
Erica tetralix L.	bog heather, cross-leaved heath	seed	+	3
		leaf	***	14
Eriophorum vaginatum L.	cotton grass	leaf base spindle	+	2
Galium saxatile L.	heath bedstraw	fruit	+	1
Juncus squarrosus L.	heath rush	seed	**	12
Luzula multiflora (Retz.) Lej.	woodrush	seed	+	3
Myrica gale L.	bog myrtle	fruit	+	3
		leaf frag	+	1
Potentilla erecta (L.) Rausch	tormentil	achene	***	22
Pteridium aquilinum (L.) Kuhn	bracken	frond frag	**	5
Selaginella selaginoides (L.) Link	lesser clubmoss	megaspore	+	2

Table 37 *(continued)*

species	common name	type	abundance	number of contexts in which fossil occurs
Viola sp. subgenus *Viola*	violet	seed	+	2

Trees

species	common name	type	abundance	number of contexts in which fossil occurs
Betula pubescens Ehrh.	birch	fruit	*	7
Salix sp	willow	fruit	*	11

Plants of wet habitats

species	common name	type	abundance	number of contexts in which fossil occurs
Ajuga reptans L.	bugle	nutlet	+	1
Bidens tripartita L.	bur-marigold	achene	+	1
Caltha palustris L.	kingcup	seed	*	7
Carex spp *distigmatae*	sedge	nut	***	30
Carex spp *tristigmatae*	sedge	nut	***	28
Eleocharis palustris (L.) Roem & Schult.	common spike-rush	nut	**	16
Epilobium parviflorum Schreb.	willowherb	seed	+	1
Filipendula ulmaria (L.) Maxim	meadowsweet	fruit	**	5
Galium palustre L.	marsh bedstraw	fruit	*	6
Glyceria fluitans (L.) R.Br.	floating sweet-grass	grain	+	1
Hydrocotyle vulgaris L.	marsh pennywort	fruit	+	2
Iris pseudocorus L.	yellow flag	seed	+	2
Isolepis setacea (L.) R. Br.	bristle club-rush	nut	**	4
Juncus articularis L.	jointed rush	seed	**	7
Juncus effusus L.	soft rush	seed	***	9
Juncus sp		seed	+	1
Lychnis flos-cuculi L.	ragged robin	seed	*	8
Lycopus europaeus L.	gipsy-wort	nutlet	*8	14
Menyanthes trifoliata L.	bogbean	seed	*	5
Montia fontana L. ssp. *fontana*	blinks	seed	*	5
Pedicularis palustris L.	red-rattle	seed	**	11
Potamogeton polygonifolius Pourr.	bog pondweed	fruit	+	2
Potentilla palustris (L.) Scop.	marsh cinquefoil	achene	*8	12

Table 37 *(continued)*

species	common name	type	abundance	number of contexts in which fossil occurs
Ranunculus flammula L.	lesser spearwort	achene	**	18
R. sceleratus L.	celery-leaved crowfoot	achene	+	3
Ranunculus sp subgenus *Batrachium*	water crowfoot	achene	+	1
Senecio cf *aquaticus* Hill	marsh ragwort	achene	*	5
Viola palustris L.	marsh violet	seed	+	3

Bryophytes

species	common name	type	abundance	number of contexts in which fossil occurs
Antitrichia curtipendula (Hedw.) Brid.			***	2
Aulacomnium palustre (Hedw.) Schwaegr.			+	3
Brachythecium rutabulum cf *Bryum* sp			+	1
Ceratodon purpureus (Hedw.) Brid.			+	1
Dicranum scoparium Hedw.			*	2
Eurhynchium praelongum (Hedw.) Br. Eur.			*	5
Hylocomium brevirostre (Brid.) Br. Eur.			**	1
H. splendens (Hedw.) Br. Eur.			***	15
Hypnum cupressiforme Hedw.			**	16
Isothecium myosuroides Brid.			+	3
Mnium hornum Hedw.			*	3
Neckera complanta (Hedw.) Hub.			+	1
Plagiomnium affine (Funck) Kop.			+	2
Pleurozium schreberi (Brid.) Lindb.			*	3
Polytrichum commune Hedw.			***	1
Polytrichum formosum Hedw.			*	4
Pseudoscleropodium purum (Hedw.) Fleisch			+	2
Rhytidiadelphus loreus (Hedw.) Warnst			***	3
Sphagnum palustre L.			**	7
Sphagnum sp		operculum	+	1
		shoot	+	3

Table 37 *(continued)*

species	common name	type	abundance	number of contexts in which fossil occurs
Thuidium tamariscinum (Hedw.) Br. Eur.			**	4
Ulota crispa (Hedw.) Brid.			+	2
Liverwort cf *Plagiochila asplenioides* (L.) Dum.			+	1

From the evidence recovered, the major crops grown were oats and bere while wheat was probably grown only in small quantities. Oats and bere provided the staples of porridge, bread and ale for the greater part of the medieval population, while wheat was presumably available to an upper class minority at least. Vegetables would seem to have been scarce. The legume seed coat fragments recovered may possibly have come from cultivated species while the carbonised legume seeds were referred to wild vetch species. Large-seeded legumes in general do not preserve well. They are unlikely to be carbonised since they do not require parching. Peas and beans were actually imported to Scotland in the 13th century along with corn and salt (Duncan 1975a, 498, 506). It was possibly still necessary to import them until at least the 16th century. 'Pess' (peas) are mentioned among other foodstuffs in an entry in the Perth Guildry Book for the year 1556, although their point of origin is not specified (Stavert 1993, 236). The *Brassica* seeds recovered may indicate cultivation of green vegetables. Fruit, both wild and cultivated, was seasonally available to supplement the diet and, for those who could afford it, the luxury of dried figs and walnuts.

Notes on some species of interest

Cereals

*Oats (*Avena sativa*), barley (*Hordeum vulgare*), rye (*Secale cereale*), wheat (*Triticum aestivum s l*)*

Many of the cereal remains consisted of carbonised grains and florets (see Table 38). Uncarbonised grain fragments of wheat, oats and barley were also present in certain samples, as well as rachis segments of barley.

The majority of oat florets came from *Avena sativa*, the common white oat. Florets of the wild oat, *A. fatua*, are easily distinguished from other species of oat likely to be encountered by their distinctive suckermouth base. It is possible, however, that some of the carbonised grains identified as *A. sativa* may be *A. fatua*. In addition to behaving as a weed, *A. fatua* may have been grown in mixed crops. Thus, Anderson (1794) in his description of the agriculture of Aberdeenshire, mentions that the wild oat is so

abundant there as often to constitute nearly half of the bere crop. In addition the size of the grains makes them difficult to separate from bere by winnowing.

The preserved evidence suggests that the main cereal crop was the common white oat *A. sativa*. It is surprising that no evidence of *A. strigosa* (grey or bristle oat) was recovered. However, although some small grains referable to *A. strigosa* have been found at other sites within the medieval burgh of Perth, at Canal Street III, Meal Vennel, King Edward Street and Blackfriars House (Fairweather 1992; Fairweather 1996a, 795, Robinson 1995; Boyd nd) this species is notably absent from Kirk Close, Canal Street II and South Methven Street in Perth (Robinson 1987a, 205). Nevertheless, *A. strigosa* has been found in St Andrews at 134 Market Street, 106–110 South Street and the Byre Theatre site, Abbey Street (Boyd 1988, 105; Holden, 2000, 131; Hastie and Holden 2001, 77) and in Dundee at 23-35 Panmure Street/72–8 Murraygate (Hastie and Holden 2000, 63). It was also thought to be present at 77–79 High Street, Arbroath (Holden 1999, 67). Although the bristle oat was not as common at Perth High Street as *A. sativa*, this does not seem to be the case in other burghs such as St Andrews, where it is considered to be the more plentiful of the two species. Its apparent poor recovery rate here may therefore be due to problems of preservation. However, Dickson (1996, 29) has suggested that bristle oats found in the 15th-century fill of the Paisley Abbey drain may have been used to feed horses, since the Cluniac monks were wealthy enough to afford imported wheat.

Table 38 *Numbers of carbonised cereal grains and florets, by species.*

species	number of carbonised grains	number of carbonised florets
Avena sativa	159	38
A. fatua		6
Hordeum vulgare	29	
Secale cereale	10	
Triticum aestivum s.l.	8	

In later centuries the bristle oat was the species commonly cultivated, particularly on poorer acid soils. In recent times *A. strigosa* is a more frequent weed in fields of *A. sativa* than is *A. fatua*, which is restricted to better soils (Findlay 1956).

The barley grains were hulled, and rachis segments (from the axis of the spike) indicated that the lax-eared variety, bere (*Hordeum vulgare tetrastichum*) was grown. Bere barley was also common in the plant assemblages from other medieval sites in Perth, for example at Kirk Close, South Methven Street and Canal Street II, where the remains occurred as frequently as those of oats (Robinson 1987a, 205), as well as at King Edward Street, Mill Street and Canal Street III (Robinson 1995; Fairweather 1996b, 727). In the burgh of St Andrews, bere was present at 134 Market Street, 106–110 South Street and the Byre Theatre site in Abbey Street (Robinson and Boyd 1997, 138; Holden 2000, 131; Hastie and Holden 2001, 77).

Much of the barley crop may have been brewed into ale; Duncan (1975a, 350–1) has suggested that perhaps as much as a third of the grain grown in Scotland each year in medieval times was used for this purpose.

Ten carbonised grains were identified as rye. According to Duncan (1975a, 323) rye is scarcely mentioned in the medieval rentals but was grown on a small scale in central Scotland in the early 14th century. The physical evidence of rye grains from 12th-century Perth is therefore of great interest. Further evidence for the presence of rye in medieval Perth comes from a latrine deposit at Kirk Close where its remains (testa fragments) were far more abundant than those of oats or barley (Robinson 1987a, 200–1). It was also recorded at King Edward Street (Robinson 1995). Sites in medieval St Andrews and Dundee have also yielded evidence of rye (Hastie and Holden 2001, 77; Hastie and Holden 2000, 63). At 77–79 High Street, Arbroath, the quantity of rye grains compared with hulled barley and bristle oat was particularly notable (Holden 1999, 66). That rye continued to be grown in Scotland in the post-medieval period is suggested by an entry of 1551 in the Perth Guildry Book, which mentions 'ry', although as the origin of the consignments is not mentioned, it is possible that it may refer to imported grain from outwith Scotland (Stavert 1993, 236).

In the 18th century oats and rye were sometimes sown together on poor land in the north of Scotland and ground to make a coarse meal. However by the end of that century rye had gone out of cultivation (Handley 1953). Its decline may have been exacerbated because of its excess demands on the soil, as was the case in the Western Isles in the 18th century (Dodgshon 1993, 682).

Wheat was cultivated on more fertile land than that required for oats, barley and rye and in particular was grown for the king's needs. For example, around the year 1170, William I commanded 'Archibald and Hugh, sons of Swain of Forgan, to render to Scone Abbey every year eight chalders of wheat, being the teind of the king's wheat at Longforgan' (*RRS*, i, no 16). Duncan (1975a, 322) states that in the royal accounts for the 1260s the sheriff of Perth received rents in oatmeal, bere and oats, but bought in wheat for the King's service.

During the 12th and 13th centuries grain was imported to Scotland, principally to the ports of Berwick and Perth. Scottish cereal production was probably insufficient to supply the needs of an increasing population, much of the land being totally unproductive and waterlogged. Even in the early 18th century the now extremely fertile Carse of Gowrie was 'in many places over-run with rushes, disfigured by pools of water. . .and the whole people subject to ague' (Donaldson 1794). Thus when in the 16th century the Perth Guildry Book refers to 'quete' at the harbour of Perth, it may be imported grain that is meant (Stavert 1993, 236).

Further evidence for the consumption of wheat in the medieval period has been found in latrine fills at Queen Street in medieval Aberdeen (Fraser and Dickson 1982, 240) and at Kirk Close, Perth, although there are well known difficulties in distinguishing between testa fragments of wheat and rye (Robinson 1987a, 200, 205). In medieval St Andrews wheat has been identified at 134 Market Street (Boyd 1988, 101), 106–110 South Street (Holden 2000, 131) and the Byre Theatre site, Abbey Street (Hastie and Holden 2001, 77). Wheat was also present in samples from 77–79 High Street, Arbroath (Holden 1999, 66).

Vegetables, fruits and nuts

Brassica *species (turnip, etc)*

Almost 150 seeds and numerous fragments were recovered. A few seeds were present in most samples; seeds were not concentrated in any particular sample. The better preserved seeds were referred to *Brassica campestris*. The seeds vary in size (1.30–1.99mm) and have marked surface reticulation. They may belong to the wild subspecies *eu-campestris*, wild turnip or wild navew. Significant numbers of *Brassica* seeds referable to turnip-rape or turnip have been recovered from Kirk Close, Perth but were comparably much less common at South Methven Street, Canal Street II and Mill Street (Robinson 1987a, 206; Robinson nd). There are no records of cultivation of *Brassica* species in Scotland in medieval times although 'kail' of an unspecified variety was grown from at least the 15th century (Fenton 1976). A statute of the 'dene of gilde and merchandis' of Perth dating to 1551 does indeed mention 'caill' as one of the foodstuffs or 'siclike small gudis' which could only be sold on a mercat day but there is no clue as to what kind is meant (Stavert 1993, 208). At the present day, Scots speakers tend to use the term 'kail' to refer either to curly kale, cabbage (*Brassica oleracea*) or indeed any broth or soup made from them, thus adding to the confusion.

Fig *(Ficus carica), walnut (*Juglans regia*)*

Nine fig seeds were recovered from a total of eight contexts. Two half walnut shells were recovered from Building 18 (Context 7320, Phase IVaa,IVb). Fig seeds have also been found in a 16th- to17th-century cess pit fill at Mill Street in Perth (Robinson 1995, 992), and in a medieval latrine fill at the Byre Theatre site in St Andrews which also contained grape pips and a variety of fruit stones (Hastie and Holden 2001, 79). The 15th-century drain fill of Paisley Abbey contained fig pips, the fruit probably having been consumed for medicinal reasons (Dickson 1996, 29). Figs found in medieval Scottish contexts are thus almost inevitably associated with sewage (Dickson 2000, 226).

Both figs and walnuts must have been imported to medieval Perth. During the 13th century wine was imported to Scotland from the north of France and Bordeaux (Duncan 1975a, 508) and also from the Wash ports (Carus-Wilson 1963). It is probable that the cargoes included other luxury goods such as dried figs and walnuts. Both figs and walnuts are native to the Middle East and eastern Mediterranean region. Figs were an important source of sugar in medieval times, sugar itself only being imported to Scotland from the late 15th century onwards (Fenton 1976).

Apple *(*Malus sylvestris *s l)*

Two apple pips were recovered, one from Midden 8a (Context 7168, Phase Va,Vaa) and one from Building 18 (Context 9279, Phase IVaa,IVb). The dimensions of the pips are as follows: 7.4mm by 5.0mm, 7.2mm by 4.3mm. In both cases the pointed end of the pip was damaged so the original lengths will have been greater. They are both larger than pips recovered from medieval Elgin which were all under 7mm in length (Fraser 1981). They probably belong to the cultivated rather than the wild (crab) variety which was local and uncommon in Perthshire in the 19th century (White 1898, 139). Apple pips, possibly from cultivated fruit, were also recovered from a latrine fill at the Byre Theatre site, St Andrews (Hastie and Holden 2001, 78) and from the drain fill at Paisley Abbey, where it is presumed the apples originated from the abbey orchard (Dickson 1996, 29).

Bullace *(Prunus domestica *ssp *institia), gean or wild cherry (*P. avium*), blackthorn or sloe (*P. spinosa*)*

One stone of bullace and 13 stones of gean (wild cherry) were recovered from Context 7234, a fill of Pit 7230 in Midden 9a (Phase IVc,IVcc). One sloe stone was re-covered from Building B18 (Context 9153, Phase IVaa, IVb). By contrast, large numbers of *Prunus* stones were found at medieval Elgin (Fraser 1981). A few bullace stones were recovered from the drain fill of Paisley Abbey (Dickson 1996, 29), while bullace, cherry and sloe stones were also found in the latrine fill at the Byre Theatre site, St Andrews (Hastie and Holden 2001, 77–9).

Gean and blackthorn are frequent trees and shrubs in woods and are still found in lowland Perthshire. The single bullace stone is large (20mm by 13.5mm) in comparison to the Elgin stones but its shape resembles stones of ssp *institia* rather than spp *domestica*, the cultivated plum. Bullace trees were probably grown in medieval times for their fruit. Today they are still occasionally planted and can be found growing naturalised.

Cloudberry *(Rubus chamaemorus)*

Half a seed of cloudberry was found in the paraffin-floated sample from Context 9235, a compact brown soil from Building 18 (Phase IVaa,IVb). Three hundred cm^3 of untreated soil from the same context was wet-sieved but no further seeds were found. The recovered seed was pale brown and 4.1mm long.

Cloudberry is a native species, more or less confined to the drier aspects of wet, acidic, peat bog in upland Britain. It is characteristic of high-level blanket bogs in which *Calluna vulgaris* and *Eriophorum vaginatum* are co-dominant. In the eastern Highlands it is found between altitudes of 300m and 1100m (Taylor 1971). Matthews (1955) classifies it as arctic–subarctic in distribution. Setting of seed is erratic and localised in Britain, presumably being influenced by grazing, burning and climatic events. The plant is strictly dioecious and Raven and Walters (1956) suggest that a greater frequency of male plants may be partly responsible for poor fruiting.

Wild forms of *Rubus chamaemorus* and other *Rubus* species are popular foods in Scandinavia, especially for making liquors (Jennings 1976). Gerard (1597) tells us that 'the fruit quencheth thirst, cooleth the stomacke, and alaieth inflammation being eaten as whortes are, or the decoction made and drunk'.

There appear to be no records of seeds of cloudberry in the British fossil record. Tallantire (1979) records it from archaeological deposits from medieval Trondheim in Norway. To account for the Perth seed we must either assume that cloudberries were deliberately brought to the site by man or else the seed reached the site in bird or mammal dung, perhaps goat droppings, since goats were frequently grazed in upland areas.

Bramble *(Rubus fruticosus), raspberry (*R. idaeus*), strawberry (*Fragaria vesca*), rose (*Rosa canina*), rowan (*Sorbus aucuparia*), elder (*Sambucus nigra*), blaeberry (*Vaccinium myrtillus*)*

The fruits of these plants no doubt helped to add variety to the diet when available. Only small numbers of seeds or achenes of each were found, however. Much larger quantities, especially of *Rubus* seeds, were found at medieval Aberdeen and Elgin (Fraser 1981). Bramble, strawberry and bilberry seeds were also recovered from a latrine fill at the Byre Theatre site, St Andrews (Hastie and Holden 2001, 78–9). Seeds from bramble or raspberry were also present in a post-medieval cess-pit fill at Mill Street, Perth (Robinson 1995, 992).

Bramble, raspberry, rowan and blaeberry were also all present in the drain fill at Paisley Abbey (Dickson 1996, 29).

Medicinally, blaeberries were valued in the Highlands as a remedy for ailments such as dysentery and kidney stones, while rowan berries were used to treat whooping cough (Beith 2004, 205–6, 237).

Trees

Hazel (Corylus avellana), oak (Quercus sp)

Hazel nutshell fragments were abundant in many samples. Half shells were frequent as well as occasional whole nuts. Many of the hand-picked botanical samples consisted of finds of hazelnuts. Only one or two pieces showed signs of gnawing by animals, most of the fragments presumably resulting from being broken by man. Hazel shrubs are common in woods and scrub and the nuts were a major item in the diet of mesolithic man (Dimbleby 1978, 34). The kernels can be ground into flour for baking and probably continued to be a convenient food in medieval times. Nutshell fragments are common at many medieval urban sites in Britain including Aberdeen, Elgin and St Andrews as well as the Paisley Abbey drain (Fraser 1981; Hastie and Holden 2001, 77; Dickson 1996, 29).

One whole acorn was recovered from Context 9261, a destruction layer in Building 18 (Phase IVa, IVaa).

Crop contaminants

Corn Cockle (Agrostemma githago), stinking mayweed (Anthemis cotula), cornflower (Centaurea cyanus), corn marigold (Chrysanthemum segetum)

These weeds of cultivated land have all decreased markedly in recent years due mainly to changes in agricultural practice. Whole seeds and fragments of corn cockle were frequent in the samples. Fragments were abundant along with cereal debris in the latrine pit sample from Building 18 (Context 7323, Phase IVb). As the seeds are poisonous, presumably this bread was rather unpalatable to the consumers. Corn cockle is very frequent in plant assemblages recorded at medieval sites.

Achenes of stinking mayweed were abundant in the sample from Context 9137 in Building 18 (Phase IVaa, IVb), a compact dung layer. This weed of arable land was rare, or overlooked, in Perthshire by the 19th century (White 1898). Achenes have been found elsewhere in Perth, at Mill Street (Robinson 1995, 990). Stinking mayweed has also been noted at medieval Aberdeen (Fraser 1981).

Medicinal and dye plants

Henbane (Hyoscyamus niger)

A total of seven seeds of henbane were recovered from six samples. Like its close relation, deadly nightshade, a large number of seeds of which were found at medieval Elgin (Fraser 1981), the plant is poisonous and narcotic. It contains the alkaloids hyoscyamine and scopolamine (Claphamet al 1962). However, early physicians found it a plant more easily handled than deadly nightshade (Grigson 1975, 315). Gerard (1597) tells us that 'henbane causeth drowsiness and mitigateth all kinds of paine. It is good against hot and sharpe distillations of the eies and other parts'. In Denmark, seeds were placed into hollow teeth as a local anaesthetic (Jensen 1979).

Henbane is native in southern England but occurs as a casual in Scotland. It has been found elsewhere in Perth, where it formed part of the medieval flora growing along the ladeside at Mill Street (Robinson 1995, 991). There are fossil records from Roman and Anglo-Saxon York (Greig 1976; Godwin and Bachem 1959) and medieval Beverley (Hall and Kenward 1980). Seeds of *Hyoscyamus* have remarkable longevity; seeds capable of germinating were found at habitation sites from the 14th century in Denmark (Ødynm 1965).

Opium poppy (Papaver somniferum)

Four seeds of opium poppy were recovered, three of which came from Context 9235 in Building 18 (Phase IVaa,IVb). The narcotic properties of this plant have long been used to alleviate pain. The poppy seed was probably imported and the plant grown for the opium which is obtained from the latex of the capsule. Seeds have been found at other medieval sites including Aberdeen and in the Paisley Abbey drain fill, as well as the Roman fort of Bearsden (Dickson et al 1979; Dickson, C 1996, 27).

Bog myrtle (Myrica gale)

Five fruits and a single leaf fragment of bog myrtle were found. This is a plant with numerous uses such as flavouring ale or beer, for use as brooms, repelling insects and as a yellow dye. Several leaf fragments and a single fruit were recovered from medieval Aberdeen (Fraser and Dickson 1982, 243). Further finds from the 45–75 Gallowgate site in Aberdeen have associated this plant with dyeing (Kenward and Hall 2001, 284, 287).

Bogbean (Menyanthes trifoliata)

Seven seeds of bogbean, a plant common in loch margins and bogs, were recovered. It has strong medicinal properties, being used for colic and internal upsets until recent times in the Highlands of Scotland

(Grant 1961, 313; Beith 2004, 206–7) and according to Tait (1947) was considered to be a specific for jaundice in Shetland. Bogbean remains have also been recovered from the Paisley Abbey drain fill (Dickson 1996, 27)

Gipsywort (Lycopus europaeus), bur-marigold (Bidens tripartita), yellow flag (Iris pseudacorus)

Nutlets of gipsywort were frequent in the samples. They have also been found at the medieval site of King Edward Street in Perth (Robinson 1995). White (1898, 239) in his *Flora of Perthshire*, however, lists the plant as being very local and rare, inhabiting wet places such as the shores of the Tay near Errol and at Perth Harbour. The plant yields a fast black dye and its use as a dye-plant was noted on Colonsay in the Hebrides (Grigson 1975, 343).

One achene of bur-marigold was found. A brilliant orange dye may be extracted from this plant. According to White (1898, 185) bur-marigold was rare and often sporadic in Perthshire in the 19th century.

Two seeds of yellow flag were found in the paraffin-floated samples while a number of the relatively large seeds were present in hand-picked botanical samples. Surprisingly there appear to be no other recorded instances of this plant from medieval contexts in Scotland. In the Highlands the roots of the plant have been used to yield a greyish-blue or black dye (Grant 1961, 230) and medicinally, a snuff made from the roots was used to alleviate colds (Beith 2004, 217–18).

Mosses

Mosses were present in varying amounts in the majority of samples. Most are common species of heathland and woodland and must have been brought in from surrounding areas. It is probable that mosses were deliberately gathered for use in a number of ways, for example as insulating materials, packing, bedding and for their absorbent qualities as 'toilet paper' or wound packing. Similar finds of moss toilet paper have been noted in latrine or cess pit fills at Kirk Close, Perth and the Byre Theatre, St Andrews (Robinson 1987a, 208; Hastie and Holden 2001, 79).

Large masses of robust mosses, in particular *Polytrichum commune* and *Hylocomium splendens*, were found in a number of hand-picked botanical samples. A piece of plaited rope (diameter 30mm) of *Polytrichum commune* was recovered from Midden 9a (Context 9016). A number of moss plaits were found at Kirk Close, Perth the main moss component consisting of *Polytrichum*, with small amounts from other species such as *Hypnum cupressiforme*, *Thuidium tamariscinum* and *Pleurozium schreberi* included (Ford and Robinson 1987, 153-4). Small *Polytrichum* ropes have also been found at medieval sites such as Durham (Donaldson 1979).

Large quantities of the robust pleurocarpous moss *Antitrichia curtipendula* were found in samples from Building 53 (Context 7129, Phase Vb) and Pit 7230 in Midden 9a (Context 7234, Phase IVc,IVcc). This moss is one of the commonest subfossils in British Pleistocene deposits (Dickson 1973). Today it is a local plant, forming mats on boulders or around tree bases in the west of Britain (Watson 1968).

Illus 44 *Wattle pathway preserved at the site.*
(Copyright Perth Museum and Art Gallery)

Conclusions: the environment of medieval Perth

Catherine Smith

Evidence for the exploitation of plants and animals

The excavations at the High Street provided a wealth of evidence for the exploitation of the animal and plant resources by the medieval population of Perth. Among the remains of plants were cereal grains, seeds and achenes, leaf fragments, wood, moss ropes, wattle pathways and hazel nut shells (Illus 44). Animal remains included the bones of mammals, birds and fish, fragments of ox horn, cattle, goat and horse hair and sheep's wool, leather from cattle, sheep and goats, shells of marine and freshwater mollusca, eggshell fragments and even feathers. In addition there was evidence of parasite infestation, represented by whipworm (*Trichuris*) eggs, and of one individual human, in the form of a single facial bone. All of these organic materials were preserved for centuries by the waterlogged conditions prevailing at the site.

Soil conditions and taphonomic factors

Waterlogging of the soil has been found to occur at archaeological sites in Perth and elsewhere in Britain, notably at York. In such anaerobic conditions, no oxygen is available (usually within a highly organic soil) to allow for the decomposition of animal and plant derived materials such as bone and leather. In addition, if the ground water is stagnant, then leaching of minerals from bones is not possible, thus skeletal parts will remain in good, uneroded condition (O'Connor 1989, 146). The concept of the well-aerated compost heap beloved of the modern organic gardener in which decomposition of plant materials is actively encouraged is perhaps an exact opposite to the anaerobic conditions which at the High Street have preserved fragments of leaves, grains and even moss ropes. Another factor influencing the preservation of organic archaeological materials is the pH level of the soil. A neutral pH will preserve both bones and molluscan shells, while at a lower (acidic) pH both will begin to dissolve. In anaerobic conditions a more acidic pH can be tolerated.

There are, however, many other factors which influence how much of what was deposited 'in antiquity' will survive; these taphonomic factors can be summarised as comprising all external and internal influences acting on a biological sample, from the time it was deposited until the time of its excavation. These factors include such considerations as the length of time a deposit takes to build up; for example, a pit which is dug in a wet soil and immediately filled with rubbish will, on excavation, be far richer in recognisable

organic remains than one to which the refuse has been added over weeks, months or even years. Where deposition of the rubbish is prolonged, the material will be exposed to the vagaries of the weather: baking in hot sun, or repeatedly freezing and thawing in winter conditions. In bones, such treatment can result in cracking and flaking of the surface until eventually the bone splits, with the result that its identifiable features can quickly become unrecognisable. Rainwater, too can play its part in the decomposition of exposed organic rubbish. In certain circumstances it can be slightly acid (because of the formation of weak carbonic acid from carbon dioxide in the air) and thus it can speed the dissolution of bones and shell by leaching of their mineral content.

Numerous pits were dug in the backlands of the High Street, some of these with a recognisable purpose, such as cess-pits, which, when their original function had ceased, were eventually filled up with refuse. Some may have been filled with both human waste and domestic refuse at the same time (Schofield and Vince 1994, 181). Some of the pits may have been intended for the disposal of rubbish only. However, much of the town waste seems to have been tipped on to open middens, where unless covered over quickly, dogs, cats, rodents and other scavengers such as ravens and buzzards would have foraged for edible scraps. There is also some evidence that by the 16th century, the streets were being deliberately cleaned of rubbish, this process possibly having been initiated in the earlier medieval period (see below, The town, for discussion). Therefore, midden material would effectively be removed from the archaeological record. This depletion of the assemblage by both human and non-human agencies is another source of bias in our interpretation of it.

Differential preservation, too, is a problem in determining what proportion of the environmental samples which were originally deposited has actually survived until the time of excavation; thus, in the case of animal remains, different parts of long bones, such as the relatively spongy articular ends of the proximal humerus, are preserved less well under adverse conditions than are dense articulations such as the distal tibia or the resilient shafts of the bones. So too, the bones of young or neonatal animals contain a higher proportion of organic to inorganic materials than do those of older animals, and so are less resistant to decay. In the case of plant materials, there may be similar problems of differential preservation. It has been noted that cess-pits which might be expected to contain sizeable amounts of cereal bran from the digestion of bread, have instead yielded only fragments of seed pods from crop contaminants, with little evidence of the crops themselves. The inference is that cereals were originally present, but have not proved as durable as the weeds in resisting decay (Robinson 1987a; Robinson 1995, 992).

The method of retrieval of the samples on excavation can also influence the composition of the final recovered assemblage. This is demonstrated particularly by the results of the fish bone analysis: the range of species recovered by hand-excavation alone was demonstrably different from that recovered by sieving. While large species such as cod dominated the hand-picked samples, smaller species such as eels and sparling were only recovered by sieving the deposits. Thus although very few bones of small mammals such as mice were recovered by hand, it would be dangerous merely to assume that they had never occurred on the site. It is salutary to remember that care is needed in interpreting the results of this, or any, environmental investigation. However, with these caveats in mind, the biological remains from the High Street are an important tool in understanding the environment of the medieval townspeople.

The burgh and its rural hinterland: Perth in its natural setting

In the medieval period, Perth enjoyed a privileged position by virtue of the burghal status conferred on it by the crown (See The mammal bone: Legal status of the burghs). The effect of these privileges in trading was to ensure that all agricultural produce from the surrounding countryside was legally obliged to pass through the burghs in order that taxes could be raised on it. Each burgh was thus encompassed by a rural hinterland on which it depended for the production of agricultural raw materials which generated the wealth of the medieval economy. In its turn the hinterland existed in a state of dependency on the burgh where its goods must be sold. The exact extent of Perth's hinterland in the medieval period is not known although its borders may have corresponded with those of the sheriffdom of Perth (Keith 1913, 455; Duncan 1975a, 475, 491). The sheriffdom of Perth, an administrative entity, probably came into existence in the reign of David I (1124–53) (Muir 1975, 30). However the boundaries of the Scottish sheriffdoms did not remain constant throughout the medieval period, and Perth's jurisdiction, for example, absorbed that of Scone by 1228 and that of Auchterarder by 1328 (ibid), although the latter had become a royal burgh by the early 14th century (Duncan 1975b, 32).

The boundaries of Perth's hinterland may be partly deduced by comparing the extent of influence of other burghs with which Perth would have competed for control over the countryside. Its main competitor would have been Dundee, some 35km by land to the east, erected into a burgh before 1195 by William the Lion (Perry 2005, 9). A later charter of David II in 1359 named the villages of Coupar Angus, Kettins, Kirriemuir and Alyth as being within Dundee's burgh liberties. Rivalry between Perth and Dundee also extended to wrangles over which of the two burghs was to control shipping in the Tay, a struggle which continued throughout the later medieval period (Stevenson and Torrie 1988, 41–2). Thus the hinterland over which Perth could exercise control, by inference, probably included the western part of the Carse of Gowrie (since the eastern part was under the influence of Dundee) as well as that portion of the modern county of Perthshire to the south-west which was not controlled by Auchterarder. In the north-west, Perth must have held sway over what is now highland Perthshire. However, the borders of the hinterland would not have remained static throughout the entire medieval period, but would have been in a state of fluctuation as territory was continually disputed and perhaps reallocated.

Perth's hinterland would thus have consisted of a variety of ecological habitats, including lowland arable suitable for the cultivation of cereal crops such as bere, oats and rye, the boggy land and water meadows of the Carse as well as the higher clay soils which bordered it, and highland grazings and muirland for the summer pasturing of sheep, goats and cattle. The more fertile and well-drained lowland soils may have been reserved for the cultivation of wheat, a prestige crop destined for the use of the wealthier classes. However, a warmer climate, with higher mean and average temperatures than at the present day, prevailed during the 11th to 13th centuries (Duncan 1975a, 309; Lamb 1995, 177–82). These more favourable climatic conditions would have allowed cultivation of what would nowadays be considered marginal land at higher altitudes of perhaps over 1000 feet in the Southern Uplands (Smout 1993, 42). During the 14th century the climate began to deteriorate, giving cold winters and wet summers, with the result that such marginal land would gradually have become unworkable and have been abandoned.

As regards the lowland tree cover in the medieval period, its extent is conjectural; that there had been a decline in the extent of woodland from approximately 50% of the Scottish land surface to about 5% between the Roman period and the late 16th century is now accepted, but the progress and rate of that decline is open to debate (Smout 1993, 41). Notably ancient trees such as the Birnam oak, still growing in modern Perthshire, may be survivors of the native woodland which was probably more extensive in the medieval period than at the present day. The heavy lowland soils of Strathearn and Strathmore, for example, supported dense oak woods (Gilbert 1979, 235). The importance of these trees was noted as late as the end of the 18th century by Robertson (1799, 236) – 'there are more oak woods and of greater value, in this county, than in all the rest of Scotland'. At higher altitudes, such as prevail in highland Perthshire, oak would have been replaced by scattered pine, ash and birch woods.

Resources from the hinterland: arable, pastoral, woodland, moorland, wetland and waterways

As well as the cultivated crops and domestic livestock raised in the hinterland, a wide range of wild plants and animals was potentially available for exploitation. Of the cultivated crops, study of the botanical remains has shown that bere barley (*Hordeum vulgare tetrastichum*), white oat (*Avena sativa*), grey or bristle oat (*Avena strigosa*) and rye (*Secale cereale*) would all have been grown locally. Of the two oat species, the remains of white oat were more abundant, although the grey or bristle oat is thought to do better than the white oat on poor soil. Wheat (*Triticum aestivum*) was probably grown in small quantities on the more fertile land, as at Craigie, just outside Perth (Duncan 1975a, 322), although some may have been imported from outwith Scotland.

Other crops which may have been grown are peas and beans, although the evidence for their presence at the site is slight, possibly because their seeds do not preserve well under burial conditions. In addition, they may not have been extensively cultivated in Scotland. Certainly both peas and beans were imported in the 13th and 14th centuries (Duncan 1975a, 324). Cultivated green vegetables were also scarce, but included *Brassica* species of uncertain type which may have been kail or turnip. The only cultivated fruit for which evidence is preserved is the apple, of which a few pips were found. However, it is well known that the Abbey of Coupar Angus maintained orchards in the Carse of Gowrie, and a tack of 10 Jan 1473/4 entrusts the tenant of Kersgrange with maintenance of the orchards by hedging and dyking and 'plantation of fruit trees of the best kind that may be gotten' (*Coupar Angus Rental*, i, 188–90). Orchard fruit continued to be grown in the Carse and in the 17th century apples and unspecified 'freuit from the Cairs' were noted as exports in the Aberdeen Shore Work Accounts (Taylor 1972, 378).

The domestic livestock for which we have evidence were cattle, sheep, pigs, goats, and horses. All of these animals were of rather smaller stature than their modern day counterparts. In appearance, the cattle were probably of a short-horned type, and there is some evidence that some of them may have had red coats, similar in colour to the modern Highland breed. Most of the cattle were either females, used for breeding or milk production, or castrated oxen kept for draught work pulling the plough. Very few bulls were found. Sheep were small spindly-legged creatures of a range of shades of grey, brown and black – very few of them would have been white – and were horned in both sexes. Some of the sheep had multiple horns, rather like the Jacob breed known today (Illus 23). They were kept chiefly for wool and woolfell production, both staples of the Scots export economy, although their milk was also valued in cheese-making for home consumption.

However, a further important function of domestic stock was as walking producers of manure. Both cattle and sheep may have been tathed (folded) on the infield at certain times of the year in order to spread the dung where it was needed. In the infield/outfield system of agriculture which prevailed in Perthshire until at least the 18th century, the outfield was seldom fertilised in this way and would have yielded progressively less as the nutrients in the soil became exhausted. The bere crop grown on the 'muckit land' was more likely to benefit from manuring than were the oats (Shaw 1994, 111). Sheep may have been housed overnight in bughts or cots, not primarily in order to protect them from the elements, although this would have been a benefit, but in order to collect their dung, which was favoured over that of cattle (ibid, 112).

Goats, however, do not seem to have played a role in this system of manuring and were less commonly kept than sheep. However, goat bones are more plentiful at Perth High Street and other sites within the burgh than elsewhere in medieval Scotland. This is possibly because the parts of the Perthshire highlands which may have been unsuitable for cereal production would have provided ample grazing for goats (which can eat almost any vegetation, however woody, because of the structure of their hard palate). The distribution of goats (as well as other livestock) in Perthshire in the late 18th and mid 19th centuries was recorded for the 'Old' and 'New' Statistical Accounts of Scotland (*OSA* and *NSA*). As for the other livestock, accounts of the numbers of goats in the *OSA* are somewhat sporadic and less well recorded than in the *NSA*, but it is notable that in the parish of Callander in 1791 they were reported as 'not so numerous as formerly' (*OSA*, xii, 161). Comrie, also a hilly location, is the only other parish where goats are mentioned; here, about one hundred were kept in 1792–3 (ibid, 271–2). No goats are recorded in any of the lowland parishes.

In the New Statistical Account, goats are mentioned several times as having been kept on the hills, but at the time of writing in the first half of the 19th century having 'entirely disappeared', as in the Parish of Muthil, or having been 'pastured on the hills of Logiealmond about fifty years ago; but. . .now all displaced by another species of stock' (*NSA*, x , 317 and 253).

However, the late 18th-century account given in the *General view of the agriculture in the county of Perth* also indicates that goats were previously numerous but gives a very succinct reason for their demise (Robertson 1799):

> Goats are such hardy creatures and their milk is so nutritious, that at one period they were very much reared over all the Highlands of Scotland; but ever since the landed proprietors began to pay attention to their woods, as an article of profit, the goats have very much decreased in number, because they eat the succulent buds and otherwise destroy woods by peeling off the bark; and since sheep-stocks have been found more profitable than goats, the latter have almost entirely disappeared in this part of the kingdom.

The goat bones from the High Street would seem to be evidence that goat-keeping was part of the highland agricultural tradition from at least the medieval period until the mid-19th century.

Pigs were not present in great numbers in the animal bone assemblage from the site, and it is quite likely that many were kept within the confines of the town itself as well as in the hinterland. Unlike cattle and sheep, which produce milk, meat and wool or hides, pigs are less valuable in terms of their by-products. Their value was in turning the pannage from oak woodlands (particularly acorns) into meat (Illus 9), and the privilege of allowing pigs to forage in this way, also known as pannage, was a jealously guarded right.

The woodlands of the hinterland would have provided far more than food for swine, however. Afforested land was probably managed in various ways in order to maintain a renewable source of raw materials. Oak woods were probably coppiced. In this process, the crowns of the trees are cut down, leaving a stool from which shoots spring. Oak shoots can be harvested every 16 years or so and the same stool can survive for 100 years or more (James 1982, 63). The principal use for oak springs is to produce bark, rich in tannins, for tanning leather. Other trees which were probably coppiced in the medieval period are hazel, from which wattling is made, ash for tool handles and sheep hurdles, alder for making turned bowls and birch for wattling, making besoms and for its bark, also used in tannery. That coppicing was practised in central Scotland in the medieval period is demonstrated by a grant to Lindores Abbey, Fife, in the year 1250, of a hundred loads of hazel rods annually (Duncan 1975a, 363; Smout 1993, 44). The remains of birch wattling (Illus 44) may have been produced in this way; however a study of wattling from various tree species found at Kirk Close found that the withies may have been the product of isolated coppiced trees, or even of hedgerow trees rather than of well regulated woodland (Crone and Barber 1987, 87). Because much of the woodland of Scotland grew within the boundaries of Royal Forests or was granted to favourites of the King and to abbeys such as Coupar Angus by Free Forest Grant (Gilbert 1979, 183, 234), access by the common people to large trees may have been restricted. Thus at Kirk Close, much of the timber was thought to have been reused and was probably gleaned from stands of trees growing beside the Tay or from hedgerows (Crone and Barber 1987, 88). It is quite likely that some of the building timbers were also obtained in this way; here, where most buildings were constructed of wood and only infrequently of stone, timbers were mainly found to be oak and ash (although birch was occasionally used) (Bogdan 1992, 6).

Wood was also the main source of domestic fuel in the early medieval period, the use of coal being uncommon and probably confined to those areas of small-scale mining such as were being worked in Fife and the Lothians by the Abbeys of Newbattle, Dunfermline, Culross, Inchcolm, Holyrood and Crossraguel

(Hall 2006). Among the locally available tree species, the best quality firewood would have come from ash, oak, birch and hazel, while willow and alder produced fuel of lesser quality (James 1982, 78–9). Given that wood for building was at a premium, however, it is likely that any available scrub wood was used for fuel. Trees and branches swept down the Tay in the numerous floods of the medieval period and deposited on the banks downriver would also be a good source of fuel; at the present day, entire oak trees, carried downstream by winter floods, particularly that of 1993, can still be seen littering the river banks and have in the last decade been salvaged for firewood by a local small business near Errol.

Wood charcoal was of importance in smelting and metal working. It was probably produced on the site where wood was gathered, in the woodland, in earth-covered kilns. Metal working debris in the form of slag and hammerscale from the site at Meal Vennel indicate a requirement for this fuel within the town (Cox 1996, 791). Ring and brooch moulds found at the site and a ring mould from 80–86 High Street (Cox 1997, 755) show that finer metal work also took place and would also have needed a source of fuel.

Woodland also provided a source of wild foods, gleaned for both human and animal consumption. Hazelnut shells were commonly found at the High Street and are ubiquitous at medieval sites throughout the town. Botanical evidence shows that fruits and berries were collected in season: strawberry, raspberry, bramble, rowan, rosehip, elderberry, gean, bullace and sloe were all found at the site. These berries could have been eaten raw, providing a valuable source of Vitamin C, or fermented to make alcoholic drinks. The rowan, for example, was known as *luis*, or 'drink' by the Gaelic speakers of Perthshire because a 'very good spirit' could be distilled from the fruit. In addition, the fruit itself was thought to confer long life to all who ate it (White 1898, lxiii). This may have had roots in the belief of the magic powers of the rowan, but the berries' vitamin content gave the tree real powers to prevent the human deficiency disease scurvy.

Woodland may also have been a source of winter fodder for animals. Leaves or leafy branches harvested in late summer, dried on racks and stored under cover until needed may have formed part of the winter feed for medieval animals (Reynolds 1987, 56). That fodder of some kind was available is amply demonstrated by the large numbers of cattle which survived through at least four winter seasons. Although straw from cereal crops would have been available for fodder, the needs of cattle would have had to compete against its use as roofing material.

A further aspect of woodland ecology which could be exploited comes from its role as a habitat for wild animals. The larger species such as deer were a potential source of meat, while the smaller animals such as pine marten were hunted for their fur. However, only a small percentage of the animal bones found at sites throughout Perth were those of red or roe deer, and there was no evidence at all for wild boar. This relative lack of bones of venison has been related to restrictions placed on hunting by the crown, in favour of the nobility and clergy, which effectively curtailed the rights of the common people (Gilbert 1979). The townspeople would not have gone without meat however, as under normal circumstances of supply, the domestic livestock would have provided a more than adequate source, judging by the large assemblage of bones recovered from the site.

Somewhat surprisingly, there was no evidence from the High Street for exploitation of woodland bird species, such as pheasant or capercaillie, although, on the evidence of feather remains from Pluscarden Priory the pheasant has been shown to have been present in 15th-century Scotland (Cerón-Carrasco 1994, 414). Perhaps, as was the case with venison, the pleasures of hawking, by which woodland birds would have been taken, were also reserved mainly to the crown, nobility and clergy. The early 16th-century rental books of the Bishopric of Dunkeld, for example, show that a fowler (*aucupi*) was employed on 'each day when my Lord left hawking' (*Dunkeld Rentale*, 65). It is perhaps significant that no bones of raptors other than buzzards were found at the site, and these were more likely to have been scavengers than trained hawking birds.

There was a wealth of archaeological evidence to show that moorland resources were imported into the town. Heather and moss fragments were frequently found at the site. The heathers were probably used as roofing material or as bedding for people and animals. Moss species such as *Polytrichum commune* were plaited into ropes, which might be used to hold roofing materials in place. Other moorland and bog plants such as bog myrtle (*Myrica gale*), tormentil (*Potentilla erecta*) and bog cotton (*Eriophorum vaginatum*) may have been incorporated into the plant assemblage in several ways: they may have been harvested accidentally from damp field margins during hay making; collected with peat dug for fuel; or collected deliberately for some other purpose. Bog myrtle, for instance, has been used to make gale beer and also yields a yellow dye. Tormentil is rich in tannins and was used to tan leather, as at medieval Gallowgate, Aberdeen. Here a stone mortar found in connection with a series of tan-pits was encrusted with residues containing the pollen of tormentil, as well as oak and birch, all used as tanning agents (Evans 1987, 13; Moffat and Penny 2001, 297-9). Some moorland plants have medicinal uses, but as there were no distinct concentrations of plant materials found at the High Street, it is not possible to say whether they had been used in this way. Furthermore, most of the wild plants native to Britain have had medicinal properties ascribed to them at one time or another, not all of which are accepted today. However, in the absence of other medicines, the medieval townspeople would have had little option than to turn to locally available plant remedies and it is worth noting that some plant-derived substances still have a place in the modern British Pharmacopoeia.

Thus mosses could have been used as a packing material for wounds, since sphagnum, for example, contains natural antiseptic and preservative phenols, as well as being highly absorbent when dried. Eleventh-century chronicles relate how after battle, 'stricken Scots stuffed their wounds with moss' and this use continued until as recently as the Second World War (Mabey 1979, 102). Sphagnum was also used in the same way as toilet paper, sanitary towels and disposable nappies are at the present day (Beith 2004, 244); a cesspit at Kirk Close contained significant quantities of heathland and woodland mosses which were almost certainly used in this way (Robinson 1987a, 200).

Further evidence of moorland and mountain resources which found their way into the town was provided by bones of bird species such as red grouse, black grouse and ptarmigan. Presumably these species would have been most successfully hunted in winter when flocks of ptarmigan leave the high tops to winter at a lower altitude in the birch forests, where red grouse are also to be found (Bruun et al 1989, 94).

There is also a body of evidence that transhumance, that is, the seasonal movement of animals and their herders known in Scotland as 'going to the shieling', took place in Perthshire in the medieval period. Bil (1992, 388) has shown from placename studies that the term 'shiel' may have been used to describe the custom of leading the cattle to summer grazing as early as the 13th century in the most southerly and easterly parts of the Perthshire lowlands. However the custom was centred more particularly on upland Perthshire, in Atholl, Rannoch and Breadalbane (ibid, 386). Shieling had several advantages: the cattle benefited from the fresh green plant growth of the summer pastures, and were not so troubled by parasitic flies since these are deterred by the stronger winds to be found at higher altitudes; red deer are known to take advantage of this relief by escaping to the heights in summer. While the cattle, sheep and their young grazed, the women and children who attended them made cheeses from their milk. This cheese was economically important, as it often contributed to payments of rent in kind. Rentals of abbeys frequently specify payments of large quantities of cheese, for example 40 stones weight (254kg) (Duncan 1975a, 358), some of which would have been sold on at market.

Rivers, waterways and wetlands

Situated as the town is at a crossing point on the River Tay, it would be highly unusual if no evidence of exploitation of freshwater resources had been found at medieval Perth. Fish were probably the most important food obtained from the river. Salmon, still an important economic species at the present day, was the most frequently occurring freshwater species found at the High Street, although bones of sparling (smelt; *Osmerus eperlanus*) and eel were also recovered. Salted salmon was a major Scottish export during the medieval period (Grant 1934, 36) and Perth was a centre of the salmon trade by the 13th century (Martin 1995, 41). Letting of the salmon fishings on the Tay was controlled by the Guildry Incorporation of Perth and only the wealthier burgesses and lairds could afford to pay the tacks (Stavert 1993, xix). The King's nets were situated at various places on the Tay below Perth and feature in the Perth Guildry Book from 1453 onwards (ibid, 416). During the later 18th century, John Richardson, merchant in Perth, became known as the 'Great Fishmonger of the Tay', leasing much of the fishing in the parish of Kinfauns, below Perth (Haldane 1981). Richardson considered that the most productive and hence valuable part of his fishings was from 'the influx of the Isla down to Newburgh on the south bank and Errol on the north (ibid, 9). Presumably this stretch of the river also yielded large catches in earlier times, either by netting or by impaling the fish with a forked spear known as a *leister* (Martin 1995, 43).

Sparling (smelt) were of much lesser economic importance than salmon, probably because the fish themselves are very small. However they were considered a delicacy and were thought to taste and smell like rushes (Martin 1995, 47), or to 21st-century taste buds, like cucumber. In 'The Dirige', a satirical 15th-century poem by the Scots makar William Dunbar, the poet invites the King to return from a religious retreat at Stirling to the comfort of the court at Edinburgh:

> 'Cum hame and dwell na mair in Stirling
> Fra hyddows hell cum hame and dwell
> Quhair fische to sell is nane bot spyrling
> Cum hame and dwell na mair in Stirling'
> (Bawcutt and Riddy 1992, 131)
> ['hyddows' hideous]

Sparling seem to have been only 'small fry' as far as Dunbar was concerned.

Freshwater shellfish were also gathered from the Tay, most notably the pearl mussel (*Margaritifera margaritifera*) (Illus 43). Although this species is edible and has been used by the sea fisherman of the Ythan in Aberdeenshire for baiting lines, it is more important for producing freshwater pearls (Goodwin 1985, 28). In the 12th century, Scottish pearls were exported to Europe, although they were of lesser value than the oriental type (Kunz and Stevenson 1908, 160). Scottish pearls are also mentioned in a statute of 1335 of the goldsmiths of Paris, indicating the value of the pearl fishing industry (Goodwin 1985, 25). Thus the freshwater mussel shells found at the site may have been collected for bait, but it is also likely that pearls were being sought. The Tay and the Isla were still being fished for pearl mussels at the end of the twentieth century, although the species had declined drastically in abundance and is now protected. Perth remains the centre of the British freshwater pearl trade.

Waterfowl from the Tay were also utilised for food. The duck bones from the site are more likely to have come the wild mallard rather than its domestic descendant. An unknown, although probably small, proportion of the goose bones may have come from greylag, while a few were from pinkfooted goose. Other members of the anatid family found at the site were swan, goosander, wigeon and shoveler duck. Large waterfowl, heron, crane and stork, although not numerous, were also found. Waterfowl would have been caught, perhaps netted, on the reedy margins of the river or in the undrained, boggy Carse lands, which may have been home to the red-throated diver whose bones were found at the site.

Wetland

Plant species of wetland habitats which were of use to man were the rushes and sedges (*Juncus* and *Carex* sp.) found growing by the margins of lochs and on riverbanks. They may have been collected deliberately, for strewn floor coverings, and in the case of rushes for making the wicks in rush lights to be burnt in vessels like the cruisie lamps of the Highlands (Grant 1961, 182). Rushes could also be plaited to make baskets and mats; although no evidence for this use survives at the site, willow was used and it might be assumed that rushes were too (see Fascicule 2, The baskets).

If not collected deliberately, the rush and sedge seeds found at the site might have been incorporated into the plant assemblage through harvesting of wet meadow species for hay, or via animal dung from animals pastured in damp habitats. In recent experiments carried out on Shetland, such species have been found to be associated with the bristle oat crop. They are often harvested accidentally along with the oats from the margins of damp fields (Hinton 1991). Such accidental collection may also account for the presence of other damp-loving species such as bogbean (*Menyanthes trifoliata*) and yellow flag (*Iris pseudacorus*) although as these particular plants have specific uses, they may have been collected deliberately. Bogbean (Gaelic name *tribhileach*) was used medicinally in the Highlands as a cure for colic and internal upsets (Grant 1961, 313). It was also used to flavour beer and to treat blockages caused by overeating in animals (Beith 2004, 207). Yellow flag, used when flowering is over (which may account for the presence of its large seeds at the site) produces a greyish-blue or black dye (Grant 1961, 230). Since yellow flag is known to be poisonous to cattle (Cooper and Johnson 1984, 133–4), it is not likely that the seeds came from either fodder or dung. The roots of yellow flag have also been used in a toothache cure, as on Mull in the 18th century (Beith 2004, 217–18)

At first sight it is surprising that no evidence of reeds (*Phragmites*) was found at the site, given the current extent and recent economic harvesting for thatch of the reed beds at Errol and elsewhere in the Carse of Gowrie. However it would appear that these beds were not deliberately planted until around the year 1735 in conjunction with a programme of drainage and embanking carried out by local lairds, thus beginning the elimination of the 'rushes ... pools of water ... (and) haunt of lapwings' (Robertson 1799, 63, 367–9). Local tradition also has it that the reed beds at Newburgh, on the opposite bank of the Tay, were not planted until the early 19th century, when Napoleonic prisoners of war housed in Perth prison were reputedly pressed into service.

Marine resources

The principal marine resource was, of course, sea fish. Species for which we have evidence at the site included cod, haddock, saithe, herring, ling, halibut and plaice or flounder. Although the Tay is tidal as far upstream as Perth Bridge, these marine fish must have been caught down river, at least as far away as Dundee and the mouth of the estuary, or perhaps Arbroath. Boats could have sailed from Perth harbour and made the journey to the open sea, where large cod could be taken on long lines. A variety of other strategies could be employed, however. Small cod could be caught, from boats, close to the shore with small lines. In the present century, codling can also be taken from the rocks, in winter when they come inshore, the nearest point to Perth probably being West Ferry, near Dundee. Flatfish such as fluke (flounder) are commonly taken on hand lines at Riverside Drive, the location of the landfall of the Tay Railway Bridge, at Dundee, or at Wormit on the Fife side, while small saithe or pollack, known locally as podles, are easily caught off Broughty Ferry pier.

Fish hooks from the site range in size from those suitable for taking small cod to large hooks for large cod and salmon. Lines may have been made from flax (seeds of which were found at the High Street). Attachments for fixing hooks to the lines (snuids) were traditionally made from horse hair (Martin 1995, 15) also found at the site (see Fascicule 3, The hair). Lines were baited with shellfish, preferably mussels, although limpets and buckies were also used. Shells from bait species were plentiful at the site. However, as these shellfish would have had to be transported from rocky shores perhaps as far down river as St Nicholas Craig, Dundee (now the site of the railway station) or Balmerino on the Fife side, it is quite likely they were also used as direct food for humans. It seems wasteful of time and energy to transport shellfish by river to Perth, then bait the lines, only to take the baited lines back to the mouth of the estuary, a distance of about 35km. In addition, unrefrigerated bait, as it must have been, goes 'off' very quickly.

Although the presence of cod head bones indicates that fresh fish were indeed landed at the harbour, some of the cod eaten in the town were probably imported as salt fish, preserved in barrels. Fish are mentioned only occasionally in the *Perth Guildry Book*, but in 1551, the 'hugstairs' (hucksters) were forbidden to sell goods including 'fissis' and herring on a Sunday or Holyday (Stavert 1993, 209). These herring were probably caught using floating nets, and could have arrived at the site fresh or preserved by salting or smoking.

Floats for herring nets were traditionally made on the east coast of Scotland from inflated dog skin 'bowies' (Shepherd 1979, 83–6) and it is interesting to recall the knife cuts on some of the dog bones indicative of skinning.

An intriguing use of shells, in this case the scallop (*Pecten maximus*), was shown by two examples in which holes had been bored. The shells could thus be suspended from thongs and worn around the neck. They were probably pilgrim badges brought back to Scotland from the shrine of Saint James the Great at Santiago de Compostela in Spain. Wearing of such badges conveyed a certain kudos in the medieval world, although the author of the late 14th-century allegory 'Piers the Ploughman' was rather scathing of a practice which he obviously considered an empty show (Goodridge 1966, 77). Scallop shells also have more mundane uses; pierced for use as milk strainers, they were in common use throughout the Highlands until recent times (Grant 1961, 214).

The town

The most important factor for preservation of environmental evidence was the waterlogged nature of the deposits at the site. Frequent flooding of the River Tay, and the burns which fed it, must have played havoc with life in the town. The most notable flood of the medieval period may have been that of 1209 which destroyed the bridge over the river, and possibly the castle too. The highest level reached by the floodwaters of the Tay in the recent period was that of 1814 when a level of 7.0m above Ordnance Datum was measured at Perth Bridge (Bowler 2004, 3, 12). Descriptions of floods in the 15th century are also recorded in the *Perth Guildry Book*, when the 'Tay flooded in revenge, as the river took on the daring and the appearance of the sea' (Stavert 1993, 493). Another dramatic inundation was recorded in the so-called *Chronicle of Perth* as having lasted for about a week in 1621 and caused such destruction the 'lyke in no manes remembrance wes sene' (Eagles 1995, 121). That bogginess at the High Street caused problems was shown by the construction, in the 12th century, of a pathway made of hurdling laid over swampy ground (Illus 44).

Surrounding the town was a wall with associated ditch and lade or watercourse which may have helped deflect some of the effects of floods. Investigations at medieval sites elsewhere in the town have also recovered evidence of encircling ditches. At Mill Street, the ditch was surrounded by tall weed species, such as henbane, stinging nettle, fat hen and dock species, while wet habitat plants such as meadow-sweet were found in the silts at the bottom of the ditch (Robinson 1995, 991). Thus it is possible that some of the wetland plants found at the High Street, such as sedge, need not have been transported far. Early town ditch deposits from

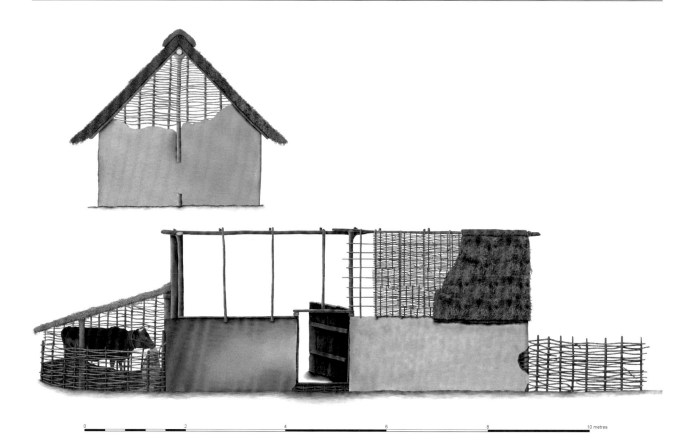

Illus 45 *Building B4 Reconstruction (by Dave Munro)*

South Methven Street were found to contain caddis fly larval cases which were not present in later deposits. Along with other evidence from the ditch, this was interpreted as an indication of a relatively unpolluted water supply which only later became infilled with rubbish (Robinson 1987a, 202). Similar pollution of the ditch is likely to have occurred at the High Street. Part of the town itself may have been wooded at an early period in its development: tree stumps were found in the backlands at the site (see Fascicule 1, The excavation). However as burgh expansion continued, scrub would have been cleared away in forming the familiar pattern of long rigs or burgage plots laid out behind the street frontage. Facing the High Street would have been the booths and tenement properties of the merchant burgesses, while the less prestigious dwellings and craftsmen's workshops lay farther behind in the backlands. There is evidence that some of the buildings, for example Building B4 (Illus 45) had byres for animals attached. Copious evidence of dung also indicates that animals were stabled within the town. However, during the day, cattle, sheep and horses were pastured on the Burghmuir, to the west of the town (an early name for one of the roads leading to this area being the Cow Causeway; Eagles 1995, 274). Pasturage was also available on the North and South Inches, but this was not without seasonal problems. Because of their proximity to the river, these areas tended to become flooded. In January 1615, for example 'great weittis' covered the North Inch, and 'scheip that war in perrell

of drwnyng' were saved by 'men rowing wt boats' (ibid 31).

Where pigs were concerned, some animals were probably kept in styes within the town. Evidence for this practice is possibly provided by several skeletons of neonatal piglets. The presence at the Blackfriars House site of a young pig suffering from the bone disease rickets, which is caused in part by a lack of sunlight, is thought to be indicative of an animal kept in a dark stye (Smith 2000a). In the *Leges Quatuor Burgorum* (Laws of the Four Burghs 'mayd and ordanyt be the Kyng David') we are warned that 'it is nocht leyfull til ony burges wythin the kyngis burghe dwellande for to halde swyne in the burgh bot gif he hase a kepar folowand thaim quhar thruch his nychtbouris inryn na scathe nor noye or than that he hald thaim in sty' (*APS* i, 349 c84). In other words, pigs should be followed by a swineherd in order to stop them damaging the property of others, or should be kept under control in a stye. However this advice was frequently ignored, and the fact that domestic animals and geese frequently wandered unchecked about the town, causing havoc by eating the contents of backland garden plots, can be traced in various burgh statutes. As late as 1715 in Dundee, the town council minutes record, rather wearily, 'no swine to be kept unless within houses; any person deprehending swine in his skaith can kill them' (Warden 1872, 392). The reason for this repeated banning of pigs from the streets ran deeper than avoidance of damage to gardens, annoying

Illus 46 *Cattle radius showing gnaw marks made by dog or other carnivore on bone shaft.*

Illus 47 *Reconstruction of medieval rubbish disposal. (Painting by Steve Earl)*

though this was. In early 17th-century Lanark the reason given for their restriction was that 'ane sow eat ane barin in this toun in credill' (Whyte 1979, 81), although as it is not noted when this incident is supposed to have happened the story may have been apocryphal.

However, destructive geese and bad-tempered pigs were not the only beastly hazard to be encountered in the medieval town. At least some of the dogs and most of the cats probably led a semi-feral existence, belonging to no-one and finding food where they could (Illus 46). This would almost certainly have lead to sporadic outbreaks of rabies, a disease known and feared from classical times and potentially fatal to both animal and man. Vicious watch dogs, too, would have been a danger to life and limb, although the dogs were so highly valued that any man who 'slais a mannis (house) hund thruch villany . . . sal wak apon that mannis myddin for a tuelf moneth and a day' (*APS*, i, XXXIII, 325).

Dangerous animals were not the only factor affecting everyday life, of course. Living conditions within the medieval burgh would have been partly influenced by the craft activities which took place there. From the site we have evidence of skinning, leather manufacture, horn working, commercial butchery, possible glue and neats' foot oil production, yarn spinning and textile manufacture. At other sites in the burgh, backland activities included grain drying and malting at Canal Street III and metal working at Meal Vennel (Coleman 1996; Cox 1996). Evidence from a watching brief at St John's Square has also provided evidence for small scale antler working (Perry and Coleman forthcoming). In addition, crafts for which we have no direct evidence were known to have been carried on in medieval burghs, for example, tallow rendering, candle making, flax retting and dyeing. All of these craft activities resulted in waste products, which in the case of tanning and skinning are potentially noxious. Some were dangerous fire hazards as are any processes which involve heating fats, such as tallow candle making. In some

burghs, composed chiefly of highly flammable wooden buildings, candle making was banned to the outer limits of the town. Flax retting, involving steeping the flax in tanks or even in free flowing water as in Henryson's 15th-century fable, where the lint 'steipit in the burne and dryit syne' (Bawcutt and Riddy 1992, 47) was notorious for engender-ing particularly noxious smells. Heckle combs, a flax-worker's mallet and flax seeds found at the site indicate that at least the later stages of lint production took place in the town. A drying area for textiles was to be found on the water meadows of the North and South Inches.

The waste from butchery, the entrails of animals, trimmings of hides and pelts, tan-pits full of steeping leather, fish heads, old horn cores buried for weeks until the horn sheaths were ripe for removal – all of these left their traces on medieval Perth. This industrial waste would have been commingled with everyday domestic food refuse, floor-sweepings, animal dung and the contents of cess-pits (Illus 47). Such unsavoury miasmas would have contributed to an interesting atmosphere about the town, to say the least. The poet Dunbar describes the typically fragrant 15th-century scene in a work dedicated to the merchants of Edinburgh:

> 'May nane pass throw your principal gaittis
> For stink of haddockis and of scattis
> For cryis of carlyngis and debaittis . . .
> Tailyeouris, soutteris and craftis vyll
> The fairest of your streittis dois fyll'
> (Bawcutt and Riddy 1992, 161–4)
> ['gaittis' streets; 'scattis' skates,
> 'soutteris' cobblers, 'vyll' vile]

The physical evidence from early Perth indicates that its gaits would have been as offensive to the refined senses of the courtly makar as those of Edinburgh two centuries later.

Some efforts (however futile) were made to keep the streets clean. In 15th-century Aberdeen, for instance, a burgh 'scaffyngir' was appointed to remove rubbish (a job still done by the 'scaffies' of the north-east) (Wyness 1966, 71, 140). Nevertheless, this possibly solitary 'waste-disposal operative' was no match for the inhabitants of medieval Aberdeen and great midden deposits were allowed to accumulate as revealed by the excavations at Queen Street, for example (Murray 1982). In Perth, the job of 'gait dychting' seems to have fallen within the province of the 'pynnouris', the shore-porters at the harbour. They were also responsible for 'sowping and dychting of the mercattis' (Stavert 1993, 237). 'Sowping' seems to have implied slopping out of the market area with water. The rubbish itself was probably thrown into the Tay; the pynnours were charged with the obligation to

> 'dicht all the mercattis of the toune and carry the muk thairof to the wattirside, and clengis the gaittis and mercattis thairof with couppis and sleddis ... and als cleng and dycht the mydding at lyis besid the peir beneath the trone and all possible haist betwix this (11th November 1511) and Youll'
> (ibid, 458)

Quite how often the gaits were dichtit is unclear – the previous tack for this job was leased some seven years previously, but it is most unlikely that rubbish would be allowed to accumulate for such an extended period of time. The tack may have been renewed regularly on a seven year cycle. Reference in the tacks to 'use and consuetude has been in tymes begane' (ibid, 446) regarding the pynnourship indicate that street cleaning was a custom of some standing, and may thus may have occurred in the period for which we have direct evidence at the site. Certainly the pynnours could not have been entirely efficient, or were responsible only for those areas directly on the street frontage, otherwise the numerous midden deposits found at the site would not have yielded such fruitful environmental evidence. However it is obvious that the pynnour of Perth, Andrew Storour, and his team of scaffies, should be included in our earlier list of taphonomic influences.

Aspects of human health and hygiene in medieval Perth

There is a strong possibility that the immediate environment of Perth was polluted to some extent by the craft industries which were indispensable to the creation of wealth in the burgh. Living conditions for the wealthiest merchants and the poorest labourers may have differed substantially, but it is probable that intestinal parasitic infestations were no respecters of social status. Whipworm (*Trichuris*) eggs were found in what may have been a cess-pit deposit at the High Street and roundworm (*Ascaris*) eggs in a latrine deposit at Kirk Close (Illus 48; Robinson 1987a, 201). Although we have no evidence for other

intestinal parasites from Perth, it is quite likely that infestations of tapeworms were contracted via the dogs and pigs which roamed freely through the burgh. Cestode tapeworms (for example *Taenia solium*) and nematode roundworms (*Trichinella*) could be ingested through eating undercooked measly pork. This was perceived, erroneously, as a source of leprosy in the middle ages (Smith 1995b, 73). The fish tapeworm, *Diphyllobothrium latum*, could also have been troublesome if undercooked fish was eaten. Infestation by this parasite may lead eventually to Vitamin B12 deficiency.

However unsavoury and malodorous the cess-pits and latrines might have been, some of the inhabitants of Perth made an effort towards a degree of comfort in their sanitary arrangements; at Kirk Close, a covered latrine was constructed with an oaken seat, on which one thoughtful user had incised a pattern of decorative lines (Ford 1987b, 145). Presumably he would also have been comforted by a plentiful supply of sphagnum moss or lint toilet 'paper', the latter type having been used at Elgin (Robinson 1987b). The botanical contents of such cess-pits reveal much about the diet of those who used them. As well as evidence of home grown cereals and wild berries found in medieval cess-pits (Robinson 1987a, 201–2), there are occasional remains of imported fruits such as figs and grapes, as at Aberdeen (Fraser 1981; Fraser and Dickson 1982, 240; Kenward and Hall 2001, 290). Only the wealthy could have afforded these exotics.

Much more common in the diet of the labouring people must have been bannocks and porridge made from oats, rye and bere. However nutritious these must have been, there was an ever present danger of common weed seeds contaminating the processed grain. Corn cockle (*Agrostemma githago*) was a serious contaminant of the rye crop (Robinson 1987a, 206) and has potentially serious poisonous effects on both people and their animals. Symptoms of githagism in man include lassitude, weight loss and gastrointestinal disturbances and, if the contaminated diet is continued, may lead to death (Cooper and Johnson 1984, 77–8). Another crop contaminant found at the site, stinking mayweed (*Anthemis cotula*) although not poisonous when ingested was potentially troublesome during harvest time. Grigson (1975, 401) is of the opinion that 'in the days of hand husbandry no weed was more hated' because the entire plant has the power to raise blisters wherever it comes in contact with the skin, and often caused such pain that men were unable to work.

Ergot of rye, caused by the parasitic fungus *Claviceps purpurea*, was also a potential hazard in the medieval period, responsible for the disease known as St Anthony's Fire. Its spores have been found at a rural medieval site at Nethermills, Grampian (Boyd 1986). Poisoning with ergot causes symptoms ranging from mild tingling in the arms and legs and burning sensations in the mouth, to severe convulsions, mental confusion and gangrene (Cooper and Johnson 1984, 49). Mass episodes of poisoning have been recorded

Illus 48 *Latrine pit, with wattle hurdling used to strengthen trampled area, Kirk Close, Perth.*

in the past, throughout Europe, from the 6th century (Stuart 1987) until as recently as the late 1920s in Manchester's Jewish community (Cooper and Johnson 1984, 49).

Further to the problems caused by accidental contamination or spoilage of food through damp or pilfering and polluting by mice, there was the very real risk of deliberate adulteration in order to make extra weight when sold. A curious practice which appears to have been indulged in by unscrupulous fleshers was to blow up joints of meat (presumably using straws) in order to make the meat appear plumper and more attractive. Documentary evidence for this trickery appears in the 16th-century burgh records of Dundee 'no flescher in brugh nor land bring blawin flesh to this merkit nor collipittit nor cuttit upon or under the skin . . . and na scheip be slitted down in the schulders' (Warden 1872, 12–13). 'Collipittit' implies cutting the meat in some way, perhaps in order to introduce air into it, or perhaps to remove identifying marks, such as ear marks, in the case of stolen animals. 'Blawin' of meat is also commented on by Sir David Lindsay (1490–1555) in *Ane satire of the thrie Estaitis*, one of the estates at which he directed his pen being the self-important wealthy merchant burgesses, thus, ironically:

> 'At our fleschers tak ye na greife
> Thocht they blaw lean mutton and beife
> That they seime fat and fair'
> (Hamer 1931, 367)

Meat was thus not to be tampered with in any way before reaching market. Part of the official duties of the appraisers of flesh who came to be responsible for setting prices may well have been to perform a carcass inspection. Quite what the medieval 'appreciatores carnibus' would have made of current meat enhancing practices, in which water or collagen (sometimes from a completely different species) is injected into 'joints' of meat, 'formed from selected cuts of pork', for example, is a matter of speculation. Food adulteration, it seems, is nothing new.

Although perishable foodstuffs may have been contaminated either accidentally or deliberately, spoilage of meats and fish could be avoided by pickling, smoking and, particularly, salting. Salt was in great demand for this reason, and commercial salt-pans were in operation around the Fife coast by at least the late 15th century (Murdoch and Lewis 1999, 5; Whatley 1984). Home-produced salt was not considered to be as good in quality as that from the Mediterranean, however, and it would have been necessary to import some. Also important to the process of salting were the barrels in which the fish or meat was to be preserved. These had to be sound and leakproof, otherwise the brine would seep away and the contents putrefy. Richardson of Pitfour's 18th-century Tay salmon empire relied on skilled cooperage: his barrel staves were of the best oak, while the barrel hoops were of willow, possibly grown in the county of Kinross (Haldane 1981, 20–1). When the 'kitts' or barrels threw their hoops, the pickle was lost and the salmon spoiled. In the 18th century, this was a matter only of economic profit and loss. In the 12th to 14th centuries the consequences may have been more far-reaching. We know that periods of crop failure and dearth occurred in the 16th century and there is every possibility that food shortages were common in earlier times, thus it was of prime importance to store food against time of famine.

Direct evidence of the value of the diet of the medieval people of Scotland may be seen in their skeletons. Only one human bone was retrieved, somewhat inexplicably, from the site. Although an explanation of foul play is not without parallel in medieval Perth (the body of a young man, probably beaten about the head and murdered, was recovered from a 14th-century pit at the Horse Cross excavations (Roberts 2007)), the human facial bone from the High Street may have originated from a burial in the cemetery of St John's Kirk. Part of the parish cemetery of St John's, as well as several other medieval graveyards in Perth, at the Carmelite and Dominican Friary sites and St Laurence's Chapel at the Horse Cross have been disturbed by modern developments and thus partly excavated (Roberts 2005; Roberts 2007; Bowler and Hall 1995, 939–52; Hall 1989, 99–110). There are further sources of evidence from both the Carmelite Friaries of Aberdeen and of Linlithgow (Stones 1989). From burials at these sites comes evidence of a condition called *cribra orbitalia*, characterised by pitting of the orbital area of the skull, which is thought to result from iron deficiency anaemia in childhood. Predisposing factors involved in this condition include parasitic infection, unhygienic living conditions (which, as we have seen, probably obtained in medieval Perth) as well as prolonged lactation in women of child-bearing age and a diet deficient in iron (Cross and Bruce 1989, 135). Eating processed meats such as puddings made from entrails stuffed with oatmeal and blood or offal – Dunbar's 'puddingis of Jok and Jame' despised of the well-to-do (Bawcutt and Riddy 1992, 162) – would have provided dietary iron, although the sufferers would not have realised that this was so. Other deficiency diseases such as rickets, osteomalacia and osteoporosis, involving among other variables a lack of Vitamin D and calcium in the skeleton, may have affected the medieval population. Possible evidence of rickets in medieval Perth was noted in the skeleton of a child aged between six and ten years old at death from the parish cemetery of St John's Kirk (Roberts 2005, 40).

Man and beast: working relationships

Several aspects of man's working relationships with his domestic animals are highlighted by the environmental evidence from this and other medieval Scottish sites. We know that not only did rich and poor people live 'cheek by jowl' within the confines of the burgh, but that they lived in fairly close proximity to their livestock too (Illus 49). At least one of the buildings at the High Street (Building B4) had an attached byre and courtyard but it is likely that some of the physical divisions between human and animal living quarters were much less well defined. The benefit, for people, of housing cattle alongside the family would have been that the beasts helped to heat the dwelling with their breath and body heat. Kept under the watchful eye of the humans, veterinary problems such as difficult calving would be quickly noticed and attended to. That domestic animals were carefully tended seems to be shown by the good survival rate of cattle to adulthood. Good stockmanship involves factors such as careful handling of animals, a basic knowledge of their requirements for food and shelter, recognition of departures from normal behaviour of individual animals and above all patience and empathy with the stock (English et al 1992, 15). Not all stockmen, of course would have been so careful of their animals, although it would have made sound economic sense to observe the rules of good animal husbandry. A neglected, unthrifty animal will produce less milk or wool when alive, and a poor, underweight carcass and hide when killed.

Some workers have equated poor husbandry with a high rate of bone pathologies and it is certainly hard to understand how some of the more gross malformations which occur in archaeological material have been allowed to occur. It is perhaps noteworthy that the foot-rots and foot infections of sheep and cattle, which can be stopped from further spread by judicious early treatment, seem to be fairly rare in the material from Perth and other medieval Scottish sites, implying good shepherding practices. By contrast, joint problems such as osteo-arthritis appear relatively frequently in medieval material, implying that when draught oxen became too lame for heavy work they were culled. Pigs in medieval Perth tended to suffer rather more from puncture injuries to the feet than did sheep and cattle, perhaps because of their free range lifestyle. They may have been less easy to corner and treat, as well as being of uncertain temperament, and left more to fend for themselves.

What is not clear, however, is just how much neo-natal mortality in livestock actually did occur. Since in many cases sick lambs would have died in the countryside shortly after or during birth rather than in the town, their carcasses are unlikely to be found in urban assemblages. This has, of course, implications for the interpretation of culling patterns. An example of the mortality rate for sheep is revealed by the Dunkeld Rental of the early 16th century. The appointed shepherd was obliged to present the skins of sheep which had died to the granitor (an official responsible for the food supply), in order to prove that no dishonesty had taken place. In August 1512, the shepherd reported 35 dead out of 199 sheep, the skins having been delivered up, but a further 23 which he affirmed 'were dead at Lent' were not allowed in the reckoning because 'the dead sheep were not presented with their skins' (*Dunkeld Rentale*, 275). The

Illus 49 *Artist's impression of Perth High Street backlands. (Drawn by Roger Dennis, 1978)*

accounting system and arithmetic used are far from clear, as some adult sheep are included in the figures, but the picture presented seems to be of a high lambing mortality rate at Westend of Birnam, near Dunkeld. The shepherd of Dunkeld was enjoined to guard his sheep 'faithfully and diligently from common danger, excepting the bites of wolves [and] foxes' (ibid, 274). Wolves were not yet extinct at this period in Scotland, and were obviously seen as a danger to livestock. The abbey of Coupar Angus, for example, required certain of their tenants to keep hounds for the purposes of dealing with 'tod and wolf' (*Coupar Angus Rental*, 107). (No bones of wolf have been identified at the High Street, however, but several were probably from fox, presumably brought into the town for their pelts.)

Domestic animals were thus valued for the wealth they brought, and most appeared to have been adequately cared for, bearing in mind the limitations of skeletal evidence; if a disease leaves no trace on the skeleton it is unlikely to be recognised in archaeological material. Some dogs, indeed may have been cossetted pets, such as the tiny dog buried in a pit after what may have been a long and sheltered life (Illus 12). However, some animals which are nowadays regarded with sentimentality, such as dogs, cats and horses, were skinned for their hides or fur, and horses, though highly valued in life, were probably eaten throughout the medieval and post-medieval periods in Scotland.

Animals also provided entertainment, most of it involving cruelty. There was apparent evidence of cock-fighting (Phase Vdd); the bony spur which occurs naturally on the lower leg of a cock bird was modified by sawing, in a way similar to a 19th-century English stuffed prize specimen illustrated by West (1982, 256). A sharp metal claw-like blade would then have been attached to the bony stump (Illus 39, 40), enhancing the bird's capacity to lethally injure its opponent.

Cock-fighting seems to have been a popular pastime in 18th-century Scotland, although this is the first evidence of the sport having been indulged in at an earlier period. Edinburgh's cock-pit regularly attracted large crowds in the late 18th century (Fittis 1891, 162). Traditionally, cock-fighting and its associated sport, cock-throwing (practised on the unfortunate losers), were also allowed to take place in schools every year on Fastren's E'en (Shrove Tuesday) at the beginning of Lent. For the privilege of taking part, the boys paid a fee to the teacher whose other perk was to be allowed to keep the corpses (Graham 1969, 430). This custom seems to be a survival from an earlier period, and is mentioned by Hazlitt (1995, 135) as being enjoyed in English schools in 1518.

There is no concrete evidence that the sport of dog-fighting took place in medieval Scotland, although a dog found in a post-medieval cess-pit at Mill Street had suffered a suppurating wound to the shoulder blade

which may have been caused by the bite of another
dog, perhaps during an organised bout (Smith 1998,
880). As with dog-fighting there is no evidence that
bear-baiting ever happened in medieval Perth; however
a cut bone of brown bear from a medieval context at
Castle Park, Dunbar, is difficult to explain in any other
way (Smith 2000b, 236). Bear-baiting with dogs was
certainly practised in England from at least the early
16th century (Hazlitt 1995, 36) and there is no reason
to suppose it was not enjoyed as a holiday sport in
Scotland.

It is easy for the early 21st-century observer to abhor
these 'sports' involving animals on moral or sentimental
grounds. When we consider, though, how harsh life
may have been for the poorer folk particularly, we
may feel inclined to excuse their natural desire for
diversionary entertainment.

For those privileged few for whom life was not so
precarious, there was time to reflect with compassion
on the lot of outcasts, including the non-human kind:

'Thocht brutall beistis be irrationall–
That is to say wantand discretioun–
Yet ilk ane in thair kynd naturall
Hes mony divers inclinatioun:
The bair busteous, the wolf, the wylde lyoun,
The fox fenyeit, craftie and cantelous,
The dog to bark and keip the hows.'
Robert Henryson *The Cock and the Fox*
(Bawcutt and Riddy 1992, 18).

The miscellaneous finds

The worked bone

Arthur G MacGregor
with contributions by the late Nicholas Q Bogdan, Mark A Hall and Catherine Smith

Introduction
Nicholas Q Bogdan

In addition to the very large amounts of animal bone recovered from the excavation (see The environmental remains), more than 80 pieces of bone which could be described as worked were also recovered. Of these, the majority were probably of medieval date.

The worked bone assemblage included some of the most interesting and exotic finds recovered from the site. The corpus was also noteworthy for its chronological spread, from the early 12th to the 14th centuries. The earliest three pieces, mounts designed to decorate a casket, may all originally have came from one object, discarded no later than the 12th century (Phase Ib). In total, 15 of the worked bone finds were recovered from the South Sector deposits which had been laid down during the 12th century. Of these, nine probably came from layers that had been deposited before 1150, based on dendrochronological dates (see Table 39).

The majority of the worked bone artefacts were recovered from the South Sector's stratified medieval deposits, most coming from layers that accumulated during the second half of the 13th and early 14th centuries (see Table 40). The inclusion of a number of offcuts, roughouts and trial pieces within these later deposits is an indication that bone and horn working was being carried out in the vicinity of the site. This was also confirmed by the recovery of a large number of horn cores (1,753 cattle and 722 goat) (see The environmental remains), indicating that horn was being gathered and even imported in a systematic manner (Spearman 1988, 140–1). Unusually, one fragment of worked horn itself, rather than the waste horn core, was recovered from a 12th-century deposit (Cat No 14).

Of the seven worked bone finds from the North Sector, four came from stratified layers. Perhaps significantly, the earliest, a fragment from a casket mount (Cat No 76) was similar to a piece (Cat No 10) recovered from the southern part of the site (Area 1). Both probably dated to the 12th century.

Of all the worked bone artefacts, one is of especial note. It has a good claim to be recognised as being the most aesthetically pleasing of all the many thousands of artefacts recovered during the excavation. The anthropomorphic ivory handle (Cat No 45) is by any standards a remarkable piece (Hall 2001).

Bobbins

Cat/Accession	Area	Rig	Feature	Phase
South Sector				
24/A05–0202	7	VII	B18 (Phase 1/2)	IVaa, IVb
33/A5369	3	VI	M1.4d	IVb, IVc
59/A1353a	4	VI	M3b	Vd
60/A1353b	4	VI	M3b	Vd
65/A2498	2	V, VI	M4a	Vaa–Vc (VI)

Within this inhomogeneous group, tentatively identified as bobbins, there is a marked difference between the two more formalised examples with the collared ends (Cat Nos 24 and 33) and the simple cylindrical types (Cat Nos 59, 60 and 65). The first type (Cat Nos 24 and 33) may be compared with two carefully turned wooden bobbins from the site (The worked wood, Cat Nos 91/A11403, 94/A10570) and also with examples in bone from York, Goltho and Norwich (MacGregor 1985, 183–5). They have been interpreted as reels for fine thread and the central cavity may have been used for holding sewing needles (MacGregor et al 1999, 1968–9). In Cat No 33, the small piece of associated wood may therefore have served as a plug, or could conceivably have been used to wedge the end of a line or yarn in the end of the bobbin.

Other, more elaborate solid bobbins are in the Norwich Castle Museum (Green 1973, 287–9) and the British Museum (OA543).

The second group (Cat Nos 59, 60 and 65) consists of items which are less certainly bobbins: handles, needle-cases, or even potters' stampers might be considered as possibilities, though there is even less evidence to support any of these alternative identifications. The all-over polish noted on two of them would not be inconsistent with a function as bobbins. Cat No 59, a rectangular section cut from a sheep metatarsal, decorated all over with a pattern of close-set incised dots may be a tally stick, and is similar to examples found at Kirk Close and Meal Vennel, Perth (Ford 1987a, 151 fig 82, no 159; Cox 1996, 786 Illus 27, no 597).

It is perhaps noteworthy that the first group (Cat Nos 24 and 33) was found in deposits which were laid down during the second half of the 13th century, Cat No 24 coming from a feature which appeared to be associated with the destruction of Building 18 (Phase 1) and its reconstruction as Building 18 (Phase 2); both buildings of some pretension, probably burgesses' houses despite their backland position. Cat No 33 came from a potentially contemporary backland midden, albeit on the adjoining property (Rig VI).

Table 39 *Worked bone artefacts by Phase and type.*

South Sector Periods

Period I	pre 1150
Period II	1150–c1200
Period III	c1200–c1250
Period IV	c1250–c1300
Period V	c1300–1350>
Period V1	Post-medieval and/or modern

phase	cat no	object type
South Sector		
Ia(Ib)	1	casket mount
Ib	2	casket mount
Ib	3	casket mount
Ic	4	playing piece
Ic	5	comb
(Icc)Id	6	pin-beater?
Id	7	die
Ie(If)	8	toggle
If	9	pin
If,IIa	10	casket mount
IIa–IIc	11	handle
IId–IIg	12	?bead
IIe–IIg	13	whorl
IIi	14	horn terminal
IIi	15	pin-beater?
IIIa–IIIc	16	perforated bone
IIIc	17	toggle
<IIIc–IVaa	18	whorl
<IIIc–IVaa	19	toggle
IVa,IVaa	20	perforated bone

phase	cat no	object type
IVa–IVb	21	offcut
IVa–IVb	22	offcut
IVaa,IVb	23	comb
IVaa,IVb	24	bobbin
IVaa,IVb	25	perforated bone
IVb	26	perforated bone
IVb	27	forked implement
IVb	28	whorl
IVb	29	needle
IVb	30	perforated bone
IVc	31	whorl
IVb,IVc	32	comb
IVb,IVc	33	bobbin
IVb,IVc	34	comb
IVb,IVc	35	die
IVc,IVcc	36	whorl
(IVc–)Va	37	needle/bale pin
IVcc,Va	38	pin
IVcc,Va	39	comb
IVcc(Va)	40	perforated bone
Va	41	offcut
Vaa	42	needle?
Vaa	43	roughout?
Va,Vaa	44	pin-beater?
Va,Vaa	45	ivory handle
Va,Vaa	46	rough–out
Va,Vaa	47	?skate
Va,Vaa	48	die

phase	cat no	object type
Va,Vaa	49	comb
Va,Vaa	50	toggle
Vbb	51	die
Vbb	52	die
Vbb	53	pin
Vbb	54	pin
Vbb	55	whorl
Vbb	56	needle
Vb–Vc	57	handle
Vc	58	?burnisher
Vd	59	bobbin?
Vd	60	bobbin?
Vd	61	toggle
Vd	62	die
(Va–)Vd(Vdd)	63	die
Vd,Vdd	64	offcut/trial piece
Vaa–Vc(VI)	65	bobbin?
VI	66	whorl
VI	67	roughout?
u/s	68	comb
u/s	69	antler offcut
u/s	70	toggle
u/s	71	comb
u/s	72	comb
u/s	73	trial piece
u/s	74	infant's teether
u/s	75	sawn horn core

phase	cat no	object type
North Sector, Area 5		
4–6	76	casket mount
6–12	77	pin-beater
14–16	78	toggle?
u/s	79	umbrella handle
u/s	80	pin-beater?
u/s	81	offcut/trial piece
North Sector, Area 6		
G	82	toggle

The second group (Cat Nos 59, 60 and 65) came from early–mid 14th-century middens, which probably relate to one property as there is reason for thinking that Rigs V and VI were combined from Phase IVb onwards.

Casket mounts

Cat/Accession	Area	Rig	Feature	Phase
South Sector				
1/A10074	1	VI	M0; Pit 3789	Ia (Ib)
2/A9815	1/2	VI	MC006	Ib
3/A9843	1/2	VI	MC006	Ib
10/A1880	1	VI	P5.3b	If, IIa
North Sector				
76/A5431	5	n/a	CG008	4–6

Mounts from two or, more probably, three caskets appear to be represented. Cat Nos 1, 2 and 3 all came from early 12th-century deposits. Cat Nos 10 and 76 are similar to one another and may both date from the mid-12th century, but they are unlikely to have come from one casket as the latter piece was recovered from the North Sector (Area 5) and the former from the South Sector (Area 1) of the site. Notwithstanding that they appear to fall into two groups which can be distinguished from each other by their incised ornament, by the shapes of their cut-out ornament and by their raw material, it may be that quite dissimilar decorative motifs could occur within the scheme of a single casket. Mounts cut from scapulae have the advantage of having large flat surface areas and may be found in combination with conventional strips cut from ribs or antlers.

Table 40 *Total number of bone artefacts by Period.*

date	century	period	number of bone objects
pre-1150	12c	I	9
1150–1200	12c	II	6
1200–1250	13c	III	2
1250–1300	13c	IV	19
1300–1350	14c	V	30
>1350	14c or later	VI	2
u/s (South Sector)		u/s	10
North Sector		all	7
total			85

The practice of applying decorative bone mounts to small wooden boxes or caskets has a long history in Britain, stretching from the late Roman period to about the 12th century. Continental examples are also known, principally in the Germanic area. The later British examples, all of about 11th/12th-century date, include the following: groups of unattached mounts from South Cadbury Castle (Greene, in Alcock 1970, 22–3) and York Minster (MacGregor 1995, 420, fig 158); a group of mounts from Ludgershall Castle from the lid of a box, the wood of which had decayed leaving the mounts in their original disposition (Wilson and Hurst 1966, 192, Plate XV); a partially surviving wooden lid with some strips still fixed in position, found in Coppergate, York (Benson 1906, 73, Plates II, III; Waterman 1959, 86) and, from more recent excavations at 16–22 Coppergate, a complete wooden lid from the same street, found with all the strips intact (MacGregor 1979, 6–8; MacGregor et al 1999, 1954–9, Fig 913).

Incised decoration in the form of lines and concentric circles is common to all but the last mentioned of the above mounts and, indeed, to most of their predecessors. The use of decorative cut-outs is also common among the later caskets, in some cases combined with a sheet-metal backing. The mounts on one of the York caskets have large circular and elliptical perforations through which shows a backing of gilt bronze sheeting (Waterman 1959, 86), while the Ludgershall mounts were backed with lead. A richer example from Emden, Ostfriesland, which features cruciform cut-outs within multiple incised circles, was backed with sheet gold (Schmidt 1969, 273–4). Other caskets with perforated mounts seem to have had no metal backing, and no trace of any can be seen on the Perth mounts.

The surviving small diameter fixing holes are also free from staining by metallic salts, raising the possibility that some at least of the mounts were

never utilised, a hypothesis that would, in turn, imply that they had been manufactured on or near the site. Alternatively, the mounts may have been stripped from the lid before they had been stained by corrosion. Bone fixing pegs were used with some mounts, but they tend to be of larger diameter than the peg holes represented here.

No Christian significance need be attached to the cruciform cut-outs; they are also commonly found on secular combs of the period (cf Cat No 49).

Of those found within the South Sector of the site, all came from Rig VI and were found relatively near the High Street frontage. In fact it seems likely that Cat Nos 1, 2 and 3, which all come from one casket, may be associated with the occupants of B17 (East), a street frontage structure dating from the early 12th century. Although Cat No 1 was recovered from a pit and Cat No 2 from a nearby deposit, they evidently originally formed part of one piece, along with Cat No 3; these have now been conserved and reconstructed at Perth Museum and Art Gallery.

Cat No 10 was recovered from the 'occupation' of a path which linked a number of backland structures, Building 6 (Phase 2), Building 16 (Phase 2) and Building 16a, with the High Street frontage.

Combs

None of the combs recovered is likely to have been manufactured any later than the 13th century when the production of antler composite combs seems finally to have been abandoned in the British Isles in favour of one-piece combs of bone, horn, or wood. (see Fascicule 2, The wood, Cat No 541/A05–0042). Stylistically, the single-sided combs appear to be the earliest among the group, an impression which finds some corroboration in the stratigraphically early position of comb Cat No 5 (*LMMC*, 291). Unfortunately, the other examples

Arabic numbers in brackets, following the Accession Number, indicate whether the comb is single or double.

Cat/Accession	Area	Rig	Feature	Phase
South Sector				
5/A9124 (1)	1/2	V, VI	M2.1b	Ic
23/A11−0024 (2)	7	VII	MC126, Pit 7402	IVaa, IVb
32/A4885 (2)	3	V	MC155	IVb, IVc
34/A5397 (2)	2	VI	M1.4d	IVb, IVc
39/A5365 (2)	3	VI	P6	IVcc, Va
49/A11−0019 (2)	7	VII	M8a	Va, Vaa
71/A11−0002 (1)	7–10	VI–VIII	unstratified	unstratified
72/A0493 (1)	7/10	VII, VIII	Sondage 2003	unstratified

of single-sided combs (Cat Nos 71 and 72) came from unstratified deposits.

The slightly concave ends of the double-sided combs from Perth are similar to Continental examples dating from the 12th to 14th centuries (Andersen et al 1971, 153; Blomquist 1942, 158; Chmielowska 1971, 98; Wiberg 1977, 209). The widely spaced side plates and pierced ornament of Cat No 49 can be compared with certain combs of this period, from Oslo (Wiberg 1977, fig 27) and Lund (Blomquist 1942, figs 73–4). Parallels from the British Isles have been found at Coppergate, York (MacGregor et al 1999, 1932, fig 892).

The stratified double-sided combs from Perth all appear to have been recovered from deposits which date from the mid-13th to very early 14th centuries. Although they are too few in number to permit generalisation, the double-sided combs show a number of common features (such as the alternation on opposite side plates of saw cuts from the cutting of the teeth) which may suggest a common origin. There is no reason to doubt that they were made locally; although no unfinished combs were found on the site, the presence of two antler offcuts (Cat Nos 21 and 69) may indicate the presence of a workshop within the near vicinity of the site: a focus of antler working has been recorded in Perth, at the site of St John's Square/ South Street (Perry and Coleman forthcoming). Three other composite antler combs, two double-sided and one single-sided, were recovered from excavations at King Edward Street, Perth (Ford 1995, 968, Illus 26). The single-sided example was found in association with pottery of 12th-century date.

Decorative terminal

Cat/Accession	Area	Rig	Feature	Phase
South Sector				
14/A8684	3	VI	M1.3	IIi

Although this was the only example of worked horn found, the very large number of horn cores recovered during the excavations led to the suggestion that they were the waste from a horner's workshop (see The

environmental remains). Cat No 14 was recovered from a backland midden dating to the 12th century.

Dice

The Arabic number in brackets indicates the class to which the dice belong.

Cat/Accession	Area	Rig	Feature	Phase
South Sector				
7/A7187 (2)	2	V	M14b(a)	Id
35/A5838 (1)	3	V	M1.4g	IVb,IVc
48/A11−0017	7	VII	M8a, T7193	Va,Vaa
51/A11−0006 (2)	7	VII	B53 (Phase 2), South Area, occupation (7a)	Vbb
52/A11−0008	7	VII	B53 (Phase 2), South Area occupation (7a)	Vbb
54/A11−0012 (1)	7	VII	B53 (Phase 2), North Area, occupation (7b)	Vbb
62/A3055 (2)	4	VI	P1a	Vd
63/A11−0009 (1)	10	VIII	MC174 Pit 7013	(Va−) Vd (Vdd)

Two principal groupings can be recognised among the eight cuboid dice recovered: on some of them (Class 1), the opposed faces are marked with values which always total seven (hence one is opposite to six, two is opposite to five, three is opposite to four), while on the others (Class 2) the values are arranged sequentially (ie, one is opposite to two, three is opposite to four, five is opposite to six). The first of these conventions (Class 1) is the one which was favoured during the Roman period, when cuboid dice were first introduced into the British Isles, and which is now normally observed on modern dice. The second (Class 2) is found predominantly from the 13th century until the end of the medieval period. One 13th-century example was found in Southampton (Platt and Coleman-Smith 1975, 271, fig 247). Nine dice of 13th- to 15th-century date are known from Winchester (Brown 1990). Thirteen were found in Dublin for which precise dates are not stated (NMI 1973, 13). One 16th-century example is known from Streatley, Bedfordshire (Dyer 1974, 19–20, fig 4). Twenty-four dice, of which twenty-one are of bone, one of antler and three of ivory have come from Anglo–Scandinavian and medieval excavations in York (MacGregor et al 1999, 1982–5).

Of the eight dice recovered from the excavation, one (Cat No 48) was an unfinished blank, another (Cat No 52) belongs to neither class and the remaining six can be equally divided between the two classes. Interestingly, the Perth dice confirm that the original method of numbering (Class 1) was never entirely displaced by the alternative practice (Class 2). Particularly noteworthy was the excavation of a Class 2 die from deposits which are dated to the mid-12th century. This (Cat No 7), the earliest of the dice recovered on the site, was something of an exception in that the remaining seven examples were all recovered from the upper, more recent, layers. With the exception of Cat No 48, which was found in a late 13th-century midden, they were all recovered from 14th-century deposits. Three (Cat Nos 51, 52 and 54) came from Building 53 (Phase 2), a structure which may have been used as a metalworker's workshop. Cat No 63 was recovered from a pit associated with the destruction of Building 50, the earliest of the stone buildings.

The frequency with which dice were found on this site, when compared with other gaming pieces, suggests that they were used in simple dice games rather than for determining the moves in board games. The comparative ease with which small dice could be lost, and the fact that unworked pebbles, bones or other commonplace objects could also have been used as playing pieces should, however, be borne in mind.

Playing piece (see also Dice)

Cat/Accession	Area	Rig	Feature	Phase
South Sector				
4/A8517	1/2	V, VI	M2.1b	Ic

This piece belongs to a type which was introduced around the time of the Norman Conquest and which became widespread in the early medieval period. Two sources of raw material were, normally, red deer antler and, as here, the mandibles of cattle. Numerous mandibles with discs excised from them have been found in excavations at Schleswig, West Germany (MacGregor 1985, 136).

Decoration is usually limited to the obverse surface and commonly consists of the motifs displayed on this piece. These are the poor relations of the elaborately carved discoid playing pieces of elephant and walrus ivory (and occasionally, cetacean bone) which are well known on the Continent and found more infrequently in this country, as in the 19th-century finds at Melrose Abbey and Leicestershire (ibid, 137).

Cat No 4 was found within a midden which lay immediately to the north of Building 15, an early street frontage structure. Wooden gaming pieces were also recovered from the site (see Fascicule 2, The wood).

Handles

Cat/Accession	Area	Rig	Feature	Phase
South Sector				
11/A11401	1	VI	MC065	IIa–IIc
45/A11–0013	7	VII	M8a	Va, Vaa
57/5368	4	V, VI	M3a	Vb–Vc
North Sector				
79/A0011	5, A	n/a	unstratified	19

Although only three medieval antler/ivory handles were recovered during the excavation, two of these are of particular interest (cf Clarke and Carter 1977, fig 143). Cat No 57 is unfinished, indicating that the manufacture of items of imported walrus ivory was being carried out on, or near to, the site. In the absence of other finds however, the scale of this activity cannot be gauged. The anthropomorphic walrus ivory handle (Cat No 45) was one of the most remarkable finds made during the excavation (Hall below and 2001, 169–88). One modern handle (Cat No 79), probably from an umbrella, was recovered from the North Sector.

It should be noted that a number of the iron artefacts recovered (eg blades, awls, etc) still had their wooden handles intact (see Fascicule 2, The wood, The metalwork). This was however not true of the bone examples.

Anthropomorphic ivory handle (45)
Mark A Hall

Cat/Accession	Area	Rig	Feature	Phase
45/A11–0013	7	VII	M8a	Va, Vaa

The history of ivory carving in medieval Europe has been outlined by Williamson (1982), Lasko (1984), MacGregor (1985, 38–41) and others. Until the 12th century, ivory was principally used to depict religious subjects. The trade in elephant ivory was intermittent, hence the principal raw material in northern Europe was walrus ivory. However, from the 13th century onwards there was a switch to elephant ivory, the major workshops being based in Paris. From this period onwards, subject material shifted from religious themes to increasingly secular motifs, on such objects as mirrorcases, writing tablets, combs, caskets and knife handles.

Since the Perth handle is secular in design rather than religious, but is made from walrus rather than elephant ivory, there are thus important implications for its place of manufacture. Continental (particularly Parisian) production is unlikely. Walrus ivory manufacture remained popular in Scandinavian countries in the 14th century and while there is a possibility of trade between Perth and Scandinavia at this period, there are other alternatives. One is that the small-scale nature of the evidence (only two other handles, one unfinished, from this excavation) is consistent with ivory recovered from walrus strandings or accidental catches from Scottish fishing boats. Another is that the ivory may have been brought by a skilled itinerant craftsman (Lasko 1984, 210).

The most likely artefact to which the handle related is a knife of the whittle-tang variety, the tang of the knife being inserted into the cylindrical socket of the handle. Knife production was apparently an important industry in Perth; on this excavation 17 leather knife sheaths (see Fascicule 3) and over 20 metal knives (see Fascicule 2) were recovered, while elsewhere in Perth, at Meal Vennel, 44 knives, 19 of which were whittletanged, were recorded, 11 dating to the 14th century (Cox 1996).

In its imagery, this handle does not conform to the general depiction of foliate heads hitherto described as Green Men, in which leaves spill from the eyes, ears and mouth. In the Perth example, foliage is present on the sides of the hood covering the head but does not emanate from the head. Instead, the Perth handle should probably be seen as representing a fully human figure indulging in the May festivities that were common across Britain in the medieval period. The leaves, possibly rowan or hornbeam on the right side and hawthorn on the left side of the hood in which the figure of the Perth handle is cloaked, are probably representative of the May celebrations. In Scotland these involved a mock king, queen or lord who presided over the May games in which all of society participated. In the later medieval period this figure was occasionally replaced by that of Robin Hood or the Abbot of Unreason. Green branches, often of hawthorn (also known as may), were brought from the hedges 'to bring the summer into town' as in Edinburgh in the 15th and 16th centuries, (Livingstone 1997, 30). Such seasonal celebrations were part of a wider dramatic culture, which included mumming, morris dancing and pageantry. After the Reformation in Scotland such practices were seen as superstitious and were successfully suppressed.

Other examples of May festivities exist in church carvings and misericords, for example in Norfolk, Exeter Cathedral, Lincoln Cathedral and Worcester Cathedral; the last being in the form of a 'man wearing a cap with a hood drawn over his ears and a cloak and sword, and bearing in each hand a large branch of foliage' representing 'May' (Remnant 1969, 168 no 6). Most tellingly in *Les Très Riches Heures* of the Duc de Berry, the illumination for the month of May show the nobility dressed in green, their horses and themselves garlanded with leaves (Longnan and Cazelle 1969, pl 6; 176). As a knife handle, complete with blade, this object would not have been out of place sheathed in the belt of one of these noblemen. It is a skilfully executed and expensive piece of art, intended perhaps for the high table of a wealthy burgh merchant or commissioning dignitary. Its clear signs of wear indicate it was a well-used, prized possession.

Pins

Decorated pin

Cat/Accession	Area	Rig	Feature	Phase
South Sector				
9/A7079	2	VI	MC044b	If

This example should perhaps be compared with the metal pins which were also recovered from the site (see Fascicule 2, The metalwork). It should also be noted that some of the bone needles (Cat Nos 38 and 53) may have been utilised as dress pins. Cat No 9 was discovered within a midden/occupation layer which should probably be associated with the occupants of Building 6 (Phase 2).

Pig fibula pins

Cat/Accession	Area	Rig	Feature	Phase
South Sector				
38/A10000	3	VI	P6	IVcc, Va
53/A11–0010	7	VII	B53 (Phase 2), South Area, occupation (7a)	Vbb

The two pig fibula pins belong to a tradition which is much in evidence on sites dating to the Iron Age and Viking periods. These are mundane, everyday objects which require no great degree of modification to the original bone (MacGregor 1985, 121). Some pins of this type have perforated heads (presumably for the attachment of a cord); others are unperforated, for example, the large collections from Cahercommaun (Hencken 1938, 38), Lagore Crannog (Hencken 1950, 194) and York (Waterman 1959; MacGregor et al 1999, 1951).

Needles

Cat/Accession	Area	Rig	Feature	Phase
South Sector				
29/A11–0021	7	VII	B18 (Phase 2b), Hall and Hall South, occupation (12a)	IVb
37/A5757a	1	V, VI	M5c	(IVc–)Va
42/A11–0018	7	VI	M1.5b	Vaa
56/A11–0007	7	VII	B53 (Phase 2), North Area occupation (14)	Vbb

This concentration of bone needles and pins (which should be associated with the metal examples also recovered from the site, see Fascicule 2, The metalwork) may be taken as a further facet of the textile industry on the High Street, although this point cannot be insisted upon. The longest example, Cat No 37, may be interpreted as a bale pin, similar to wooden examples from the site, which may have been used to hold sacking coverings around bales of raw wool (see Fascicule 2, The wood). Other bale pins in wood have been recovered from sites in Perth at the Horse Cross (Cox and Smith 2007), King Edward Street and 1–5 High Street (Ford 1987b, 145).

Whorls

Cat/Accession	Area	Rig	Feature	Phase
South Sector				
13/A9510	4	VI	B12, occupation (2a)	IIe–IIg
18/A5455	1	VI	B20 occupation (1a)	<IIId–IVaa
28/A11–0022	7	VII	B18 (Phase 2b), North Room, Hall and Hall South – occupation (10)	IVb
31/A11–0023	10	VIII	M9b(a)	IVc
36/A05–0119b	9	VII	M9a	IVc, IVcc
55/A11–0011	7	VII	B53 (Phase 2), North Area, occupation (9b)	Vbb
66/A11502	2	VI	Building T Well 3819	VI

Femur heads were commonly utilised in the manufacture of whorls from the late Iron Age until the early medieval period (Carver 1979, 24–5; Waterman 1959, fig 7); their natural shape recommended them for this purpose, a straightforward saw-cut being all that was required to detach the naturally domed epiphysis from the femur. In immature bones the epiphysis would not even be fused to the femur neck, but most of those utilised at Perth come from mature animals in which fusion of the epiphysis had already taken place.

Of the seven bone whorls recovered, six came from medieval levels. A number came from features from which stone whorls were also retrieved (see The stone objects). The location and chronology of all the whorls (stone, bone and wood) are discussed in Fascicule 3, The textiles.

Although it was only fragmentary and appeared to have been burnt, Cat No 36 is noteworthy for it was found with a spindle (see Fascicule 2, The wood, Wood Cat No 374).

Pin-beaters

Cat/Accession	Area	Rig	Feature	Phase
South Sector				
6/A8104	1/2	VI	B8, occupation (2)	(Icc) Id
15/A9895	3	VI	M1.3	IIi
44/A11–0015	7	VII	M8a	Va,Vaa
North Sector				
77/A0339	5, A	n/a	lade (4)	6–12(b-e)
80/A0021	5, A	n/a	unstratified	19

All these pointed implements appear to be pin-beaters for use in conjunction with a warp-weighted loom (Clarke and Carter 1977, 311–13). Variations on this type of beater are known in the British Isles from the late Roman period until the early medieval period when the warp-weighted loom and its associated tool-kit were replaced by the horizontal loom. For an account of these looms which survived until comparatively recently in Scandinavia, and of the methods of beating up the warps which were used on them, see Fascicule 3, The textiles; Clarke and Carter 1977, 311–12; Hoffman 1964. The possibility that some of the numerous wooden points also recovered during the excavation were used for the same purpose should be borne in mind (see Fascicule 2, The wood).

It is noteworthy that of the four-pin-beaters recovered from the South Sector, three may have come from Rig VI, albeit they were recovered from deposits of greatly different date.

Together with the bobbins of bone and wood, the spindle whorls identified above, and certain of the metal and glass artefacts, these pin-beaters indicate a significant involvement in textile production on the site; seemingly more than would have been necessary to fulfil domestic needs (see Fascicule 3, The textiles).

Toggles

Cat/Accession	Area	Rig	Feature	Phase
South Sector				
8/A12486	3	V	MC034a	Ie(1f)
17/A11–0028	9	VII	P8.1c PH9458	IIIc
19/A5367	1	VI	B20, occupation (4)	<IIId–IVaa
50/A11–0027	7	VII	M8a	Va, Vaa
61/A3486	4	VI	M3b	Vd
70/A11–0025	7–10	VI–VIII	unstratified	unstratified
North Sector				
78/A0238	5, A	n/a	CG024	14–16
82/A3127	6	n/a	garden	G

All are made from pig metapodia, perforated through the bone at midshaft, with the exception of Cat No 78, a goat horn core. Items of this type are well-known from the Viking period and early medieval settlements both in the British Isles and on the Continent. None of them show any more elaboration than that accorded to these Perth examples. Their function has never been decisively identified; it is possible that they served as bobbins of some sort although they all lack the fine polish which is frequently to be found on items associated with textile working. They may, as was surmised from the group from Freswick, Caithness (Curle et al 1954, 51–2) and the example from Durham (Carver 1979, 21, fig 14), have functioned as toggles or dress fasteners, though the roughly cut perforations show no sign of wear from abrasion by a cord. Alternatively, they may simply have been toys, mounted in doubled and twisted cord and caused to spin by pulling on the ends of the cord, as was suggested for similar bones from Moravia by Hruby (1957, fig 29).

Two of the Perth examples (Cat Nos 17 and 19) date from the mid-13th century; two (Cat Nos 50 and 61) came from 14th-century middens; another is unstratified (Cat No 70). The identification of the perforated goat horn core (Cat No 78), as a toggle is, at best, tentative. Although sheep were sometimes tethered in Scotland by a rope attached to the horn, the lack of wear around the hole, or indeed, any signs of healing of the bone, indicates that this was not so in this instance and that the hole was drilled post-mortem.

Forked implement

Cat/Accession	Area	Rig	Feature	Phase
South Sector				
27/A11–0031	7	VII	P8.2b, levelling	IVb

Implements of this class are being recognised in increasing numbers from archaeological sites covering a considerable time span. One of the earliest examples comes from the Iron Age fort at Close ny Chollagh, Isle of Man (Gelling 1958, 59), followed by one from a Roman sewer at York (MacGregor 1976, 13). Two were noted from excavations at Lochlee Crannog, Ayrshire (Munro 1879, 215) and several come from Viking or early medieval levels at York (MacGregor 1981).

Although their form has been little changed from that of the natural bone, the smoothing noted on this and other examples is indicative of some utilisation. Such wear as has been noted (MacGregor 1985, 175–6) is usually confined to the tips, both of which are damaged in this example from Perth. No wear ever appears in the bottom of the terminal U-notch as might be expected if they had been used as netting implements or bobbins. A possible use as forks has been suggested (MacGregor 1981).

Cat No 27 was recovered from the construction layer of a path which served and adjoined Building 18 (Phase 2), probably a burgess's house despite its backland position.

Miscellaneous worked bone

Cat/Accession	Area	Rig	Feature	Phase
South Sector				
12/A9504	4	V	M10	IId–IIg
47/A02–0267	7	VII	M8a, T7193	Va, Vaa
58/A11–0035	7	VII	M7	Vc

Little can be said of this disparate group. Cat No 12, which was probably a bead, came from a midden (M10) from which a glass bead was also recovered (The glass, Cat No 3). Although M10 lay within Rig V, there is reason for thinking some, at least, of its finds may relate to a backland building (B12) in the adjacent Rig VI. It seems likely that the backland parts of Rigs V and VI may have been combined during the late 12th century.

Cat No 58 may have been a burnisher. It was recovered from an early 14th-century midden. Cat No 47, a trimmed horse tibia, may be part of a broken ice skate, although metapodia were more commonly used in the manufacture of these items, as at King Edward Street, Perth (Ford 1995, 968, Illus 26) and 80–86 High Street, Perth (Cox 1997, 746, Illus 18, 751).

Offcuts, roughouts and trial pieces

All bone unless otherwise stated.

Cat/Accession	Area	Rig	Feature	Phase
South Sector				
21/A11–0029 offcut (antler)	7	VI	P3.3	IVa–IVb
22/A11–0030 offcut (horn core)	7	VI	P3.3	IVa–IVb
41/A11–0020 offcut	7	VI	B34, courtyard	Va
43/A11–0026 roughout?	7	VI	M1.5b	Vaa
46/A11–0016 roughout?	7	VII	M8a	Va, Vaa
64/A1178 offcut / trial piece	2	V	M4e MF2713	Vd, Vdd
67/A11–0003 rough-out?	7/9	VII	modern, T7014	VI
69/A11–0004 offcut (antler)	7–10	VI–VIII	unstratified	unstratified
73/A02–0280 trial piece	7	VII	unstratified	unstratified
75/A110001 offcut (horn core)	3/4	V, VI	unstratified	unstratified
North Sector				
81/A0217 offcut / trial piece	5, A	n/a	unstratified	19

The presence of these pieces confirms the impression given by some of the unfinished pieces listed above (die, Cat No 48; handle, Cat No 57; bobbin Cat No 60) that the manufacture of ivory, bone and antler implements was being carried out on, or near, the High Street site during the early 12th century and the second half of the 13th and early 14th centuries. The antler beam fragment (Cat No 21) is of particular interest, demonstrating as it does the same routines of antler utilisation as has been noted elsewhere (MacGregor 1978, 48), which savours of a professional, rather than a haphazard, use of this material. Too little material was found to demonstrate the presence of a workshop dealing exclusively with skeletal materials. If a related activity that might have been practised in parallel were to be sought, then the working of horn as suggested by the presence of numerous horn cores (see The mammal bone) and the single decorated horn point (decorated terminal Cat No 14) would constitute an appropriate possibility. It should be noted that most of the pieces from the South Sector came from Area 7, in particular, Rig VI.

Perforated bones

Cat/Accession	Area	Rig	Feature	Phase
South Sector				
16/7918	4	VI	M1.4a(a)	IIIa–IIIc
20/A02–0925	9	VII	B18 (Phase 1b), South Room, occupation (2b)	IVa, IVaa
25/A02–0634	9	VII	B18 (Phase 1/2), MF9194	IVaa, IVb
26/A02–0745	9	VII	B18 (Phase 2a), Hall and Hall South, construction (3)	IVb
30/A?	7	VII	P8.2b	IVb
40/A4381	3	VI	M1.4e	IVcc

A number of perforated sheep/goat long bones, five metapodia and one tibia, were recovered from the site. The perforations were cut into the proximal articulation, extending into the marrow cavity. Examples are known from elsewhere in Perth: King Edward Street (metatarsal) and Meal Vennel (two metacarpals, one metatarsal; two proximal radii). The explanation for the perforations is not clear, and it is likely that the bones are not strictly speaking artefacts. Bigelow (1993) has reviewed the occurrence of bi-perforated sheep metapodials from Norse sites on Shetland. These bones are usually pierced twice, once in the anterior or posterior surface just above the distal articulation, and again in the proximal articulation, as in the medieval examples from Perth (ibid, 441). The author suggests that these holes have been made in order to extract marrow, the hole near the distal end being used to create a draught when sucking out the marrow. If this is indeed the reason for most of the perforations in medieval sheep bones, it would also explain why the holes occur in not only the metapodia but also in the radius and distal tibia.

All of the perforated bones from the excavation came from 13th-century features, from Phase IIIa–IIIc to Phase IVcc.

Teether

Cat/Accession	Area	Rig	Feature	Phase
South Sector				
74/A11–0001	7–10	VI–VIII	unstratified	unstratified

Cat No 74 is an infant's teether or soother, probably of late Victorian or Edwardian date. Such items were designed to help cool babies' gums while the painful process of teething took place, and while earlier versions, in the form of sticks, are known in coral from at least the 16th century, ivory or bone versions were commonly available in the mid-19th century (Kevill-Davies 1991, 55–61). Ivory teethers took the form of rings, due to the natural form of the original material. By the later 19th century, the stick form typified by the coral examples

was replaced by a flattened pad shape and was also being manufactured in rubber. A rubber teether similar to Cat No 74 in its tear-drop shape, with suspension loop, but in 'dark pure gum rubber: the infants' delight' is illustrated in the Montgomery Ward & Co catalogue for 1895 (Emmet 1969, 107).

Catalogue

South Sector

1 Casket mount Bone
Length 32mm; width 26mm; thickness 1.5mm. (part of Cat No 2)
Cut from a scapula. Obverse decorated with incised ornament comprising part of a large motif consisting of multiple concentric circles, the interval between one pair of circles filled with ring-and-dot ornament; the centre of the circular ornament cut away in a complex of cruciform motifs. Broken. Early medieval.
A10074; C3835–1; M0, Pit 3789; Phase Ia(Ib); Rig VI
Illus 50

2 Casket mount Bone
Length 122mm; width 54mm; thickness 1.5mm.
Cut from scapula, perforated by two small fixing holes. Obverse surface is decorated with incised ornament comprising a double border line; triangular groups of ring-and-dot ornament in two corners and in the cube; two large motifs consisting of multiple concentric circles, the interval between one pair of circles filled with ring-and-dot ornament. The centres of the large circular motifs are each cut away in a complex of six cruciform shapes, possibly originally with a seventh in the centre. Broken. Early medieval–12th century?
A9815; C3770–1/2; MC006; Phase Ib; Rig VI
Illus 50

3 Casket mount (probably part of 2/A9815) Bone
Length 29mm; width 27mm; thickness 1.5mm.
Cut from a scapula. Obverse decorated with incised ornament comprising part of a large motif consisting of multiple concentric circles; around the outermost of those surviving are traces of incised ring-and-dot decoration; the centre of the circle is marked with a dot, around which are disposed four complete or partial cruciform cut-outs. Broken. Early medieval – 12th century?
A9843; C3770–1/2; MC006; Phase Ib; Rig VI
Illus 50

4 Playing piece Bone
Diameter 53mm.
Discoid playing piece cut from a bovine mandible. Obverse decorated with incised concentric circles, the central area and the space between the outermost pair of rings filled with incised ring-and-dot motifs. Early medieval – 12th/13th century.
A8517; C3742–1/2; M2.1b; Phase Ic; Rigs V and VI
Illus 52

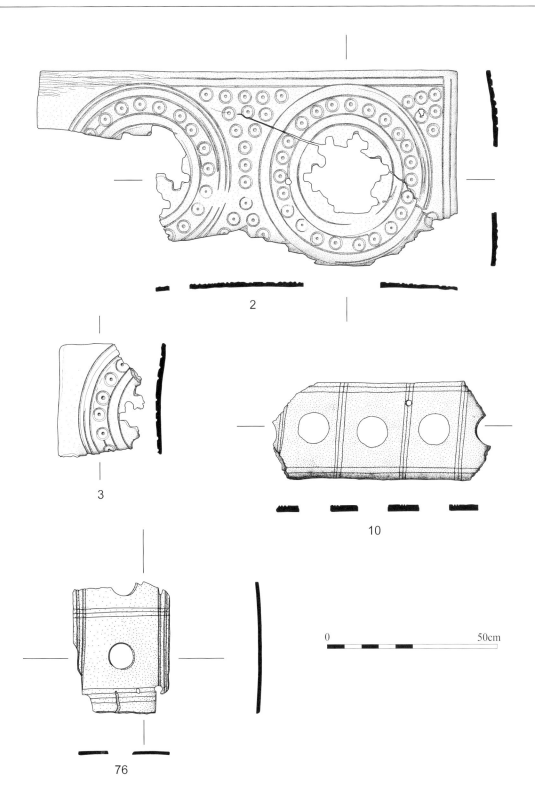

Illus 50 *Worked bone. Casket mounts Cat Nos 1/2 (reconstructed), 3, 10 and 76.*

5 Comb (single) Antler and iron
Length (to break) 95mm; height 25mm; thickness 8.5mm.
   Single-sided composite comb with close-set iron rivets. Five tooth-plates with evenly-sized teeth survive, including one end plate with teeth of graduated length. Side plates have flat edges and curved faces; decorated with incised marginal line on upper edge and two rows of ring-and-dot motifs linked by tangential lines. Both side plates marked intermittently on lower edge by saw cuts from cutting of teeth. Broken. Early medieval.
   A9124; C3767–1/2; M2.1b; Phase Ic; Rigs V and VI
   Not illustrated

6 Pin-beater? Bone
Length (to break?) 92mm.
   Point, unperforated; broken? cf Clarke and Carter 1977, 311–13. Early medieval.
   A8104; C3728–1/2; B8, Occupation (2); Phase (Icc)Id; Rig VI
   Not illustrated

7 Die (Class 2) Bone/antler
Dimensions 6.5mm by 7mm by 7.5mm.
   Values marked in ring-and-dot motifs. 1:2, 3:4, 5:6. Medieval.
   A7187; C3620–2; M14b(a); Phase Id; Rig V
   Not illustrated

8 Toggle Bone
Length 59.5mm; width 14.8mm; thickness 16.6mm.
   Pig metacarpal (right metacarpal IV). Hole bored through anterior and posterior midshaft. Diameter of hole on anterior 3.3mm, on posterior 4mm. Proximal articulation intact, distal epiphysis unfused. cf Cat Nos 8, 17, 19, 50, 61, 70, 82.
   A12486; C5067–3; MC034a; Phase Ie(If); Rig V
   Illus 54

9 Decorated pin Bone
Length 106mm.
Irregularly-cut thistle head and tapering shank. cf Clarke and Carter 1977, 314, Illus 143. Early medieval.
A7079; C3604–2; MC044b; Phase If; Rig VI
Illus 53

10 Casket mount Bone
Length 64mm; width 27mm; thickness 1.5mm.
Cut from a rib. Perforated with one fixing hole of diameter 2mm and five complete or partial decorative holes of diameter 9mm. Incised decoration on obverse comprising a pair of border lines along the longer edges and groups of three transverse lines alternating with the ornamental perforations. Broken. cf Cat No 76. Early medieval.
A1880; C3062–1; P5.3b; Phase If,IIa; Rig VI
Illus 50

11 Handle Antler
Length 100mm; diameter 15mm.
   Cylindrical in form, but with a slight 'keel' along one side. Ovoid axial perforation 30mm deep. Early medieval.
   A11401; C3886–1; MC065; Phase IIa–IIc; Rig VI
   Not illustrated

12 Miscellaneous, ?bead Bone
Fragments of bead? Broken.
   A9504; C2314–4; M10; Phase IId–IIg; Rig V
   Not illustrated

13 Whorl Bone
Diameter 58mm; internal diameter 9mm.
   Spindle whorl made from proximal head of a femur (bovine).
   No evidence of wear around the internal drilled hole. cf Cat No 18, 28, 31; Carver 1979, 24–5; Waterman 1959, Fig 7.
   A9510; C4603–4; B12, Occupation (2a); Phase IIe–IIg; Rig VI
   Not illustrated

14 ?Decorative terminal Horn
Length 87mm; thickness c1mm.
   Point cut from distal end of a cattle horn. Much of the thickness is shaved away. A series of irregularly spaced holes c2mm in diameter are cut around the open edge. The tip is cut into a series of regular flutings, each terminating in a point and distinguished from the rest of the horn by greater thickness.
   A8684; C2462C–3; M1.3; Phase IIi; Rig VI
   Illus 54

15 ?Pin-beater Bone
Length (to break) 100mm.
   Point, perforated by a hole of diameter 4 mm. Point broken. cf Clarke and Carter 1977, 311–13. Early medieval.
   A9895; C2462C–3; M1.3; Phase IIi; Rig VI
   Not illustrated

16 Perforated bone Bone
Sheep/goat metatarsal. Hole bored through proximal surface. Marrow extraction?
   A7918; C2190B–4; M1.4a(a); Phase IIIa–IIIc; Rig VI
   Not illustrated

17 Toggle Bone
Length 62mm.
   Consisting of a metapodial of a pig. Unworked except for a transversely perforated hole with a diameter of 4mm. cf Cat Nos 8, 19, 50, 61, 70, 82; Carver 1979, 21, Fig 14. Early medieval.
   A11–0028; C9459–9; P8.1c, PH9458; Phase IIIc; Rig VII
   Not illustrated

18 Whorl Bone
Diameter 40mm; internal diameter 10mm; weight 12.2g.
   Spindle whorl made from proximal head of a bovine femur. cf Cat Nos 13, 28, 31, 66; Carver 1979, 24–5; Waterman 1959, Fig 7. Early medieval.
   A5455; C3553–1; B20, Occupation (1a); Phase <IIId–IVaa; Rig VI
   Not illustrated

19 Toggle Bone
Length 53mm.
Consisting of a metapodial of a pig. Unworked except for a transversely perforated hole with a diameter of 4mm. cf Cat Nos 8, 17, 50, 61, 70, 82; cf Carver 1979, 21, Fig 14. Early medieval.
A5367; C3550–1; B20, Occupation (4); Phase <IIId–IVaa; Rig VI
Not illustrated

20 Perforated bone Bone
Sheep/goat metatarsal. Hole bored through proximal surface. Marrow extraction?
A02–0925; C9385–9; B18 (Phase 1b), South Room – Occupation (2b); Phase IVa,IVaa; Rig VII
Not illustrated

21 Offcut Antler
Length 52mm; width 50mm; thickness 20mm.
Fragment of red deer antler beam from junction with a tine; sawn on three sides (above, below and at base of tine). Compact outer tissue has been split off from two sides.
A11–0029; C7364–7; P3.3; Phase IVa–IVb; Rig VI
Not illustrated

22 Offcut Bone
Length 14mm; diameter 29mm.
Cylindrical section of goat horn core; sawn at both ends. cf Clarke and Carter 1977, Fig 143.
A11–0030; C7364–7; P3.3; Phase IVa–IVb; Rig VI
Not illustrated

23 Comb (double) Antler and bronze
Length 80mm; height 24mm; thickness 7.5mm.
Double-sided composite comb with bronze rivets. Cut with coarse teeth on one side, fine on the other; end plates slightly concave in outline. Side plates D-shaped in section. Most teeth lost or broken. Early medieval.
A11–0024; C7336–7; MC126, Pit 7402; Phase IVaa,IVb; Rig VII
Not illustrated

24 Bobbin Bone (originally identified as wood)
Length 58mm; diameter (max) 9mm.
Turned, drilled axially with a hole of diameter 4mm. Expanded centrally and at either end; decorated at both ends with three bands of four (in one instance five) incised circumferential lines; part of a further single line visible at either obliquely-cut end. Early medieval.
A05–0202; C7307–7; B18 (Phase 1/2), MF7307; Phase IVaa,IVb; Rig VII
Not illustrated

25 Perforated bone Bone
Sheep/goat metatarsal. Hole bored through proximal surface. Marrow extraction?
A02–0634; C9159–9; B18 (Phase 1/2), MF9194; Phase IVaa,IVb; Rig VII
Not illustrated

26 Perforated bone Bone
Sheep/goat metacarpal. Hole bored through proximal surface. Marrow extraction?
A02–0745; C9197–9; B18 (Phase 2a), Hall and Hall South – Construction (3); Phase IVb; Rig VII
Not illustrated

27 Forked implement Bone
Length 135mm.
Double pronged implement made from a bovine nasal bone. Retains natural double prong at one end, broken at the other end. cf Gelling 1958, 98; Munro 1879, 215. Early medieval.
A11–0031; C7354–7; P8.2b, Levelling; Phase IVb; Rig VII
Not illustrated

28 Whorl Bone
Diameter 37mm; internal diameter 12mm; weight 9.7g.
Spindle whorl made from the proximal head of a bovine femur. cf Cat Nos 13, 18, 31, 66; Carver 1979, 24–5; Waterman 1959, Fig 7. Early medieval.
A11–0022; C7299–7; B18 (Phase 2b), North Room, Hall and Hall South – Occupation (10); Phase IVb; Rig VII
Not illustrated

29 Needle Bone
Length (to break) 71mm.
Needle with flattened, expanded head pierced by an ovoid eye. Tapering shank, broken at tip. Early medieval.
A11–0021; C7289–7; B18 (Phase 2b), Hall and Hall South – Occupation (12a); Phase IVb; Rig VII
Illus 53

30 Perforated bone Bone
Sheep/goat metatarsal. Hole bored through proximal surface. Marrow extraction?
A?; C7350–7; P8.2b; Phase IVb; Rig VII
Not illustrated

31 Whorl Bone
Diameter 45mm; internal diameter 7mm; weight 11.4g.
Spindle whorl made from the proximal head of a bovine femur.
cf Cat Nos 13, 18, 28, 66; Carver 1979, 24–5; Waterman 1959, Fig 7. Early medieval.
A11–0023; C6162–10; M9b(a); Phase IVc; Rig VIII
Not illustrated

32 Comb (double) Antler
Length 17mm; height 29.5mm; thickness 2.5mm.
Tooth plate from double-sided composite comb. Cut with coarse teeth on one side, fine on the other. Half rivet holes on either side. Three teeth missing. Early medieval.
A4885; C2483–3; MC155; Phase IVb,IVc; Rig V
Illus 51

33 Bobbin Bone and wood

Length 79.7mm; external diameter 9.9mm; internal diameter 7.6mm.

Bobbin, partially broken at one end, with natural axial perforation, slight central expansion and hand cut collar mouldings at either end. Three incised dots disposed axially towards one end, three more arranged circumferentially near the centre, where trace of natural central groove remains. Most probably derived from sheep/goat metatarsal. Found with a small wooden plug in the intact end (dimensions of wood fragment: length 17.3mm, width 5.2mm, thickness 2.7mm). Early medieval.

A5369; C2476–3; M1.4d; Phase IVb,IVc; Rig VI
Not illustrated.

34 Comb (double) Antler

Tooth plate from a double-sided composite comb. Cut with coarse teeth on one side, fine on the other. Half rivet holes on either side. One tooth (coarse) missing. Dimensions not available. Early medieval.

A5397; C2790–2; M1.4d; Phase IVb,IVc; Rig VI
Not illustrated

35 Die (Class 1) Bone/antler

Dimensions 5.5mm by 5.5mm by 5.5mm.
Values marked in ring-and-dot motif. 1:6, 2:5, 3:4. Medieval.
A5838; C2473–3; M1.4g; Phase IVb,IVc; Rig V
Not illustrated

36 Whorl (associated with wooden spindle A05–0119a) Bone

Diameter c41mm; weight 3.8g.
Spindle whorl cut from a proximal head of a femur; burnt and fragmentary. Early medieval.
A05–0119b; C9050–9; M9a; Phase IVc,IVcc; Rig VII
Not illustrated

37 Needle/bale pin Bone

Length 134.6mm; width 12.6mm; thickness 9.2mm.
Bale pin, made from a section of large ungulate long bone shaft. The bony trabeculae from the internal cavity of the bone are exposed on the reverse side of the object at the head of the pin. The wider end of the pin has been pared to form a rounded head. A small hole (diameter 2.5mm) has been bored through the head of the pin. The lower end of the object has been pared to a rough point. The object shows signs of polishing on the shaft, more markedly towards the point. Pins of a similar size, in wood, have been recovered at sites in Perth at the Horse Cross (Cox and Smith 2007) and King Edward Street and 1–5 High Street (Ford 1987b, 145) as well as from PHSAE where about 200 examples were found, mainly dating to the 14th century (The wood). The wooden examples have been interpreted as bale pins, used to hold sacking coverings around bales of raw wool (ibid).

A5757a; C3505–1; M5c; Phase (IVc–)Va; Rigs V and VI
Not illustrated.

38 Pin Bone

Length 71mm.
Cut from a pig's fibula, head formed by the natural articular end, perforated. Rounded shank, broken. Early medieval.
A10000; C2481–3; P6; Phase IVcc,Va; Rig VI
Illus 53

39 Comb (double) Antler, iron and bronze

Length (to break) 70mm; height 32mm; thickness 9mm.
Double-sided composite comb with iron rivets and a bronze pin at one end, possibly the remnants of a suspension loop. Cut with coarse teeth on one side, fine on the other. Surviving end plates are slightly concave in profile and rounded at the corners. Plano-convex side plates marked with a single incised line along the upper and lower edges. Saw-cuts from cutting of one set of teeth mark the lower edge of one side plate and those from the other set mark the upper edge of opposite side plates. Early medieval.

A5365; C2484–3; P6; Phase IVcc,Va; Rig VI
Not illustrated

40 Perforated bone Bone

Sheep/goat tibia. Hole bored through distal surface. Marrow extraction?
A4381; C2456–3; M1.4e; Phase IVcc, (Va); Rig VI
Not illustrated

41 Offcut Bone

Length (to break) 33mm; width 7mm; thickness 6mm.
Fragment cut to tapering outline; rectangular in section. Broken at one end.
A11–0020; C7200–7; B34, Courtyard; Phase Va; Rig VI
Not illustrated

42 ?Needle Bone

Length (to break) 69mm.
Ovoid shank, broken at the head, but apparently perforated. Early medieval.
A11–0018; C7169–7; M1.5b; Phase Vaa; Rig VI
Not illustrated

43 ?Roughout Bone

Length 74mm; diameter 9mm.
Irregular rod of solid bone, marked with central incised dot at one end.
A11–0026; C7169–7; M1.5b; Phase Vaa; Rig VI
Not illustrated

44 ?Pin-beater Bone

Length 164mm.
Point with roughly-cut irregular head, perforated by a hole of diameter 2mm. Marked over much of its length by oblique grooves. cf Clarke and Carter 1977, 311–13. Early medieval.
A11–0015; C7140–7; M8a; Phase Va,Vaa; Rig VII
Not illustrated

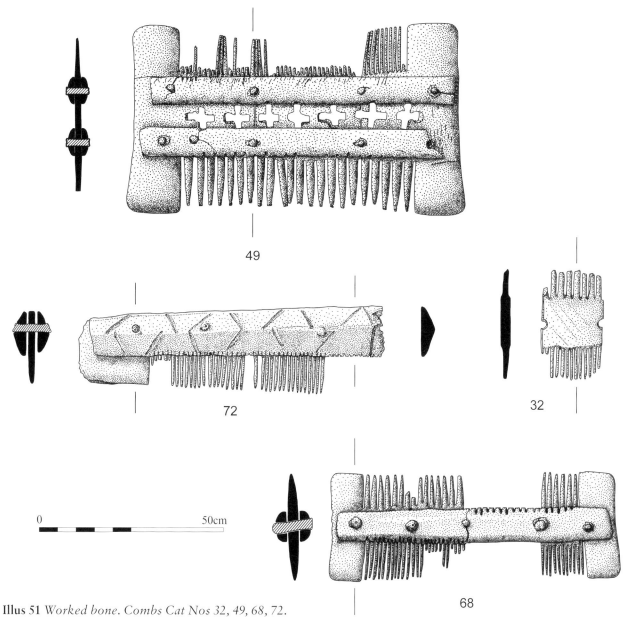

Illus 51 *Worked bone. Combs Cat Nos 32, 49, 68, 72.*

45 Anthropomorphic handle Walrus ivory

Length 120.5mm; maximum width 22.6mm; minimum width 16.5mm; thickness 14.5mm; weight 35.71g. Socket: internal diameter 9mm by 4.8mm; external diameter 16.4mm by 9.9mm; depth c50.5mm.

Decorated, socketed handle of oval cross-section, derived from walrus ivory. Intricately carved to represent grinning, hooded male face with folds of cloak draped along length of handle. Possible collar arrangement at socket end of handle has phallic appearance. Carved, naturalistic leaves on right and left hand sides of head may be rowan or hornbeam and hawthorn, respectively. Leaves terminate at shoulder of carving, possibly held by very minimally depicted hands. The coarse dentine of the original walrus tooth has been exposed in a band of c3mm width along right side of handle. Object has slight wear damage to left nostril and to rudimentary hands. Handle has a deep, all-over polish, is predominantly rich, translucent dark brown in colour with patches of lighter, buttery colour. Medieval (14th century).

A11–0013; C7159–7; M8a; Phase Va,Vaa; Rig VII

Illus 52

46 ?Roughout Bone

Length 95mm; width 10mm; thickness 6mm.

Fragment cut from the shaft of a cattle long bone, rectangular in section, rounded and tapered at one end, broken at the other.

A11–0016; C7163–7; M8a; Phase Va,Vaa; Rig VII

Not illustrated

47 Miscellaneous, ?skate Bone

Length 170mm; width 28.2mm; thickness 28.4mm.

Split long bone shaft, probably a horse right tibia shaft. Distal end of shaft trimmed with a sharp implement, probably an axe. Trimming marks on anterior, posterior and lateral surfaces. May be a broken ice-skate, although metapodia are usually preferred for this type of object. Unfinished or broken during manufacture.

A02–0267; C7172–7; M8a, T7193; Phase Va,Vaa; Rig VII

Illus 54

48 Die Bone/antler
Dimensions 7mm by 7.5mm by 8mm.
Die blank, squared, chipped at two corners, unfinished. ?Medieval.
A11–0017; C7172–7; M8a, T7193; Phase Va,Vaa; Rig VII
Not illustrated

49 Comb (double) Antler and iron
Length 93mm; height 50mm; thickness 5.5mm.
Double-sided composite comb with iron rivets. Cut with coarse teeth on one side, fine on the other. Two widely-spaced pairs of flat side plates, one set marked on one edge with cuts from sawing of fine teeth, the other set marked on the opposite edge by cuts from coarse teeth; the side plates adjacent to the fine teeth are further marked by fine transverse scratchings. The area between the two pairs of side plates is pierced by a series of seven cruciform perforations. End plates filed thin after assembly? Some teeth missing. Early medieval.
A11–0019; C7196–7; M8a; Phase Va,Vaa; Rig VII
Illus 51

50 Toggle Bone
Length 63mm.
Consisting of a metapodial of a pig. Unworked except for a transversely perforated hole with a diameter of 5mm. cf Cat Nos 8, 17, 19, 61, 70, 82; Carver 1979, 21, Fig 14. Early medieval.
A11–0027; C7196–7; M8a; Phase Va,Vaa, Rig VII
Not illustrated

51 Die (Class 2) Bone/antler
Dimensions 8mm by 8mm by 8mm.
Values marked in ring-and-dot motifs. 1:2, 3:4, 5:6. Medieval.
A11–0006; C7071–7; B53 (Phase 2), South Area – Occupation (7a); Phase Vbb; Rig VII
Illus 52

52 Die Bone/antler
Dimensions 7.5mm (max) by 7.5mm by 7.5mm.
Values marked in incised dots. 1:3, 2:4, 5:6. Irregularly shaped. ?Medieval.
A11–0008; C7071–7; B53 (Phase 2), South Area – Occupation (7a); Phase Vbb; Rig VII
Not illustrated.

53 Pin Bone
Length (to break) 52mm.
Cut from the fibula of a pig. The head is formed by the natural articular end; shank broken. ?Medieval
A11–0010; C7071–7; B53 (Phase 2), South Area – Occupation (7a); Phase Vbb; Rig VII
Illus 53

54 Die (Class 1) Bone/antler
Dimensions 6.5mm by 6.5mm by 6.5mm.
Values marked in ring-and-dot motifs. 1:6, 2:5, 3:4. ?medieval.
A11–0012; C7093–7; B53 (Phase 2), North Area – Occupation (7b); Phase Vbb; Rig VII
Not illustrated

55 Whorl Bone
Diameter 36mm; internal diameter 7mm; weight 17.7g.
Spindle whorl comprising an almost complete proximal head of a bovine femur. cf Cat Nos 13, 18, 28, 31, 66. Early medieval.
A11–0011; C7095–7; B53 (Phase 2), North Area – Occupation (9b); Phase Vbb; Rig VII
Not illustrated

56 Needle Bone
Length 80mm.
Needle with large irregular perforation. Early medieval.
A11–0007; C7077–7; B53 (Phase 2), North Area – Occupation (14); Phase Vbb; Rig VII
Illus 53

57 Handle (knife) Walrus ivory
Length 84mm; width (maximum) 19mm; thickness 9.5mm.
Rectangular in section, tapering towards the blade end. A tapering perforation intended to receive the tang penetrates only 15mm and is clearly unfinished, perhaps having been abandoned due to a split developing. Each corner on the long sides has a rudimentary scribed moulding; one of the principal faces has additional scribed mouldings, abandoned at an early stage. Early medieval.
A5368; C2176–4; M3a; Phase Vb–Vc; Rigs V and VI
Illus 52

58 Miscellaneous, ?burnisher Bone
Length 75mm; width 32mm; thickness (maximum) 12mm.
Section of rib, broken at one end, rounded at the other as though from prolonged abrasion.
A11–0035; C7035–7; M7; Phase Vc; Rig VII
Not illustrated

59 Bobbin/tally stick Bone
Length 81mm; width (maximum) 10mm; thickness 10mm.
Cut from sheep metatarsal, rectangular in section, with a natural axial perforation, and evidence of some wear at both ends. Decorated overall with close-set incised dots. Broken at one end. cf Ford 1987a, 151 fig 82, no 159; Cox 1996, 786 Illus 27, no 597.
A1353a; C2110–4; M3b; Phase Vd; Rig VI
Illus 53

60 ?Bobbin Bone
Length 72mm; width 12mm; thickness 12mm.
Cut from sheep metapodial; D-shaped in section. Some polishing and cut marks; probably unfinished.
A1353b; C2110–4; M3b; Phase Vd; Rig VI
Not illustrated

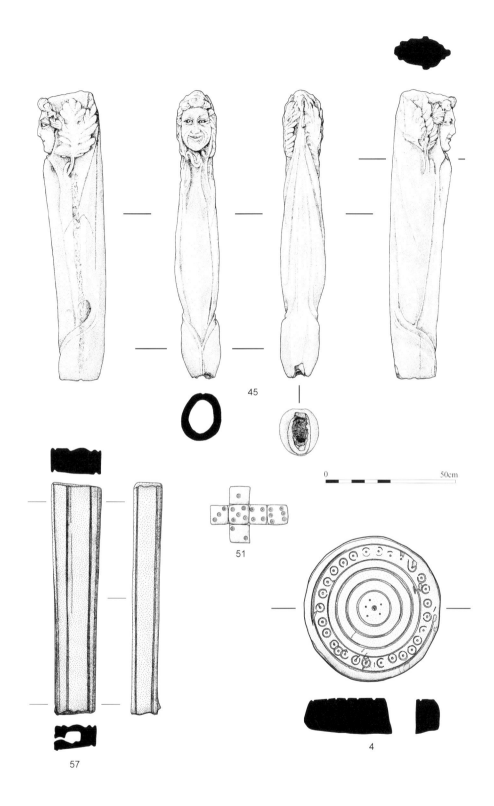

Illus 52 *Worked bone. Handles Cat Nos 45, 57. Playing piece Cat No 4. Die Cat No 51.*

61 Toggle Bone

Length 51.3mm; width 14.1mm; thickness 14.3mm.

Pig metapodial with large perforation (diameter 7.5mm) drilled through posterior and anterior mid shaft. Proximal end of bone chopped across medio-laterally, distal end broken but epiphysis probably unfused. cf Cat Nos 8, 17, 19, 50, 70, 82.

A3486; C2148–4; M3b; Phase Vd; Rig VI

Illus 54

62 Die (Class 2) Bone/antler

Dimensions 7.5mm by 7mm by 5.5mm.

Values marked in ring-and-dot motifs. 1:2, 3:4, 5:6. Not a regular cube; the sides with the smallest area (that is, most difficult to throw) carry values 3 and 4, the largest 5 and 6. The excavators noted evidence of blue pigment on the incised ring-and-dot motifs. No trace of this remains. Medieval.

A3055; C2168–4; P1a; Phase Vd; Rig VI

Not illustrated

63 Die (Class 1) Bone/antler

Dimensions 7mm by 7mm by 6.5mm.

Values marked in ring-and-dot motifs. 1:6, 2:5, 3:4. ?Medieval.

A11–0009; C7013–10; MC174, Pit 7013; Phase (Va–) Vd(Vdd); Rig VIII

Not illustrated

64 ? Offcut/trial piece Bone

Dimensions 34mm by 23mm by 6mm.

Trapezoidal plaque cut from a bovine scapula, marked on obverse surface by saw-cut grid and around each edge by a single saw-cut line.

A1178; C2714–2; M4e, MF2713; Phase Vd,Vdd; Rig V

Not illustrated

65 ?Bobbin Bone

Length 82mm; diameter (maximum) 14mm.

Bobbin made from a sheep metatarsal, with natural axial perforation and slightly expanded ends; decorated on its four principal faces with a line of ten/twelve incised dots. Polished all over (including the ends) by handling.

A2498; C2737–2; M4a; Phase Vaa–Vc(VI); Rigs V and VI

Not illustrated

66 Whorl Bone

Diameter 39mm; internal diameter 7mm; weight 19.5g.

Spindle whorl comprising an almost complete proximal head of a femur. Early medieval. cf Cat Nos 13, 18, 28, 31, 55.

A11502; C3848–2; Building T, Well 3819; Phase VI; Rig VI

Illus 54

67 ?Roughout Bone

Length 106mm; width 8mm; thickness 7mm.

Fragment cut from the shaft of a cattle long bone, rectangular in section, broken at both ends. Medieval?

A11–0003; C7001–7/9; Modern, T7014; Phase VI; Rig VII

Not illustrated

68 Comb (double) Antler and iron

Length 81.5mm; height 29mm; thickness 10mm.

Double-sided composite comb with iron rivets. Cut with coarse teeth on one side and fine on the other. End plates ungraduated with slightly concave profiles. Side plates plano-convex in section, tapering slightly towards either end. Each is marked along half of one edge by saw cuts from cutting of coarse teeth and along the other half of the opposite edge with those from fine teeth. One tooth plate missing, some teeth broken. Early medieval.

A0680; C2006–3/4; unstratified; Rigs V and VI

Illus 51

69 Offcut Antler

Length 64mm.

Fragment of ?roe deer tine, sawn at the tip and base. Utilised.

A11–0004; C7000–7–10; unstratified; Rigs VI–VIII

Not illustrated.

70 Toggle Bone

Length 50mm.

Consisting of a metapodial of a pig. Unworked except for a transversely perforated hole with a diameter of 5mm. Broken. cf Cat Nos 8, 17, 19, 50, 61, 82; Carver 1979, 21, Fig 14. Early medieval.

A11–0025; C7000–7–10; unstratified; Rigs VI–VIII

Not illustrated

71 Comb side plate Antler

Length 73.5mm; width 13.7mm; thickness 2.7mm.

In two conjoining fragments. Curving, flat plate with fixing hole at unbroken termination. Decorated with single incised lines at each long edge (top and bottom of plate) and ring and dot motifs closely spaced together within central field. Decorated front of plate polished smooth; reverse shows fine pores typical of antler. Iron rivet may have been present when object first excavated but now missing?

A11–0002; C7000–7–10; unstratified; Rigs VI–VIII

Not illustrated

72 Comb (single) Antler and iron

Length (to break) 84mm; height 23.5mm; thickness 11mm.

Single-sided composite comb with iron rivets. Four tooth plates cut with fine teeth survive, including one end plate with two ungraduated teeth only. The side plates have a slight axial ridge marked by a pair of incised lines with the edges of the plates delineated by single border lines; in the intervening spaces are random oblique incisions. The saw cuts from the cutting of the teeth have been carefully extended to mark the lower edge of one side plate, while on the other side plate only occasional cuts are registered in this way. Note irregular teeth at the junction and the thinning of the tooth plates, apparently after assembly. Broken. Early medieval.

A0493; C2003–7/10; Sondage 2003; unstratified; Rigs VII and VIII

Illus 51

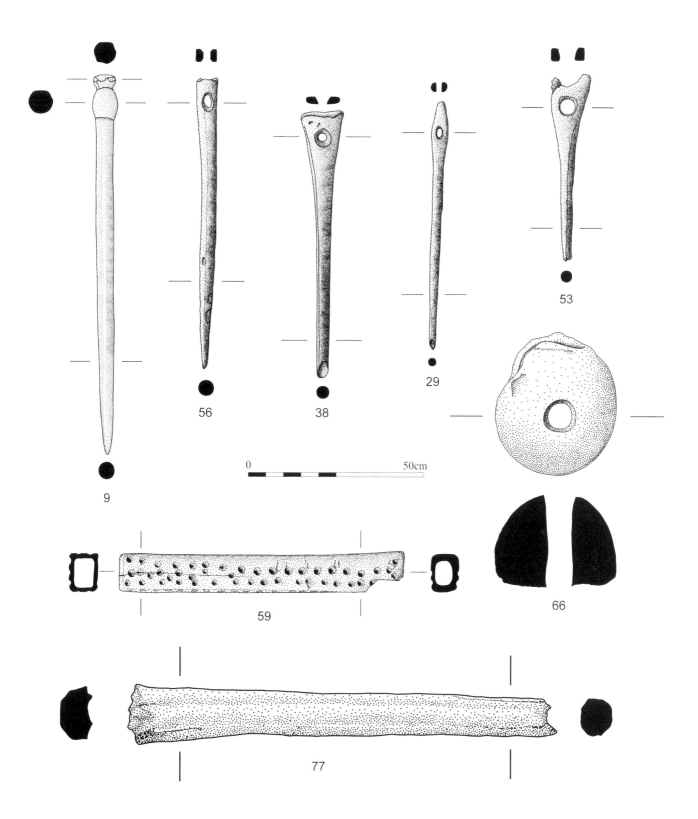

Illus 53 *Worked bone. Pins/needles Cat Nos 9, 29, 38, 53, 56. Whorl Cat No 66. Tally stick/bobbin Cat No 59. Pin beater Cat No 77.*

73 Trial piece Bone

Length 142.5mm; width 28.6mm; thickness 10.1mm.

Split long bone shaft, probably of cattle. Four irregularly spaced ring and dot motifs incised near one end of shaft. Three motifs are cut with same tool, ring diameter 3.2mm. Fourth ring is smaller, measuring 2.1mm and presumably cut using a different tool.

A02–0280; C7085–7; unstratified; Rig VII

Illus 54

74 Teether / infant's soother Bone

Length 70.6mm; width 13.6mm; thickness 5.4mm.

Composed of bone rather than ivory. Probably a long bone shaft of large ungulate. Object is of an elongated tear-drop shape, tapering to a smooth terminal point. Pierced with a tear-drop shaped hole at wider end, probably for a suspension cord. Below suspension loop are three incised grooves, which continue on to the medial and lateral sides of the object. At a further distance are two similar incised grooves. The entire object is polished smooth, although file scratches are present on the front and back and on the inside of the suspension loop. Modern.

A11–0001; C7000–7–10; unstratified; Rigs VI–VIII

Illus 54

75 Offcut Bone

Length 95.3mm; width 42.7mm; thickness 28.7mm.

Sawn left sheep horn core. Base is sawn cleanly across, with small edge lug remaining on posterior aspect. Tip is roughly broken or possibly chopped.

A0686; C2006–3/4; unstratified; Rigs V and VI

Not illustrated

North Sector

Trench A and Area 5

76 Casket Mount Bone

Length 36mm; width 27mm; thickness 1.5mm.

Cut from a rib, perforated with one fixing hole of diameter 1.5mm and two large decorative holes of diameter 8mm. Incised ornament on obverse comprising four border lines on the intact narrow edge and two border lines on each of the other edges, with three transverse lines across the centre; groups of three lines alternate with the ornamental perforations. cf Cat No 10. Early medieval.

A5431; C0295–5; CG008; Phase 4–6

Illus 50

77 Pin-beater Bone

Length 123.5mm; width15.3mm; thickness 7.7mm.

Single-ended pin-beater cut from a long bone shaft, probably of cattle. Wider end is roughly chopped, revealing cancellous bone tissue (from internal marrow cavity of bone). Tapered end (now broken) has been smoothed to such an extent that cancellous tissue cannot be seen. Longitudinal striations present on tapered, outer surface of bone. cf MacGregor 1985, 186, fig 101, no 16, 189; MacGregor et al 1999, 1967, Fig 923, nos 7033, 7039, 7721).

A0339; C0036–5 and A; Lade (4); Phase 6–12(b-e)

Illus 53

78 ?Toggle Bone

Length 99mm.

Horn core of goat, unworked except for a transversely perforated hole with a diameter of 6.5mm. No wear around the hole.

A0238; C0026–5 and A; CG024; Phase 14–16

Not illustrated

79 Handle Elephant ivory

Thickness 15mm; width (maximum) 61mm.

?Umbrella handle made from a transverse section of elephant ivory. Ovoid in section, with opposed expansions near base, which is threaded internally and narrowed to receive a ferule externally. Modern.

A0011; C0001–5 and A; unstratified; Phase 19

Illus 54

80 ?Pin-beater Bone

Length (to break) 100mm.

Point with slightly expanded head, perforated by a hole of diameter 6mm. Broken at tip, considerably eroded. cf Clarke and Carter 1977, 311–13. Early medieval.

A0021; C0001–5 and A; unstratified; Phase 19

Not illustrated

81 ? Offcut/trial piece Bone

Length 35mm; width 25.5mm; thickness 7mm.

Plaque cut from a bovine scapula or pelvis, rectangular, with a wide notch cut in one end. The corners have been rounded off on the obverse side.

A0217; C0001–5 and A; unstratified; Phase 19

Illus 54

Area 6

82 Toggle Bone

Length 73.6mm; width 22.5mm; thickness 18.0mm.

Pig metatarsal (right metatarsal IV). Hole bored through anterior and posterior midshaft. Diameter of hole on anterior aspect 2.2mm, posterior aspect 1.9mm. Proximal articulation intact; distal epiphysis unfused but intact. cf Cat Nos 8, 17, 19, 50, 61.

A3127; C1028–6; Garden; Phase G

Not illustrated

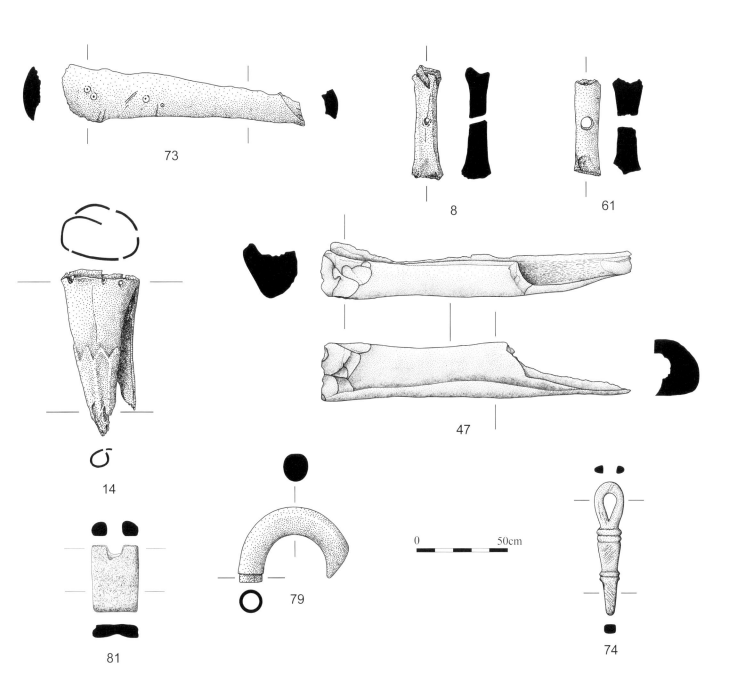

Illus 54 *Worked bone. Trial pieces Cat Nos 73, 81. Toggles Cat Nos 8, 61. Horn terminal Cat No 14. Skate Cat No 47. Handle Cat No 79. Teether Cat No 74.*

The medieval glass

John Hunter
with additional material by the late Nicholas Q Bogdan and George Dalgleish

This excavation provides a valuable opportunity to examine the use and frequency of glass in medieval urban Scotland. Glass of the 12th–14th centuries is not well evidenced in Scotland. While the potential is therefore promising, it should be pointed out that this is counter-balanced by factors of composition. Glass produced at this time in Europe mostly contained a relatively high potassium content as a direct consequence of using woodland materials in production. The resulting glass was of low durability and extremely vulnerable to weathering and decay, particularly under buried conditions. The more durable high soda-lime glasses appear not to have been produced much beyond the 10th century. Little is known of medieval glass in Scotland but the situation is unlikely to have differed significantly from that in England at the same period, where known production sites are relatively few in number and where glass itself was still a prized commodity. Indeed, judging from the English evidence at this time it is highly probable that the majority of Perth's examples would have been imported. In view of Perth's importance as a trading centre and in view of England's traditional weakness at producing quality glass prior to the 16th century, the finds are likely to reflect the upper end of the market and may be atypical of glasses in the rest of Scotland.

The glasses recovered are in a condition that does little justice to their original state and it is almost impossible to gain useful information from them. Although 27 items (Cat Nos 1–22, 28–32) were re-covered from the closed stratigraphy they are unlikely to be representative of either type or quality. They should simply be considered as survivors.

However, it is possibly noteworthy that only seven (25%) out of the 27 were recovered from deposits which dated from earlier than c1250. While perhaps 16 (59%) were deposited during the next half century, only five (17%) items came from 14th-century deposits. Perhaps significantly 17 (63%) of the glass examples were recovered during the second season when Parliament Close (Path P8) and the rigs to the east of it were excavated. Only ten (37%) pieces were recovered during the initial 1975–6 excavation season.

Glass beads

Of the eight glass beads recovered, all are circular in form. One (Cat No 4/A8365) is of durable glass and is therefore possibly residual. The others are similar in form although they tend to differ in overall proportion.

All have a basic rounded profile and appear to be consistent as regards material. Their general similarity may suggest localised production.

Five of the eight came from Area 7 and were all lost during the second half of the 13th century. Of these five, three (Cat No 15/A10–0027, Cat No 13/A10–0028a, Cat No 14/A10–0028b) came from deposits which are associated with the destruction of Building 18 (Phase 1) and the construction of Building 18 (Phase 2b); one (Cat No 16/A10–0022) from a floor of the latter; and the remaining example (Cat No 10/A10–0030) from an adjacent path (P3.3).

The two earliest (Cat No 3/A9109 and Cat No 4/A8365) came from middens which were being laid down in Area 4 during the late 12th century. The third (Cat No 6/A10–0021) was recovered from a midden (M15) which probably belongs to the second quarter of the 13th century.

Glass mounts

The earliest piece of glass recovered during the excavation was a rounded blue glass piece, the mount of a dress ring, which had been deposited in Pit 3789 early in the 12th century (Cat No 1/A9999). The only other such discovery was a green glass mount (Cat No 7/A8364) which may have been used to decorate a book cover or an item of decorative metalwork. It came from a midden, M6b, which was laid down during the first half of the 13th century (or possibly slightly earlier).

Linen smoothers

Four glass objects belong to a group usually interpreted as linen smoothers. These are of solid glass with a concave surface and here are seen to be approximately 65–80mm in diameter. They have a rounded surface and are of a convenient form to hold in the hand. They appear to be a traditional item and are known in Britain from the end of the first millennium. Their presence here evidences their continuity in Perth until at least the second half of the 13th century (see also Fascicule 3, The textiles).

Two of the smoothers (Cat No 11/A10–0017 and Cat No 12/A10–0029) were recovered from contexts which were probably associated with Building 18. Another (Cat No 21/A10–0023) came from a midden (M9b(b)) in an adjoining rig, while the fourth (Cat No 9/A7872) was found in the most westerly rig excavated, Rig V.

Vessel glass

Of the seven fragments of vessel glass recovered, four came from Area 3. One of these (Cat No 5/A9936) is highly durable and likely to be residual. This fragment which shows a pushed base is from a small flask or jar and is probably of Roman origin. It was, however, recovered from a midden (M1.3) which was probably being deposited during the last decades of the 12th century. Three other vessel fragments may all date from the second half of the 13th century (Cat No 8/ A6322, Cat No 17/A5457) or early 14th century (Cat No 23/A2123). Certainly Cat No 8/A6322, which has a rounded and thickened rim, belongs to that period. The size and condition of all the fragments leaves little scope for comment. The earliest (Cat No 2/A7055) shows a horizontally applied tail. It was recovered from Midden 14b, which was deposited behind a street frontage property in Area 2, immediately before 1150. Unfortunately it is impossible to suggest vessel types although the foot fragment (Cat No 29/A10–0005), which was recovered from an occupation layer from within what was probably an early 14th-century metal-worker's open workshop/yard (Building 53), seems to belong to a stemmed form of vessel.

Window glass

Seven window fragments were recorded of which only two (Cat No 20/A10–0009 and Cat No 32/A3399) give indications of quarry shape. The former perhaps belongs to a diamond-shaped quarry and the remains of grozing can be seen on two adjacent edges. The other is basically complete and in the form of a curved rectangle with all four edges grozed. Both are likely to have been used in patterned form, presumably in ecclesiastical buildings. Little comment can be made on the rest of the window material, nor indeed on the method of production. Three fragments have flame-rounded edges (Cat No 18/A10–0018, Cat No 19/A10–0019 and Cat No 28/A10–0004) indicating that they had been cut from the edge of a manufactured sheet. These quarrels may have been finished by cutting but any evidence for this has been lost through weathering. None of the fragments exhibited any surviving traces of decoration.

It would appear that the earliest fragments all came from a midden (M9) which was being laid down during the last decade of the 13th century. While it is possible that this glass (Cat No 18/A10–0018, Cat No 19/A10–0019, Cat No 20/A10–0009) may be associated with Building 18 (Phase 2b), a substantial timber structure, it seems more likely that they came from a street frontage building, all trace of which was destroyed when the cellar of Building W was constructed (Fascicule 1, CD insert, the Architecture Survey). Of the remaining pieces, two were found in Building 50, a substantial stone structure which was probably erected shortly before 1300. The remaining pieces were recovered from middens in different parts of the site, and from different properties, one (Cat No 32/A3399) being from Midden 3c and the other (Cat No 28/A10–0004) from Midden 1.5b.

Catalogue

The Catalogue numbers allocated in an earlier version of the intended report start at No 70, but have here been changed to reflect additions to the worked bone catalogue (Cat Nos 1–85) and the arrangement of the other Fascicules in the series, and now begin at Cat No 1. Superseded catalogue numbers are given in brackets.

Post-medieval glass has been identified by George Dalgleish.

South Sector

1 (70) Mount (in dress ring) Glass and bronze
Ring with a very thin hoop set with a tubular bezel made from strip of bronze and containing a piece of rounded blue glass. Diameter of ring 17mm. See Fascicule 2, The metalwork.
    A9999; C3826–1; M0; Pit 3789; Phase Ia(Ib); Rig VI
    Not illustrated

2 (71) Vessel Glass
Body fragment; thickness c2mm. Applied horizontal tail. Vessel type indeterminable. Weathered and opaque.
    A7055; C3601–1/2; M14b(c); Phase Ie,If; Rig V
    Not illustrated

3 (72) Bead Glass
Small fragments of circular bead. Rounded profile with flattened inner wall. Weathered and opaque.
    A9109; C2304–3; M10; Phase IId–IIg; Rig V
    Not illustrated

4 (73) Bead Glass
Circular, diameter 7mm; diameter of bore 3mm; thickness c2mm. Rounded profile with flattened inner wall. Durable glass. Yellow.
    A8365; C2239–4; M11; Phase IIh; Rigs V and VI
    Not illustrated

5 (74) Vessel Glass
Base fragment showing pushed base. Blown vessel. Thickness 1–2mm. Probably from a flask or small jar. Durable glass. Light blue/green. Probably Roman.
    A9936; C2597–3; M1.3; Phase IIi; Rig VI
    Not illustrated

6 (75) Bead Glass
Fragments of circular bead, thickness 4–5mm. Rounded profile with flattened inner wall. Weathered and opaque.
    A10–0021; C9404–9; M15; Phase IIId; Rig VII
    Not illustrated

7 (76) Mount Glass

Oval in form, c30 by 20mm. Rounded edges. Base side flattened. Maximum thickness 7mm. Bubbly durable glass. Green.

A8364; C2581–3; M6b; Phase IIg–IIId; Rig V

Not illustrated

8 (77) Vessel Glass

Rim fragments. Rim rounded and thickened with slightly out-splayed profile. Thick-walled vessel c3–5mm. Vessel type indeterminable. Weathered and opaque.

A6322; C2528–3; P2.2b; Phase IVa; Rig V

Not illustrated

9 (78) Linen smoother Glass

Fragment. Pushed concave base. Convex upper surface. Estimated maximum depth 30mm. Estimated diameter 65–70mm. Opaque. Early medieval.

A7872; C2236–4; MC143; Phase IVaa; Rig V

Not illustrated

10 (79) Bead Glass

Fragment of circular bead. Unevenly formed with estimated diameter of 15mm and bore diameter of 7mm. Thickness c4mm. Rounded profile slightly flattened on one side. Weathered and opaque.

A10–0030; C7364–7; P3.3; Phase IVa–IVb; Rig VI

Not illustrated

11 (80) Linen smoother Glass

Fragments. Pushed concave base. Convex upper surface. Estimated maximum depth 30mm. Weathered and opaque. Early medieval.

A10–0017; C9193–9; B18(Phase 1b); Destruction; Phase IVa,IVaa; Rig VII

Not illustrated

12 (81) Linen smoother Glass

Fragment. Pushed concave base. Convex upper surface. Estimated maximum depth 30mm. Estimated diameter 80mm. Weathered and opaque. Early medieval.

A10–0029; C7342–7; MC126; Pit 7402; Phase IVaa,IVb; Rig VII

Not illustrated

13 (82) Bead Glass

Fragment from circular bead; diameter 18mm; diameter of bore 5mm; thickness c5mm. Rounded profile with one side flattened. Weathered and opaque.

A10–0028a; C7306–7; B18(Phase 2a); NR and Hall–Construction (2); Phase IVb; Rig VII

Not illustrated

14 (83) Bead Glass

Fragment from crudely formed circular bead. Estimated diameter 17mm; bore diameter 7mm; thickness c5mm. Badly weathered and opaque.

A10–0028b; C7306–7; B18(Phase 2a); NR and Hall–Construction (2); Phase IVb; Rig VII

Not illustrated

15 (84) Bead Glass

Fragment of glass bead; thickness c3mm. Rounded profile. Weathered and opaque.

A10–0027; C7304–7; B18(Phase 2a); NR and Hall–Construction (2); Phase IVb; Rig VII

Not illustrated

16 (85) Bead Glass

Fragment of circular bead; diameter 15mm; bore diameter 7mm; thickness c5mm. Rounded profile. One side slightly flattened. Weathered and opaque.

A10–0022; C7235–7; B18(Phase 2b); NR and Hall–Floor(2); Phase IVb; Rig VII

Not illustrated

17 (86) Vessel Glass

Body fragment; thickness c3mm. Vessel type indeterminable. Weathered and opaque.

A5457; C2462A–3; M1.4c; Phase IIIa–IVcc; Rigs V and VI

Not illustrated

18 (87) Window Glass Glass

Fragment; thickness 3–4mm. Flame-rounded edge. Weathered and opaque.

A10–0018; C7231–7; M9a; Phase IVc, IVcc; Rig VII

Not illustrated

19 (88) Window glass Glass

Fragment; thickness 3–4mm. Flame-rounded edge. Weathered and opaque.

A10–0019; C7247–7; M9a; Phase IVc, IVcc; Rig VII

Not illustrated

20 (89) Window glass Glass

Fragment; thickness 2–3mm. Grooved on two adjacent edges. Possibly diamond shaped quarry. Weathered and opaque.

A10–0009; C9089–9; M9a; Phase IVc, IVcc; Rig VII

Not illustrated

21 (90) Linen smoother? Glass

Fragment. Weathered and opaque. Early medieval.

A10–0023; C6141–10; M9b(b); Phase IVc, IVcc; Rig VIII

Not illustrated

22 (91) Vessel Glass

Body fragments. Vessel type indeterminable. Weathered and opaque.

A10–0026; C6142–10; M9b(b); T6142; Phase IVc, IVcc; Rig VIII

Not illustrated

23 (92) Vessel Glass

Body fragment; thickness 2–3mm. Vessel type indeterminable. Weathered and opaque.

A2123; C2423–3; MC165; Pit 2465; Phase Va(VI); Rig V

Not illustrated

24–27 (93–6) Bottle Glass

Four fragments of dark green/brown glass; all from the same bottle, forming the base and lower body of a free blown cylinder type wine bottle. The pontil mark is visible on the kick. Late eighteenth–early nineteenth century

A8614a–d; C2465–3; MC165; Pit 2465; Phase Va(VI); Rig V

Not illustrated

28 (97) Window Glass Glass

Fragments; thickness c3mm. Flame-rounded edge. Weathered and opaque.

A10–0004; C7079–7; M1.5b; Phase Vaa; Rig VI

Not illustrated

29 (98) Vessel Glass

Main part of foot of stemmed vessel. Approximate diameter 40mm. Concave base. Weathered and opaque.

A10–0005; C7090–7; B53 (Phase 2); NA–Occupation (8); Phase Vbb; Rig VII

Not illustrated

30 (99) Window glass Glass

Fragment; thickness 2–3mm. Weathered and opaque.

A10–0002; C7044–10; B50(a); H7044; Phase IVcc–Vc(–Vdd); Rig VIII

Not illustrated

31 (100) Window glass Glass

Fragment; thickness 2–3mm. Weathered and opaque.

A10–0003; C7055–10; B50(a); H7056; Phase IVcc–Vc(–Vdd); Rig VIII

Not illustrated

32 (101) Window glass Glass

Almost complete quarry approximately 50 by 20mm; thickness 4–5mm. Slightly curved along length and probably part of mosaic patterned window. Groved on all four edges. Weathered and opaque.

A3399; C2164–4; M3c; Phase Vd; Rig V

Not illustrated

33 (102) Bottle Glass

Fragment of light brown/amber bottle glass; possibly from a beer or wine bottle. ?Relatively modern.

A2097; C2424–3; Building G; Well 2009, T2467; Phase VIa–VIf; Rig V

Not illustrated

34–37 (103–6) Bottle Glass

Base, part body and three fragments of dark green/brown glass wine bottle. Free blown of late cylinder type, the pontil mark on the kick is clearly visible. Late 18th–early 19th century.

A3944a–d; C2724–2; Building T; Wall 2724; Phase VI; Rigs V and VI

Not illustrated

38 (107) Bottle Glass

Dark green/brown glass beer or wine bottle; lacking neck. Lines from three-part mould visible. Post-1822.

A10802a; C3848–2; Building T; Well 3819; Phase VI; Rig VI

Not illustrated

39 (108) Bottle Glass

Dark green/brown glass beer or wine bottle; almost complete. Lines from three-part mould visible. Post-1822.

A10802b; C3848–2; Building T; Well 3819; Phase VI; Rig VI

Not illustrated

40 (109) Bottle Glass

Dark green/brown glass beer or wine bottle; lacking neck an shoulders. Lines from a three-part mould visible. Post-1822.

A10802c; C3848–2; Building T; Well 3819; Phase VI; Rig VI

Not illustrated

41 (110) Bottle Glass

Fragment of dark green/brown glass from neck and mouth of a wine bottle; possibly an early moulded type. Post-1822.

A10805a; C3848–2; Building T; Well 3819; PhaseVI; Rig VI

Not illustrated

42 (111) Bottle Glass

Green glass bottle seal marked 'RENAULT & CO/COGNAC' around a representation of two brandy casks. Probably relatively modern.

A10805b; C3848–2; Building T; Well 3819; Phase VI; Rig VI

Not illustrated

43 (112) Bottle Glass

Opaque green/blue octagonal medicine type bottle (in two pieces). Late 19th century.

A11491a; C3848–2; Building T; Well 3819; Phase VI; Rig VI

Not illustrated

44 (113) Bottle Glass

Neck from dark green glass wine bottle; possibly free blown. Early 19th century.

A11491b; C3848–2; Building T; Well 3819; Phase VI; Rig VI

Not illustrated

45 (114) Bottle Glass

Light blue glass oval medicine type bottle. Moulding lines visible. Late 19th century.

A11492; C3848–2; Building T; Well 3819; Phase VI; Rig VI

Not illustrated

46 (115) Bottle Glass

Body of light green (aqua) glass egg-shaped or 'Hamilton' mineral water bottle. The moulding seam is clearly visible. Late 19th–early 20th centuries.

A11678a; C3848–2; Building T; Well 3819; Phase VI; Rig VI

Not illustrated

47 (116) Bottle Glass

Base of dark green/brown glass free blown cylinder type bottle. The pontil mark is visible on the kick. Late 18th–early 19th century.

A11678b; C3848–2; Building T; Well 3819; Phase VI; Rig VI
Not illustrated

48 (117) Bottle Glass

Cobalt blue body and base of cylinder medicine type bottle. Moulded. Mid–late 19th century.

A11678c; C3848–2; Building T; Well 3819; Phase VI; Rig VI
Not illustrated

49 (118) Bottle Glass

Base of small dark green/brown glass bottle free blown cylinder type wine bottle. pontil mark visible on kick. Late 18th–early 19th century.

A11678d; C3848–2; Building T; Well 3819; Phase VI; Rig VI
Not illustrated

50 (119) Bottle Glass

Complete green (aqua) glass egg-shaped or 'Hamilton' mineral water bottle. The moulding seam is clearly visible. Late 19th (1870)–early 20th centuries.

A11678e; C3848–2; Building T; Well 3819; Phase VI; Rig VI
Not illustrated

51 (120) Bottle Glass

Fragment of base of brown moulded glass wine/beer bottle. Base has the figure '6' embossed on it. Post-1822; probably second half of 19th century.

A11678f; C3848–2; Building T; Well 3819; Phase VI; Rig VI
Not illustrated

52 (121) Bottle Glass

Two fragments of green (aqua) glass forming the square base of a medicine type bottle, moulded. The base has a Registry mark embossed on it. The year letter is illegible but the style of mark dates it to 1842 x 1867. Mid–later 19th century.

A11678g–h; C3848–2; Building T; Well 3819; Phase VI; Rig VI
Not illustrated

53 (123) Bottle Glass

Fragment of cobalt blue oval base of medicine type bottle. Moulding seam visible. Mid–late 19th century.

A11678i; C3848–2; Building T; Well 3819; Phase VI; Rig VI
Not illustrated

54–55 (124–5) Bottles (2) Glass

Two fragments of cobalt blue glass, probably from egg-shaped bottles, both moulded. One has the letters 'LO' and 'T' embossed on it. Late 19th–early 20th centuries.

A11678j–k; C3848–2; Building T; Well 3819; Phase VI; Rig VI
Not illustrated

56–57 (126–7) Bottles (2) Glass

Two fragments of light blue glass, one with moulding line visible, possibly from medicine type bottles. ?Late 19th century.

A11678l–m; C3848–2; Building T; Well 3819; Phase VI; Rig VI
Not illustrated

58 (128) Bottle Glass

Fragment of dark green/brown bottle glass. 18th–19th centuries.

A11678n; C3848–2; Building T; Well 3819; Phase VI; Rig VI
Not illustrated

59 (129) Bottle Glass

Fragment of green (aqua) glass, probably from an egg-shaped bottle. Late 19th–early 20th century.

A11678o; C3848–2; Building T; Well 3819; Phase VI; Rig VI
Not illustrated

60–63 (130–3) Bottles (4) Glass

Four fragments of dark green/brown bottle glass, possibly from early 19th-century wine bottles. ?Early 19th century.

A11678p–s; C3848–2; Building T; Well 3819; Phase VI; Rig VI
Not illustrated

64 (134) Bottle Glass

Fragment of light blue glass, moulding line visible. Possibly from mid–late 19th-century medicine type bottle. ?Mid–late 19th century.

A11678t; C3848–2; Building T; Well 3819; Phase VI; Rig VI
Not illustrated

65 (135) Bottle Glass

Dark green/brown neck of free blown wine bottle. Early 19th century.

A11678u; C3848–2; Building T; Well 3819; Phase VI; Rig VI
Not illustrated

66 (136) Bottle Glass

Neck of light blue medicine type bottle, moulding line visible. Probably late 19th century.

A11678v; C3848–2; Building T; Well 3819; Phase VI; Rig VI
Not illustrated

67 (137) Bottle Glass

Light green (aqua) glass neck of egg-shaped bottle. Possibly free blown or twisted in the mould. Early 19th century.

A11678w; C3848–2; Building T; Well 3819; Phase VI; Rig VI
Not illustrated

68 (138) Bottle Glass

Fragment of green (aqua) glass base of egg-shaped bottle. Moulding line visible. Late 19th–early 20th century.

A11678y; C3848–2; Building T; Well 3819; Phase VI; Rig VI
Not illustrated

69–70 (139–140) Bottle Glass
Two fragments of green (aqua) glass, possibly from an egg-shaped bottle. The letters 'EDINBU...' embossed on them. Late 19th–early 20th century.
A11678z–aa; C3848–2; Building T; Well 3819; Phase VI; Rig VI
Not illustrated

71 (141) Bottle Glass
Fragment of green (aqua) glass end of egg-shaped bottle. Probably moulded. Late 19th century.
A11678bb; C3848–2; Building T; Well 3819; Phase VI; Rig VI
Not illustrated

72 (142) Bottle Glass
Fragment of green (aqua) glass base of a very small bottle, possibly for medicine or perfume. Probably late 19th century.
A11678cc; C3848–2; Building T; Well 3819; Phase VI; Rig VI
Not illustrated

73 (143) Mirror glass? Glass
Several fragments of thin flat glass; heavily irradiated. Were possibly originally silvered on one side; possibly from a mirror.
A2662; C2743–2; Building V; Pit 2743; Phase VI; Rig V
Not illustrated

74 (144) Bottle Glass
Fragment of light blue moulded glass with lettering 'HOP' embossed on it; possibly mineral water bottle. Mid 19th–early 20th century.
A1435; C3011–1; Modern; Pit 3012; Phase VI; Rig V
Not illustrated

75 (145) Bottle Glass
Fragment of light green (aqua) glass from base of egg-shaped bottle. Moulding line visible. Late 19th–early 20th century.
A1460; C3011–1; Modern; Pit 3012; Phase VI; Rig V
Not illustrated

76 (146) Bottle Glass
Fragment of dark green/brown bottle glass. 18th–19th century.
A2970; C2047–1; U/S; Rigs V and VI
Not illustrated

77 (147) Bottle Glass
Fragment of cobalt blue glass, with part of a moulding line visible; possibly from a medicine type bottle. Mid 19th–early 20th century.
A1322; C3001–1; U/S; Rigs V and VI
Not illustrated

78 (148) Bottle Glass
Fragment of dark green/brown glass from mouth of a bottle. Possibly moulded. Post-1822.
A1342; C3001–1; U/S; Rigs V and VI
Not illustrated

79–81 (149–151) Bottle(s) Glass
Three fragments of dark green/brown bottle glass. One possibly from the shoulder of a three part moulded bottle. Post-1822.
A1977a–c; C3001–1; U/S; Rigs V and VI
Not illustrated

82 (152) Bottle Glass
Fragment of very light green (aqua) glass; possibly from the neck of a 'Codd' type mineral water bottle. Late 19th (1870–)–early 20th centuries.
A2017; C2046–2; U/S; Rigs V and VI
Not illustrated

83 (153) Bottle Glass
Fragment of dark green/brown glass; possibly from near the base of a wine bottle. 18th–19th centuries.
A4151a; C2716–2; U/S; Rigs V and VI
Not illustrated

84 (154) Bottle Glass
Fragment of light green glass with part of mould line visible; possibly from a medicine type bottle. Mid 19th–early 20th century.
A4151b; C2716–2; U/S; Rigs V and VI
Not illustrated

85 (155) Window glass Glass
Piece of green tinged clear 'crown glass' window glass. This piece is from the centre of the crown, where the pontil rod was attached when spinning out the glass bubble and is known as the 'bullion' or 'bull's eye'. It was usually thrown away but could be used in basement or transom windows, through which no one needed to look. 17th–19th century.
A0529; C2001–3/4; U/S; Rigs V and VI
Not illustrated

86 (156) Bottle Glass
Fragment of blue/green (aqua) glass of egg-shaped bottle. Moulding line is visible. Late 19th–early 20th century.
A1505a; C2001–3/4; U/S; Rigs V and VI
Not illustrated

87 (157) Bottle Glass
Fragment of dark green/brown glass, possibly from the kick of a free blown wine bottle. Possibly late 18th century.
A1505b; C2001–3/4; U/S; Rigs V and VI
Not illustrated

88 (158) Window glass Glass
Fragment of clear glass, possibly from a plate glass window. Possibly 20th century.
A1949; C2001–3/4; U/S; Rigs V and VI
Not illustrated

89 (159) Window glass Glass
Fragment of brown opaque window glass. Medieval?
A0559; C2002–3/4; U/S; Rigs V and VI
Not illustrated

90 (160) Bottle Glass

Fragment of dark green bottle glass; heavily irradiated. Probably 18th–19th century.

A1160; C2006–3/4; U/S; Rigs V and VI

Not illustrated

91 (161) Bottle Glass

Fragment of dark green/brown bottle glass. 18th–19th centuries.

A1307; C2006–3/4; U/S; Rigs V and VI

Not illustrated

92 (162) Bottle Glass

Dark green/brown glass kick of either globe or mallet shaped wine bottle. Pontil mark visible, glass heavily irradiated. Late 17th–mid 18th century.

A1449; C2003–7/10; U/S; Sondage 2003; Rigs VII and VIII

Not illustrated

North Sector

Area 5 and Trench A

93 (163) Bottle? Glass

Small fragment of opaque green glass.

A2501; C0218–5 & A; Garden 1; Phase 15

Not illustrated

94 (164) Bottle Glass

Fragment of dark green bottle glass; heavily irradiated. Possibly 18th–19th centuries.

A0265; C0042–5 & A; CG028; Phase 15–18; Rig VII

Not illustrated

Area 6

95–106 (165–176) Bottle Glass

Twelve fragments of dark green/brown glass all from the base and body of a free blown cylinder type wine bottle. Pontil mark is visible on the kick. Late 18th–19th century.

A3472a-l; C1021–6; Building A(a); T1023; Phase I; Rigs V and VI

Not illustrated

107–109 (177–179) Bottle Glass

Three fragments of dark green/brown glass; two forming the neck and part of the shoulders of a cylinder type wine bottle. Possibly late 18th–early 19th century.

A4978a–c; C1023–6; Building A(a); T1023; Phase I; Rigs V and VI

Not illustrated

110 (180) Bottle Glass

One small piece from a base (possibly the same bottle as **107–109 (177–9)**; A4978a–c) [see above] of a free blown bottle. Possibly late 18th–early 19th century.

A4978d; C1023–6; Building A(a); T1023; Phase I; Rigs V and VI

Not illustrated

111 (181) Vessel Glass

Fragment of light green (aqua) glass. Unlikely to be from a bottle – possibly from some larger glass vessel.

A2614; C1049–6; Modern; T1049, D1049; Phase I, J; Rig IV

Not illustrated

112–113 (182–3) Bottle Glass

Two fragments of dark green/brown bottle glass, one possibly from near the base of a cylinder type free blown bottle. Late 18th–early 19th century.

A1317a,b; C1015–6; U/S; Phase K

Not illustrated

114 (184) Bottle Glass

Fragment of dark green/brown bottle glass, possibly from the shoulder of a bottle. 18th–19th century.

A2082; C1029–6; U/S; Phase K

Not illustrated

Trench B

115 (185) Bottle Glass

Fragment of green/brown bottle glass with part of the moulding line across it. Post-1822.

A0284; C1002–B; U/S

Not illustrated

The stone objects

Catherine Smith, J Lawson Brown and Mark A Hall

Introduction: geological study of the stone objects and samples

Geological identifications are taken from two archive reports by J Lawson Brown (1979 and 1980). Brown thin-sectioned some of the spindle whorls, and other stone artefacts perhaps somewhat reluctantly. The introduction to his main report is reproduced here as it indicates some of the problems encountered in carrying out intrusive scientific study some thirty years ago. The identification sheets relating to this report may be consulted in the site archive lodged in RCAHMS (Box number 8/A/4; Folder 1).

Geology

J Lawson Brown

The problems involved in the geological examination and evaluation of archaeological specimens may generally be regarded as being twofold, firstly, to what extent the partial or complete destruction of the specimen for detailed examination can be justified by the likely benefit of the results of the process, and secondly the difficulties in, and often impossibilities of, delineating the possible origins and provenance of material with any certainty.

The specimens collected at the excavation are no exception to this general rule and the above-mentioned problems were rapidly encountered. They are of course interrelated: there is for example little point in cutting up a section of a common sandstone for detailed examination when there may be no specimen available for comparison and in any case the sample is not distinctive enough in itself to allow more than a generalised idea as to its possible place of origin to be suggested. At present the detailed data and knowledge of many of the rocks required for comparative purposes with the samples is just not available, and in the examination of the samples this has been constantly borne in mind. However, where it is felt that further work might cast some light on the possible origin of a specimen at some time in the future this is suggested in the appropriate place.

The question of provenance, or the likely place of origin of the material of which the specimens is composed, must now be considered. It should be made clear that, in the sense applied here, the provenance or origin has no implications as to where the specimen was worked or embellished and is only a suggestion as to the source from which the material was originally derived. It should also be understood that by the nature of rocks and in the light of the often great similarity between the same rock-type from widely separated areas it is impossible to be absolutely certain as to the origin in the majority of cases, and indeed only the most distinctive of specimens can be ascribed with certainty to any one locality. For the majority of specimens composed of more common rock-types it is usually possible, particularly with the above-mentioned dearth of comparative information available, to give only an idea of the areas where similar material may be found and of the relative possibilities as to which are the more likely places of origin, and this will of course be influenced by any other non-geological evidence which may also be available. Care should be taken therefore to subscribe no more certainty to the suggested origin of a specimen than is indicated in the following descriptions, at least not on the geological evidence alone.

Finally the further complication should be noted that a specimen may be moved many miles from the locality of its original outcrop without the involvement of the agency of man, but by the geological processes of glacial and fluviatile transport. The erosive and transportive power of glacial ice is considerable and glacial erratics, often of considerable size, are found throughout the area around Perth. These erratics include material from north of the Highland Boundary Fault which has often been transported over some distance. Smaller material can also be transported by river action, and although in comparative terms the sediment which can be transported by the River Tay is less than might be expected from its size, the movement of objects of up to pebble size over fairly long distances would still be expected, and these pebbles might perhaps be picked up for ornamental use, or some other purpose, a considerable distance from their original source. In the writer's opinion, however, the possibility of the material for the Perth artefacts having been transported far, by water in particular but also by glacial action, is not considered to be very likely in most cases, but has still been taken into account when necessary in the descriptions following.

Origins of the stone samples

This section has been summarised from Appendices A and B in the original archive report, in which all samples examined, including unworked samples, are listed by accession number (Brown 1979 and 1980). Building materials are discussed in Fascicule 1, CD Insert: Geology.

Chalk

The origin of the specimens examined could not be determined by the methods available, and several possibilities are apparent. The chalk could be derived from Ireland, continental Europe, or from England; the nearest exposures to Perth are in the Cretaceous rocks of Yorkshire. It is also possible, although unlikely, that the chalk could have derived from material glacially transported from the Cretaceous strata under the North Sea. The origin of the chalk might well be determined more conclusively by study of the microfossils present.

Accession numbers 06–0046, 06–0079, 06–0111, 06–0115

Crystalline limestone

The origin of this relatively pure white limestone is equally difficult to determine and much the same comments apply here as for the specimens of chalk, above.

Accession numbers 5958, 8175, 9151, 9464, 9537, 06–0014

Gastropod limestone

Although certainty is difficult this limestone appears to be the 'Purbeck marble' of the Dorset area of England, although similar limestones are known elsewhere, for example in the Cretaceous rocks of the Weald.

Accession numbers 5678, 8221, 8450

Flint

Flints are predominantly found in the Upper Cretaceous rocks, associated with chalk, and the same areas of possible origin may be suggested, namely Ireland, England and continental Europe. The possibility of these flints having been found in glacially transported material also exists.

Accession numbers 8321 and 11185.

Sandstones, siltstones etc

The origin of the majority of these specimens can be assigned with almost complete certainty to the extensive outcrop of the Old Red Sandstone (ORS; Devonian strata) around Perth and in the Strathmore area. Examples of the same rock types as the specimens all occur in this area, and although it is most unlikely that specimens could be assigned to any particular horizon, it seems unnecessary to postulate a more distant origin. In addition, quarries are known to have been in operation in the ORS as long ago as the 14th century. In 1328 Robert Bruce asked permission of the Abbey of Scone for hewn stone to be taken from

the quarries at Kincarrathie and Balcormac for 'the edification of the Church of Perth and of the bridges of Perth and Earn' across the River Tay (*RRS*, v, no 350).

Accession numbers 0133, 0522, 0668, 2622, 3108, 4500, 4501, 4502, 5392, 6035, 6843, 6964, 7527, 7645, 8074, 8484, 8512, 9019, 9541, 9692, 10077, 10164, 10285, 11150, 11430, 12517, 06–0010, 06–0011, 06–0013, 06–0015, 06–0021, 06–0023, 06–0027, 06–0028, 06–0032, 06–0033, 06–0034, 06–0055, 06–0064, 06–0066, 06–0067, 06–0068, 06–0069, 06–0072, 06–0076

Mudstones

Several specimens are thought to be natural 'mudstones' or compacted clays, rather than 'man-made' clays such as are present in bricks and daub from the site. The mudstones contain fine quartz grains in the matrix which indicate a quartz-rich source for the material which might well be the ORS strata from which material has been eroded and eventually redeposited as muds on the flood plain of the River Tay.

These clays are thought to be natural rather than 'man-made' since, firstly there is no evidence of working in the clays, for example in the form of laminations or 'flow structures'. Secondly clay minerals are abundant. These tend to be lost during the firing of worked clays. Thirdly, in worked clays haematite staining, generally orange in colour, is generally fairly widespread, whereas in these specimens it is very limited (although A06–0054 does contain dark-brown ore dust).

Accession numbers 12281, 06–0026, 06–0054 and 06–0078

The stone artefacts

Amethyst
Mark A Hall

1 Amethyst Stone
Length 9.6mm; width 7.9mm; height 5.2mm; weight 0.52gms
Identified by eye with aid of a microscope by M Simmons and M Hall at Perth Museum and Art Gallery (PMAG).

Translucent cut and polished amethyst, made for the setting of a finger-ring (and not a bead as originally recorded in the site archive). The excavations produced several finger-rings with a range of settings including glass, pearl and precious stones (see Fascicule 2, The metalwork); for a gold and sapphire ring and a broken ring with an empty setting for a stone, both from Meal Vennel see Cox 1996, 760–1, Cat No 1 and 764, Cat No 43). Amethyst was regarded in classical and medieval thought as having various beneficial attributes: as an antidote to drunkenness, as well as those intoxicated with love; as a control over evil thoughts; as a booster of intelligence and shrewdness in business; as a deflector of disease; as an aid to the hunter and as a protection for soldiers (Kunz 1971, 58). It was also symbolically linked to the apostle Matthias and to the divine male sacrifice (Kunz 1971, 373 and 269). As part of a ring, the stone is likely to have belonged to someone of, if not of the highest status of nobility, then at least a well-to-do merchant or town dignitary. As Cox (1996, 761) observed, legal restrictions limited the wearing of luxurious rings to the upper classes, which may have included wealthy merchants and craftsmen. The earliest surviving Scottish sumptuary law is dated March 1429/30 (The textiles; Shaw 1979, 81). The stone may of course never have been set into a ring, but had perhaps been part of the stock of an artisan working in the vicinity of the High Street. The dating of Midden 3c in Phase Vd gives a mid-14th-century date for the loss or deposition of the stone. Amethyst is an appealingly colourful purple variety of quartz. It need not be an exotic import to medieval Perth as it is common across Scotland (Heddle 1901, 49–50) and the PMAG collections include an example of the natural mineral from the Corsiehill quarry area of Kinnoull Hill, on the opposite bank of the river to Perth.

A2120; C2102–4; M3c; Phase Vd; Rig V
Not illustrated

Whorls (Illus 55, 56)
Catherine Smith

Comparison with J L Brown's notes from 1979 and 1980 indicate that the whorls may have become darker in colour (oxidised) since the objects were first excavated. The colour stated here is that first recorded by Brown, with any substantial differences observed some thirty years later noted. Two whorls (Cat Nos 16/A06–0013 and 25/A06–0025) were not found at the time of writing, but had been seen by Brown in 1979; his valuable archive notes therefore form the catalogue entries for these items (abbreviated 'JLB'). The abbreviation ORS used below refers to the local Old Red Sandstone strata.

Whorl types

Walton Rogers (1997, 1736) has described three main stone whorl forms occurring at the Anglo-Scandinavian and medieval site of 16–22 Coppergate in York. Form A types date mainly to the 9th and 10th centuries, Form B to the late 10th to early 12th century and Form C to the medieval period, particularly of the north and east of Britain (ibid). In the site assemblage, whorl Cat No 32/A1077 appeared to be of the earlier Form A associated with the Anglian tradition. Unfortunately this example came from an unstratified context. Three examples were thought to be of Form B (Cat Nos 6/A8484 and 12/A06–0034 and 31/A6035) and are comparable to examples found at Goltho and north Lincolnshire (ibid, 1737). With these exceptions the majority of the stone whorls most closely resembled Form C. To date

all other whorls known to have been recovered from medieval urban sites in Scotland, for example Canal Street I, Meal Vennel and 80–86 High Street in Perth and Broad Street and 42 St Paul Street in Aberdeen, are of Form C (Ford 1987c, Illus 81, 149; Cox 1996, Illus 26, 785; Cox 1997, Illus 19, 754–5; Trewin 1982, Illus 106, 185). Whorls of Forms A and B are however known from the multi-period Northumbrian and medieval site of Castle Park, Dunbar (Cox 2000, Cat Nos 331 and 338 Illus 100, 140–1).

As regards raw materials for their manufacture, Walton Rogers (2000, 2531) has analysed the sources for whorls from sites throughout Britain dating from the 6th to the 14th centuries and concluded that the use of local stone is entirely typical of the period. In this the whorls from the site are no exception.

2 Whorl Stone
Diameter 28.3mm; thickness 21.3mm; weight 20.62g
Complete but sampled globular spindle whorl with equally flattened base and upper surfaces. Central circular hole, diameter 8.2mm. Decorated with bands of polished surface alternating with rougher surface, giving a light and shade effect. In grey clay or mudstone, probably originating from the local ORS strata. York Form C (Walton Rogers 1997, 1736).
A12281; C3889–1/2; MC071; Phase IIb–IIf; Rig VI
Not illustrated

3 Whorl Stone

Diameter 26.8mm; thickness 23.2mm; weight 14g
Complete globular spindle whorl with flattened base and upper surfaces. Central circular hole, diameter 7.7mm. heavy wear around hole. Traces of polished alternate decorative bands, as whorl Cat No 2, although more worn by use. In smooth light grey-brown fine-grained sandstone, probably of local ORS origin. Traces of wood noted on surface on examination in 1979. York Form C.
A12517; C3902–1; MC071; Phase IIb–IIf; Rig VI
Illus 55

4 Whorl Stone
Diameter 32.3mm; thickness 6.0mm, weight 5.89g
Rough discoid whorl, probably lathe-turned. Laminated horizontally; probably part of much larger biconical or globular whorl (cf Cat No 13). In fine-grained light grey siltstone, probably originating from the local ORS strata. York Form C.
A8512; C2581–3; M6b; Phase IIg–IIId; Rig V
Illus 55

5 Whorl Stone
Diameter 25.2mm; thickness 21.6mm; weight 15.33g
Globular whorl with flattened base and irregularly flattened upper surface, higher on one side than another, possibly due to uneven wear. Central circular hole, diameter 9.3mm. Decorated with horizontal and vertical incised lines. In light brown, fairly coarse-grained sandstone, probably originating from the local ORS strata. York Form C.
A06–0072; C9447–9; P8.1c; Phase IIIc; Rig VII
Not illustrated

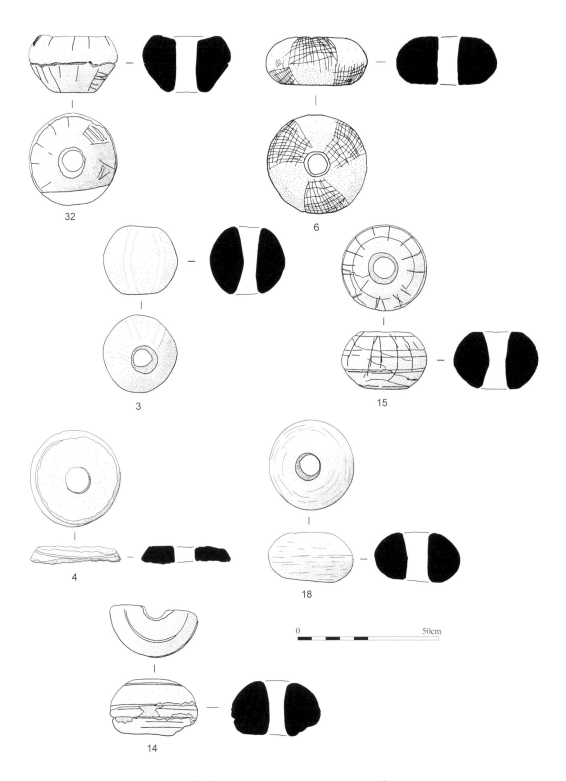

Illus 55 *Stone whorls. Cat Nos 3, 4, 6, 14, 15, 18 and 32.*

6 Whorl Stone

Diameter 34mm; thickness 16.7mm; weight 27.56g

Biconical whorl with flattened base and upper surface with central circular hole, diameter 7.6mm. Decorated all over with three alternating bands of cross-hatching. Evidence of use wear. In light grey fine-grained sandstone, weathered darker, probably originating from the local ORS strata. cf more finely decorated Form C example from Meal Vennel, Perth (Cox 1996, 784, Cat No 566; Illus 26). York Form B.

A8484; C2593–3; P2.2b; Phase IVa; Rig V

Illus 55

7 Whorl Stone

Diameter 30.1mm; thickness 4.4mm; weight 2.44g

Flat discoid, circular whorl with central hole diameter 8.3mm. laminated horizontally and broken across middle of hole. Probably fragment of larger Form C whorl; cf Cat No 4 above and Ford 1987c, Cat Nos 146 and 149 and Illus 80. In light grey-brown fine-grained sandstone, probably from local ORS strata.

A9541; C2677–3; B2, T2846; Phase IVa,IVaa; Rig V

Not illustrated

8 Whorl Stone

Diameter 28.7mm; thickness 20.8mm; weight 17.81g

Biconical whorl, flattened on base and upper surface. Damaged at base and upper surface. Central circular hole, diameter 8.0mm. Decorated with alternate bands of incised horizontal lines confined within vertical lines. cf Meal Vennel, Perth (Cox 1996, 784, Cat No 566 and Illus 26). Thin-sectioned. In dark grey clay or mudstone, probably of local origin. York Form C.

A06–0078; C7327–7; B18 (Phase 1b), North Room and South Room–Occupation (6); Phase IVa,IVaa; Rig VII

Not illustrated

9 Whorl Stone

Diameter 33.1mm; thickness 23.2mm; weight 27.44g

Asymmetrical biconical whorl, flattened base and upper surface. Central circular hole, diameter 11.2mm. Base of whorl worn and broken unevenly across hole. Decorated with incised horizontal lathe-turned bands. cf Cat No 8 and Walton Rogers 1997, 1739, Cat No 6572 and Fig 807. Thin sectioned: in dark grey clay or mudstone, probably of local origin. York Form C.

A06–0054; C 9317–9; B18 (Phase 1/2), Pit 9301; Phase IVaa,IVb; Rig VII

Not illustrated

10 Whorl Stone

Diameter 33.1mm, thickness 16.6mm, weight 20.24g

Biconical whorl with off-centre circular hole, diameter 10.0mm. Flattened base and upper surface. Knife trimmed. Decorated with radiating incised lines, meeting at bevel in centre of outer face of whorl. In light brown very fine-grained sandstone, probably of local ORS origin. York Form C.

A06–0067; C 7298–7; B18 (Phase 2b), North Room, Hall and Hall South–Occupation (10); Phase IVb; Rig VII

Not illustrated

11 Whorl Stone

Diameter 20.0mm; thickness 16.7mm; weight 23.81g

Biconical whorl with flattened base and upper surface and central circular hole, diameter 8.2mm. Decorated with crude incised radiating lines, meeting at knife trimmed bevel in centre of outer face of whorl. In dark weathered light brown fine-grained sandstone, probably of local ORS origin. York Form C.

A06–0066; C 7299–7; B18 (Phase 2b), North Room, Hall and Hall South–Occupation (10); Phase IVb; Rig VII

Not illustrated

12 Whorl Stone

Diameter not available (broken); thickness 13.5mm; weight 3.47g

Fragment of discoid whorl with central circular hole. No evidence of decoration. cf Walton Rogers 1997, 1739, Cat 6555 and Fig 807. In fawn/white micaceous siltstone, probably of local ORS origin. York Form B.

A06–0034; C9130–9; B18 (Phase 2b), Hall–Occupation (11b); Phase IVb; Rig VII.

Not illustrated

13 Whorl Stone

Diameter 30.6mm; thickness 16.6mm; weight 19.09g

Biconical/doughnut-shaped whorl with flattened base and upper surface and central circular hole, diameter 7.2mm. Undecorated; wavy horizontal lines are remains of worn knife-trimming marks. Walton Rogers 1997, Cat 6575. In light brown very fine-grained sandstone, probably of local ORS origin. York Form C.

A06–0076; C 6169–10; MC153; Phase IVb; Rig VIII

Not illustrated

14 Whorl Stone

Diameter 31.0mm; thickness (reconstructed) 17.6mm, weight 11.00g

Three conjoining fragments of biconical whorl with central circular hole, diameter 8.9mm. Flattened base and upper surface. Laminated horizontally, creating 'discoid' fragment which compares well with rough whorl Cat No 4. In light grey micaceous schist, probably from metamorphic strata to the N of Highland Boundary Fault. Probably York Form C.

A5182; C2462A–3; M1.4c; Phase IIIa–IVcc; Rigs V and VI

Illus 55

15 Whorl Stone

Diameter 30.1mm, thickness 24.4mm, weight 21.19g

Biconical whorl with central circular hole, diameter 14.5mm. Flattened base and upper surface. Decorated with lathe-turned horizontal lines and incised vertical lines. In light grey highly micaceous siltstone, probably of local ORS origin. York Form C.

A06–0055; C7231–7; M9a; Phase IVc,IVcc; Rig VII

Illus 55

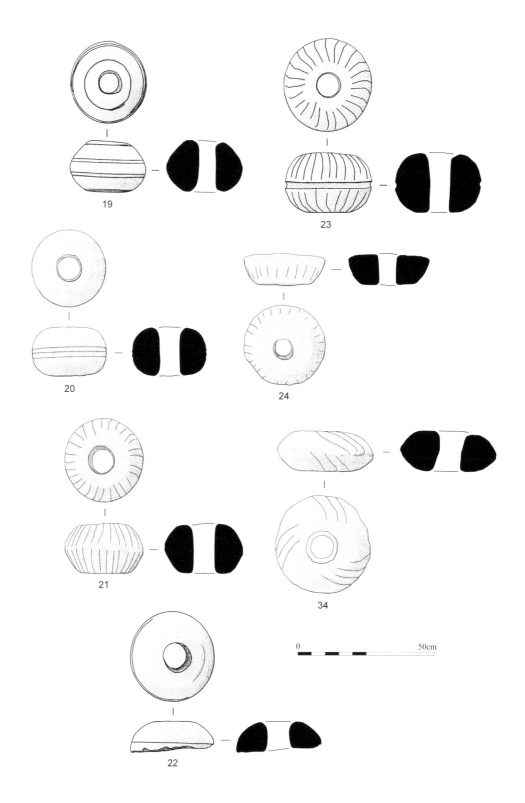

Illus 56 *Stone whorls. Cat Nos 19, 20, 21, 22, 23, 24 and 34.*

16 Whorl Stone

Weight 11.56g

Whorl seen by JLB in 1979. In white/light grey medium-grained sandstone, probably of local ORS origin.

A06–0013; C9001–9; M9a; Phase IVc,IVcc; Rig VII

Not illustrated

17 Whorl Stone

Diameter 13.2mm; thickness 20.5mm; weight 27.08g

Flattened globular whorl with central circular hole, diameter 8.9mm. Undecorated but lathe-turning marks visible on outer, upper and lower surfaces. In light grey fine-grained sandstone of local ORS origin. Probably York Form C (although upper surface more flattened than lower surface).

A06–0062; C6145–10; M9b(b); Phase IVc,IVcc; Rig VIII

Not illustrated

18 Whorl Stone

Diameter 30.3mm, thickness 16.4mm; weight 20.00g

Flattened biconical whorl with central circular hole, diameter 6.8mm. Many horizontal lathe-turning marks visible. In very fine-grained light grey sandstone, weathered almost black. York Form C.

A4500; C2759–2; B34, MF2759; Phase Va; Rig VI

Illus 55

19 Whorl Stone

Diameter 28.4mm; thickness 18.2mm; weight 17.73g

Flattened biconical whorl with central circular hole, diameter 7.5mm. Decorated with double horizontal lathe-turned lines. In light grey micaceous fine-grained sandstone, probably of local ORS origin. York Form C.

A06–0022; C9012–9; M8a; Phase Va,Vaa; Rig VII

Illus 56

20 Whorl Stone

Diameter 27.3mm; thickness 16.6mm; weight 16.88g

Flattened biconical whorl with central circular hole, diameter 7.9mm. Decorated with three parallel clean-cut lathe-turned horizontal lines. In light grey clay or mudstone, weathered dark, probably of local origin. York Form C.

A06–0026; C9012–9; M8a; Phase Va,Vaa; Rig VII

Illus 56

21 Whorl Stone

Diameter 29.4mm; thickness 17.1mm; weight 17.62g

Biconical whorl with central circular hole, diameter 8.4mm. Knife trimmed. Decorated with fairly thick vertical incised lines. In light grey non-micaceous very fine-grained sandstone, probably of local ORS origin. York Form C.

A06–0032; C7113–7; B53 (Phase 1), Central Area–Occupation (2a); Phase Vb; Rig VII

Illus 56

22 Whorl Stone

Diameter 31.4mm; thickness 9.1mm; weight 10.97g

Incomplete whorl, probably biconical, with central circular hole, diameter 9.1mm. Broken surface shows signs of abrasion indicating whorl may have continued in use after breakage. In light grey fine-grained micaceous sandstone, probably of local ORS origin.

A06–0033; C7113–7; B53 (Phase 1), Central Area–Occupation (2a); Phase Vb; Rig VII

Illus 56

23 Whorl Stone

Diameter 32.7mm; thickness 21.2mm; weight 30.54g

Biconical whorl with central circular hole, diameter 8.1mm. Lower surface more flattened than upper. Decorated with deep lathe-turned central horizontal groove and knife-cut incised vertical lines. Originally described as 'white/fawn' in colour, has now apparently oxidised to grey-green. In coarse-grained sandstone, probably of local ORS origin. York Form C.

A06–0021; C7071–7; B53 (Phase 2), North Area–Occupation (7a); Phase Vbb; Rig VII

Illus 56

24 Whorl Stone

Diameter 29.4mm; thickness 10.5mm; weight 10g

Incomplete biconical whorl, split in half at centre (cf Cat No 22) with central circular hole, diameter varying from 6.2–7mm, drilled inwards towards centre. Has possibly been knife-trimmed on upper and lower surfaces in order to prolong use. Decorated with incised vertical lines. In light grey very fine-grained micaceous sandstone, probably of local ORS origin. York Form C.

A06–0028; C 7071–7; B53 (Phase 2), North Area–Occupation (7a); Phase Vbb; Rig VII

Illus 56

25 Whorl Stone

Weight 15.12g

Seen by JLB in 1979. Whorl in grey-brown micaceous schist. Probably derived from Dalradian metamorphic rocks N of Highland Boundary Fault.

A06–0025; C7084–7; B53 (Phase 2), North Area–Occupation (12); Phase Vbb; Rig VII

Not illustrated

26 Whorl Stone

Diameter 30.3mm; thickness 18.8mm; weight 19g

Broken biconical whorl with central circular hole, diameter 8.5mm. Decorated with double bands of horizontal lathe-turned lines. In light grey micaceous siltstone, probably of local ORS origin. York Form C.

A06–0027; C7060–10; M8b; Phase Va,Vaa(–Vc); Rig VIII

Not illustrated

27 Whorl Stone

Diameter 31.8mm; thickness 14.2mm; weight 18.4g

Broken biconical or doughnut-shaped undecorated whorl with central circular hole, diameter 10.7mm. Probably not reused after breakage (no wear on broken surface). In white/light brown coarse-grained sandstone, probably of local ORS origin. Probably York Form C.

A3108; C2750–2; M4a; Phase Vaa–Vc; Rigs V and VI
Not illustrated

28 Whorl Stone

Diameter 28.7mm; thickness 17.2mm; weight 17.85g

Biconical, undecorated whorl with central circular hole diameter 6.8mm. Base roughened or abraded; damage to upper surface. In light grey, slightly micaceous medium-grained sandstone, weathered to rust colour, probably of local ORS origin. York Form C.

A4501; C2750–2; M4a; Phase Vaa–Vc; Rigs V and VI
Not illustrated

29 Whorl Stone

Diameter 33.3mm; thickness 8.8mm; weight 10.47g

Broken half of biconical whorl with central circular hole, diameter 9.2mm. Decorated with incised vertical lines. Broken face is abraded indicating whorl may have been reused after breakage. In light brown micaceous siltstone, probably of local ORS origin. York Form C.

A4502; C2750–2; M4a; Phase Vaa–Vc; Rigs V and VI
Not illustrated

30 Whorl / perforated ?counter Stone

Length 41.2mm; breadth 36.1mm; thickness 6.5mm; weight 14.98g

Roughly trimmed flat sub-circular/rectangular whorl or ?counter with cleanly drilled central circular perforation, diameter 8.0mm. May have been fabricated from a reused roof tile. Rather roughly made for use as a whorl; may possibly have been a rough and ready gaming piece. Other disc-shaped playing pieces from the site have been fashioned in bone and wood, although these are more finely finished and are decorated (The worked bone, Cat No 4; The wood, Cat No 428). In dark grey highly micaceous schist, probably from metamorphic rocks of Grampians, N of Highland Boundary Fault.

A3815; C2404–3; M1.5a; PhaseVa,Vaa(VI); Rigs V and VI
Not illustrated

31 Whorl Stone

Diameter 33.4mm; thickness 13.5mm; weight 20.60g

Flattened doughnut-shaped whorl with central circular hole, diameter 8.2mm. Upper and lower surfaces decorated with radiating incised lines. Outer surface undecorated, but with traces of lathe-turning. cf whorl Cat Nos 6 and 12. In white/light brown fairly coarse-grained sandstone (now oxidised to grey), probably of local ORS origin. York Form B.

A6035; C3578–1/2; Building T, Well 3819; T3578; Phase VI; Rig VI
Not illustrated

32 Whorl Stone

Diameter 32.1mm; thickness 18.8mm; weight 21.9g

Biconical whorl with flattened upper surface wider than lower; central circular hole diameter 7.9mm. Outer surface decorated with crude incised horizontal and vertical lines. In strongly laminated micaceous light grey shale, possibly of local origin, perhaps Fife shales in the Carboniferous succession. Thin-sectioned. York Form A, most likely A2 (one face wider than other).

A1077; C2006–3/4; unstratified; Rigs V and VI
Illus 55

33 Whorl Stone

Diameter 28.9mm; thickness 19.2mm; weight 17.83g

Undecorated biconical whorl with central circular hole, diameter from 7.6mm (lower side) to 10.5mm (upper side). Surface abrasion damage. In white carbonate fine-grained crystalline limestone, weathered orange; possibly glacially transported. York Form C.

A06–0014; C7000–7–10; unstratified; Rigs VI–VIII
Not illustrated

34 Whorl Stone

Diameter 35.3mm; thickness 13.4mm; weight 19g

Flattened biconical whorl, with central circular hole, diameter 9.0mm. Much worn by use. Decoration consists of crude diagonal incised lines. In white/fawn fine-grained sandstone, weathered dark brown, probably of local ORS origin. ?York Form C.

A06–0015; C9000–9; unstratified; Rig VII
Illus 56

Hones (Illus 57)

Only four hone stones could be located at the time of writing. As these had not been seen by Lawson Brown, a geological identification has kindly been provided by Mark Simmons, (MS) Perth Museum and Art Gallery. All four of the surviving hones had been perforated to accommodate a thong or cord, probably so that the tool could be conveniently secured to a belt. Hones, or sharpening stones, of varying sizes are a common find on medieval sites throughout Britain and similar examples have been recovered from sites in Perth at 80–86 High Street, (Cox 1997, 753; Illus 117), 1–5 High Street, Canal Street II and Kirk Close (Ford 1987c, 147–8; Illus 80) and Horse Cross (Smith et al 2007, 167).

All were manufactured from a hard micaceous schist or quartzite, probably of fairly local Highland origin. There was no evidence that the hones or the stone from which they were made had been imported from any great distance as may have been the case at Canal Street II, where one example may possibly have originated in Scandinavia (Ford 1987c, 147).

35 Hone Stone

Length 117.6mm; breadth 12.6mm; thickness 11.2mm
Complete tapering hone stone. Rectangular section,
tapering to rounded point. Circular drilled perforation
for suspension, diameter 4.3mm. Quartz mica schist of
?Highland origin (MS).
A12606; C4727–4; B16b; Pit 4726; Phase Id–IIa; Rig V
Illus 57

36 Hone Stone

Length 65.2mm; breadth 11.2mm; thickness 6.4mm
Broken hone stone. Rectangular section. Circular
drilled perforation, diameter 4.4mm. Wear on broken end
implies continued use after breakage. Quartzite of ?Highland
origin (MS).
A6316; C3509–1; M5d; Phase Vc–Vdd; Rig V
Illus 57

37 Hone Stone

Length 106.4mm; breadth 17.0mm; thickness 9.5mm
Incomplete hone stone. Broken at suspension perforation
(drilled, circular). Quartz mica schist of ?Highland origin (MS).
A06-0001; C7000–7–10; Rigs VI–VIII
Illus 57

38 Hone Stone

Length 42.9mm; breadth 11.6mm; thickness 6.0mm
Hone stone, possibly broken at one end. Rectangular
section, circular drilled perforation, diameter 4.6mm. Quartz
mica schist of ?Highland origin (MS).
A3465; C0001–5 & A (North Sector); U/S; Phase 19; Rig VII
Illus 57

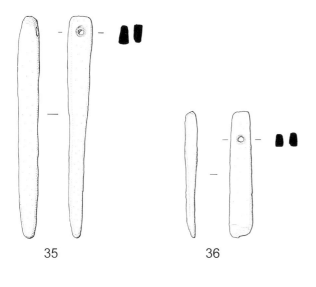

35   36

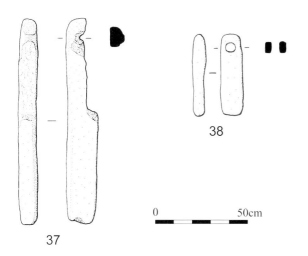

37

38

0   50cm

Illus 57 *Hones. Cat Nos 35, 36, 37 and 38.*

Two-part moulds (Illus 58–63)

Five pieces of two-part stone moulds used in casting
decorative metalwork were recovered, providing
important evidence for the production of penannular
brooches, brooch pins and mounts on the site. The
brooch moulds would have been used to produce cast
objects in two sizes: larger brooches of approximately
24–25mm diameter, with a constriction to allow the
brooch-pin to be attached, and smaller ring-brooches or
ringlets from approximately 8–11mm diameter, without
constrictions for a pin. Copper alloy brooches recovered
from the site may therefore have been made fairly locally
(see Fascicule 2, The metalwork). Similar two-part
moulds have been recovered from other sites on or near
the High Street. Both the upper and lower parts of a
mould used to cast decorative penannular brooches
came from a watching brief in the Skinnergate (Cachart
2004) and another fine example from 80–86 High Street
was used to cast a series of decorative finger-rings (Cox
1997, 755 and Illus 19). One mould appears to have been
used on both faces (Cat No 42/A06–0040) and may
represent a reused fragment. However in two examples
from Bedern, York both faces of the mould also have
artefact impressions (Ottaway and Rogers 2002, 2712–
3, Nos 13436 and 13437; Fig 1321).

The moulds from the site are made from fine-grained
limestone or siltstone, probably of fairly local origin;
the moulds from York were likewise made from chalk
available locally (ibid, 2712).

0   5cm

Illus 58 Mould for casting penannular brooches, brooch pins and ringlets. Cat No 39.

0   5cm

Illus 59 Mould for a decorative mount (above) shown with a computerised model of the inverse (positive) surface (below). Cat No 40.

0   5cm

Illus 60 Mould. Cat No 41.

39 Mould Stone

Length 109.5mm; breadth 67.1mm; thickness 19.8mm. Half of two-part rectangular brooch mould in fine-grained carbonate clay/limestone with feldspar, quartz and mafic fragments (JLB). Working surface of mould has channels at top for introduction of molten metal, leading to two circular impressions for penannular brooches, two pins of a size suitable to the brooches and three small ring-brooch or ringlet fittings. Penannular brooch external diameter 24.4mm; pin length 26.8mm; ringlet diameter 11.2mm. Remains of lead plug on internal face and external short edge. Four incised lines on unbroken external short edge. Empty (receiving) plug holes on one long edge, opposite to origin of channels. cf mould Cat No 41, and example for producing decorated brooches from Skinnergate (Cachart 2004).

A4750; C2817–2; B26, Floor/Occupation (10c); IIg–IVaa; Rig V

Illus 58

Illus 61 *Mould (upper surface).*
Cat No 42.

Illus 62 *Mould (lower surface).*
Cat No 42.

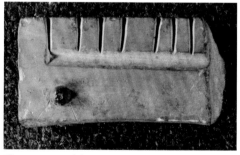

Illus 63 *Mould. Cat No 43.*

0 ─────────────── 5cm

40 Mould Stone
Length 61.8mm; breadth 61.8mm; thickness 11.1mm
Half of broken rectangular siltstone mould with incised form of decorative mount. Snapped off across decoration. Not part of mould Cat No 41, but found in same pit. In light grey fine-grained siltstone, originating in local ORS strata (JLB).
A8074; C2580–3; M1.4d, Pit 2566; Phase IVb,IVc; Rig VI
Illus 59

41 Mould Stone
Length 85.8mm; breadth 66.4mm; thickness 21.7mm
Half of trapezoidal two-part limestone brooch mould with channels cut to supply two circular forms for pen-annular brooches. Separate channel leads to two brooch pin impressions. cf mould Cat No 39. External diameter of brooch 25.5mm; pin length 25.2mm. Two small circular depressions for receiving lead plugs which held upper and lower parts of mould together when casting was in progress. A brown deposit on the inner face of the mould may be metallic (?Cu) residue. Parallel knife marks and chips on each long edge may indicate where mould parts were prised apart after casting. Outer surface (back) of mould bears lightly incised marks which may be a crude diagram or symbol, although there is no evidence that this was contemporary with useful life of mould.
A10909; C2580–3; M1.4d, Pit 2566; Phase IVb,IVc; Rig VI
Illus 60

42 Mould Stone
Length 60.2mm; breadth 46.3mm; thickness 11.7mm
Broken piece of two-part limestone mould in poor condition. Upper surface has three impressions for small ring-brooches (cf mould Cat No 39), external diameter 8.0mm, and remains of channels supplying five more. Possible depression for receiving lead plug in upper corner. Reverse surface has remains of impression for full-size brooch pin, as in moulds Cat Nos 39 and 41, but not suitable for ringlets. May represent reused fragment, but cf 13436 and 13437 from Bedern, York in which both faces of mould have artefact impressions (Ottaway and Rogers 2002, 2712). Brown staining may be metallic oxide residue. In fine-grained white carbonate clay with quartz, feldspar and no mafic fragments. Origin local/unknown? (JLB)
A06–0040; C7170–7; P8.4; Phase Va; Rig VII
Illus 61, 62

43 Mould Stone
Length 56.3mm; breadth 29.2mm; thickness 15.7mm
Part of broken two-part mould. Evidence of knife paring on outer surface, which appears polished through use or handling. Hole containing lead plug on one long edge. One long channel on working surface leads to seven tapering impressions, possibly for pins or rivets (without heads). Pin length 9.3mm. In light grey siltstone, probably originating in local ORS strata (JLB).
A06–0023; C7079–7; M1.5b; Phase Va,Vaa; Rigs VI and VII
Illus 63

Stone mortar

Part of the rim of a heavy stone vessel, a mortar in an attractive imported stone, probably Purbeck marble, was found in a late medieval midden. A sandstone example to which it bears superficial resemblance was found at 1–5 High Street, Perth (Ford 1987c, 147, Illus 80). Mortars were employed to grind up foodstuffs and were used in England from the 13th century onwards, when they began to replace rotary querns (Ottaway and Rogers 2002, 2803). Purbeck marble was used to make mortars found at King's Lynn in Norfolk and the Bedern in York (ibid, 2800). Two other samples of Purbeck marble were identified by Brown, A8221 and A5678, both described in his notes as 'shaped' so it is possible that they too may have been parts of mortars.

44 Mortar Stone
> External rim diameter 250mm; thickness of rim 31.0mm
>> Broken rim of heavy stone vessel or mortar. Externally fairly roughly trimmed but polished by use/wear. No evidence of lugs on rim. In gastropod limestone, probably Purbeck marble; white weathered brown (JLB).
>> A8450; C2476–3; M1.4d; Phase IVb,IVc; Rig VI
>> Not illustrated

Possible die
Mark A Hall

A small cube of chalk was probably fashioned as a die blank, and may be compared with several examples from the site in bone, one of which was, as in this example, blank (The worked bone; Cat No 48; Phase Va,Vaa). On the face of it, chalk is an unlikely substance for a die because of its softness and friability. There is no obvious fault or damage in this piece which might have lead to the abandonment of its manufacture. Chalk was used to make a range of gaming equipment. A selection of boards and playing pieces is known from Castle Acre Castle, Norfolk, for example (Hinton 1983, 260–3). However that assemblage did not include any stone dice: all eight dice found were of bone (Margeson 1983, 253). Excavations at Lurk Lane, Beverley did however recover a die of chalk as well as a chalk playing piece, albeit of a very crude/highly degraded form (Foreman 1981, 112, no. 81). In Perth, chalk was an exotic material most likely imported from England. Lumps of chalk from the High Street excavations have been identified as ship's ballast (Fascicule 1, The excavation: discussion) and this cube may well derive from that source, possibly fashioned as an expedient or an experimental venture. An alternative possibility for the blank cube is that it was a tessera.

45 Die Stone
> Dimensions 9.3mm by 8.6mm by 9.1mm
>> Six-sided chalk cube. Faces plain, without markings. May be a blank for a die, or perhaps a tessera.
>> A10257; C2530–3; MC155, Pit 2691; Phase IVb,IVc; Rig V
>> Not illustrated

Tile

A fragment of an ornamental tile, probably a floor tile, in a green translucent marble, was recovered from an unstratified context in Area 3/4. The raw material has been quarried in Scotland, for example Iona, Tiree and Skye since the medieval period.

46 Tile Stone
> Length 38.0mm; breadth 31.0mm; thickness 12.9mm
>> Broken tile fragment. Upper surface flat, polished, smooth. Lower surface flat but less highly finished. In green translucent marble; fairly pure recrystallised limestone. May originate in Scotland although England or continental Europe are also possibilities (JLB/MS).
>> A0638; C2001–3/4; U/S; Rigs V and VI
>> Not illustrated

Pot lids

A number of stone pot lids are noted in the site records, but were recorded by Brown in 1979 as 'not ... located for examination' or indeed subsequently (A06–0100, C7294–7). These were probably only roughly worked and most likely similar to a collection of stone lids and discs found at the Horse Cross, Perth made from locally obtained sandstones and Dalradian micaceous schists (Smith et al 2007, 167–8; Illus 57–61). Not illustrated.

Querns

At least two, and possibly three quern fragments were noted in the site records, although these were not seen at the time of writing. Two were examined by Brown (A06–0010, C7030–10; and A06–0011, C7052–10, both in Rig VIII). The former was associated with an internal wall of Building 50(b) and the latter found in Well 7048. Both were in local stone, a light brown (weathered dark) micaceous medium-grained sandstone, from the local ORS strata. Not illustrated.

The flint

The late James B Kenworthy

Introduction

The recovery of flint from a medieval town site should occasion no surprise, since flint-and-steel would have been essential for making fire, and in much later periods flintlock weapons required gun-flints. There are other reasons, too, why the occurrence of flint may have significance. The paucity of reports of flint from other town sites is indeed surprising. The reason for this neglect may well in part stem from the fact that flint is a seemingly unimportant material, and may often remain unrecognised in areas where it is naturally abundant. At Perth, however, the only naturally occurring flint is in the form of small pebbles found sparsely in gravels; the nearest substantial cobbles come from the coasts of Fife and Angus, and much of the material found can be shown to derive from further afield. Despite the small number of pieces recovered, it is hoped that this report makes clear the potential which larger assemblages may have for providing information useful to the medievalist.

Discussion

A total of 120 pieces was recovered, all from the South Sector, with the exception of two from Area 5 in the North Sector. This total includes two pieces of jasper, and two pieces of other material which, with one of the jasper pieces, were found in a single group of 67 pieces. Flint occurs over the whole chronological range of the site, and may be divided into the following five categories (in the catalogue the flints are assigned to these categories or classes):

Class 1 derived from the local natural
Class 2 derived prehistoric pieces, of presumably
     East Scottish flint
Class 3 chalk flint ballast
Class 4 other ballast (non-local river/beach cobbles)
Class 5 undiagnostic pieces.

Class 1: local natural (68 pieces)

As might be expected, these occur during the site's earlier history, but not after early Period IV, when disturbances of the subsoil on the site will have almost ceased. In most cases, their occurrence may be taken as an indication of the degree to which subsoil was being dug into at any phase. The finds come from natural (1), paths (4), and buildings (63), but are absent from middens and pits. Association with path material is to be expected, but one group (Cat No 9/A10447) found in Occupation 1b of Building 16 (Phase 1) is notable. Here, 61 pieces, plus a jasper pebble, a fossilised wood fragment, a worn quartzite pebble and three possibly struck flakes (undiagnostic, but possibly of Class 2) had been deliberately deposited together. 'Magical' collections including pebbles are known from earlier periods (cf Stevenson 1967), and this might explain the present group, although alternative explanations may be advanced – that they are the hoard of a magpie-minded child, or (although none show signs of such use) that they were a store for use as strike-a-lights. Their small size makes the last unlikely, their average dimensions being 18mm in length, 13mm in width and 8.5mm in thickness.

Class 2: derived prehistoric (3 pieces)

Apart from the possible, but undiagnostic, pieces in Cat No 9/A10447, noted above, two prehistoric artefacts come from Period IV in the South Sector and one from Phase 3 in Area 5 in the North Sector. The raw material for these pieces is likely to have come from eastern Scottish coastal deposits, or less probably from one of the other Scottish flint sources (Wickham-Jones and Collins 1978). Cat No 52/A7152, from Area 5, is merely an undateable flake, but both the other pieces warrant detailed comment.

A barbed-and-tanged flint arrowhead (Cat No 34/A06–0041; Illus 64) was found in posthole PH9242 of Building18 (Phase 1b). The material is dark orange-brown flint with iron staining. The arrowhead is triangular in plan, with finely but irregularly serrated edges and barbs which taper to a point, and is apparently intermediate between the Sutton c and Kilmarnock types (Green 1980, 49–52). It corresponds more closely to the former type in breadth and thickness, while the careful manufacture and proportions are closer to the latter form. Serration, although associated with both types, has a high correlation with Sutton c arrowheads, and occurs on 13% of those with pointed barbs (ibid, 53). Green (ibid, 199) has, indeed, hinted at a relationship between the two types, and both are common Scottish forms. Although barbed-and-tanged arrowheads span the whole early Bronze Age and perhaps the early middle Bronze Age, Kilmarnock types belong to the later part of the period, say 1800–1300BC, and lack Beaker associations (ibid, 141). The present arrowhead may either belong to a type ancestral to Kilmarnock forms, or could have been influenced in form by them.

The presence of the arrowhead in a medieval urban context may be compared with similar finds from Aberdeen, and can be explained in several ways. Its context makes it unlikely that we are dealing with a piece accidentally derived from the subsoil beneath the site, but it might simply have been picked up and brought to the site as a curiosity. Again, in areas where natural flint was scarce, prehistoric flints, including arrowheads, were collected for use in fire-making (see Brodie 1872, 499, for 19th-century examples from Kincardineshire); the absence of signs of such use on this piece make this explanation unlikely. Perhaps more probable is that the find results from the use of such 'elf-shot' as apotropaic charms in the Middle Ages and later, as described, for example by Robert Gordon c1660 (cited in Robertson 1843, 7–8) and discussed by Wilson (1863, 178–81) and Evans (1872, 323–7).

The most recent treatment of the subject is by Penney (1976) for Ireland. Dr Hilary Murray (pers comm) has suggested that this arrowhead may have been placed in the posthole as a foundation deposit. This might be related to the practice, recorded by Gastaldi (1865, 6) of some Italian peasants who carefully kept arrowheads (believed to be thunderbolts) in order to protect their houses from lightning (on the principle of like repels like). A magical use, then, is the best explanation for the presence of this piece.

The second derived prehistoric piece (Cat No 47/ A08–0070, Illus 64), comes from Midden 9a. It is a deliberately struck flake, the material and surface alterations of which are similar to those of the arrowhead. It is entirely undiagnostic. The interest of the piece lies in the flaking along each edge, where continuous steep direct retouch has removed the stained and patinated surface on the dorsal face. This is consonant with the damage expected from use with a steel; the piece may thus be identified as a thirteenth-century strike-a-light, evidence for a use for prehistoric flints discussed above.

Class 3: chalk flint ballast
(18 pieces, two fitting, from one nodule)

This fine dark grey to black flint with thin chalk cortex is eastern English in origin. The chronological spread shows concentrations (although the sample is small) in Periods II and IV. Cat No 50/A7607, although unstratified, is worn and clearly derived from an earlier phase. There can be no doubt that this flint came to Perth as ship's ballast, unloaded when vessels took on cargo at the harbour, and thus evidence for trading patterns. It is notable that this ballast occurs from the start of Period I. All damage to the pieces is consonant with accidental knocking and crushing, with no evidence for utilisation. The bulk of the flint comes from middens, pits and paths, as would be expected.

Class 4: other ballast (12 pieces)

This category is represented by cobbles of low-grade mainly pale grey flint, often with variegation or mottling. The cobbles are medium-sized, and seem to come mainly from beach sources. This material corresponds superficially to no raw material sources known to the writer, but it is clearly not local, and probably not Scottish, in origin. Similar pieces have been recovered from medieval levels in Aberdeen (Kenworthy 1982). It is probable that we have here evidence for a second source for ships in ballast calling at eastern Scottish ports. Further work on identifying the source (which may prove difficult) may lend support to trading patterns implied by other imports.

The distribution by phase is similar to that of the chalk flint ballast. The appearance of this material, then, might be linked with the appearance of French pottery imports in Period II.

One piece (Cat No 51/A7487) comes from Ditch 0526 in Area 5; on the main site, four pieces come from paths and seven from middens. Most of the pieces are broken, mainly accidentally, though some may have been deliberately smashed, perhaps for strike-a-lights. No pieces show reuse.

Class 5: undiagnostic (16 pieces)

These pieces cannot be classified with confidence. Most belong to Period IV with five from Midden 1.4d, although three were found in the group Cat No 9/ A10447 noted above. Some at least may be struck prehistoric pieces, but this cannot be demonstrated. Most are probably derived from the original ground surface below the town. The chronological distribution corresponds with that expected (see above), falling off with time.

Conclusion

Despite the unpromising nature of the material here reported on, it has been possible to derive some useful information. Only one piece, the strike-a-light (Cat No 47/A08–0070), is a medieval artefact, but the ballast pieces, although unutilised, may have some significance. The distinction of the ballast from the other categories is supported by the different pattern of occurrence by phase. Unfortunately the sample is too small to be statistically useful: the best we can do is to state that there is a 9 in 10 chance that the apparent difference is the result of a true difference in the original state of affairs. Research on ballast from other sites, and on the determination of sources is clearly needed before detailed conclusions can be drawn about the shipping pattern represented.

Catalogue

South Sector

1 Cortical angular fragment Flint (Class 1)
Pale cherty flint. Patinated, (?smoke-) stained and
heated. Abraded. Chalk cortex? No technological pattern.
Dimensions: 41mm by 22mm by 21mm.
> A11545; C4630–4; Natural; Phase 0; Rigs V and VI
> Not illustrated

2 Chalk flint nodule Flint (Class 3)
Dark grey/black flint. Unworn chalk cortex. One projection
broken off by accidental fracture. Dimensions: 67mm by
34mm by 30mm.
> A10270; C3835-1; M0, Pit 3789; Phase Ia(Ib); Rig VI
> Not illustrated

3 Angular fragment ?Flint (Class 1)
?Pale grey flint. Abraded, patinated, corticated and iron-
stained. Not worked, but lacks cortical surfaces. Dimensions
36mm by 4mm by 20mm.
> A10939; C3866–1; B17 West-construction/levelling;
> Phase Ib; Rig V
> Not illustrated

4 Secondary flake Flint (Class 4)
Light grey cherty flint. Unworn, unpatinated. Dorsal spine
shows crushing, as does right-hand edge. Detached by
'soft' hammer or natural blow. Material unique from site.
Indeterminate. Dimensions 64mm by 27mm by 13mm.
> A9704; C3801–1/2; MC005, Pit 3805; Phase (Ia–)Ic; Rig V
> Not illustrated

5 Chalk flint nodule Flint (Class 3)
Dark grey flint. Wishbone-shaped. Fresh. Flaked naturally at
apex. Dimensions 54mm by 45mm by 20mm ('arms' 20mm
diameter).
> A8776; C3737–1/2; M2.1b and B10 South Room, Floor/
> Occupation (1); Phase Ic,Icc; Rig V
> Not illustrated

6 Beach nodule fragment Flint (Class 3)
Grey flint with lighter inclusions. Fresh, unpatinated.
'Smashed', no technological pattern. Chalky cortex with
beach type abrasions. About a quarter of a nodule?
Dimensions 78mm by 53mm by 33mm.
> A10915; C4533–4; MC017; Phase Ia–Icc>; Rigs V and VI
> Not illustrated

7 Angular fragment Flint (Class 4)
Red-brown flint. Only very slightly abraded; ?slightly
patinated. No technological pattern. Dimensions 22mm by
12mm by 12mm.
> A11082; C4538–4; MC017; Phase Ia–Icc>; Rigs V and VI
> Not illustrated

8 Angular fragment Flint (Class 4)
Banded red-brown/white flint. Fresh, unpatinated but
probably heated. Small patch of beach/river pebble cortex
present. No technological pattern. Material unique on site.
Dimensions 31mm by 17mm by 10mm.
> A11069; C5097–3; MC025, Pit 5337; Phase (Ia–)Id; Rig V
> Not illustrated

9 Sixty-seven flakes and fragments Flint (Classes 1 and 5),
Jasper, Quartzite etc
> Mainly flint. Mainly naturally broken pieces with no
> modification, as follows:

a sixteen angular pieces with marked cortication (white) and
some with patination. Abrasion ranges from slight to heavy.
Staining generally absent.
b forty angular pieces, corticated, patinated and with medium
to heavy iron-staining. Abrasion slight to heavy. A few have
slight, recent (but not necessarily modern) edge damage.
c five angular pieces, corticated, patinated and with dark grey
staining in addition to some iron-staining. Heavily abraded.
d one split ?jasper pebble.
e one chip ?fossilised wood?
f one worn quartzite pebble

The following may have been deliberately struck or show
signs of possible wear:
g one possible secondary flake of very pale grey flint,
patinated, corticated but only slightly abraded. Recent
damage: inverse removals along one edge. Both ends
broken off. Dimensions 28mm by 2.5mm by 1.5mm.
h ?distal end of large secondary flake. All surfaces corticated
and patinated. Slightly abraded. Pale flint. Recent damage
on one edge. Dimensions 25mm by 28mm by 8.5mm.
i angular fragment, corticated, patinated and slightly iron-
stained. Slight abrasion. Two edges bear damage which is
not modern.

General: length range 10.41mm (interquartile range 14–
22mm), width range 6–23mm (interquartile range 10-16mm),
thickness 4–18mm (interquartile range 6–11mm).
> A10447; C4505–4; B16(Phase 1), Occupation (1b); Phase
> (Id) Ie; Rig VI
> Not illustrated

10 Beach nodule fragment Flint (Class 4)
Mottled medium grey flint. Fresh, unpatinated. 'Smashed',
no technological pattern. One facet bears small 'crushing'
removals over its surface. Dimensions 61mm by 59mm by
43mm.
> A11311; C5105–3; MC053c; Phase If; Rig VI
> Not illustrated

11 Cortical angular fragment Flint (Class ?5)

Dark grey flint beach nodule. Fresh, unpatinated, 'smashed', no technological pattern. Dimensions 57mm by 42mm by 22mm.

   A1870; C3023–1; P5.3b; Phase If,IIa; Rig VI
   Not illustrated

12 Cortical angular fragment Flint (Class 4)

Purplish-brown to pale grey flint Abraded, patinated. No technological pattern. Dimensions 23mm by 21mm by 18mm.

   A11185; C5052–3; P5.3b; Phase If,IIa; Rig VI
   Not illustrated

13 Angular fragment Flint (Class 4)

Burnt (?pale grey) flint. Calcined. A minute patch of beach/river cortex remains. Naturally (heat) fractured. Dimensions 53mm by 38mm by 26mm.

   A11450; C5077–3; P5.3b; Phase If,IIa; Rig VI
   Not illustrated

14 Flake/angular fragment Flint (Class 1)

Pale grey flint with darker patches. Edges crushed, patinated. Apparently natural, bulb lacking. Triangular cross-section. Dimensions 16mm by 10mm by 5mm.

   A08–0069; C5312–3; P5.3b; Phase If,IIa; Rig VI
   Not illustrated

15 Chalk flint nodule Flint (Class 3)

Black flint. Fresh, unpatinated. Chalk cortex. One end broken off and crushed by 'natural' blow. Dimensions 68mm by 48mm by 29mm.

   A10468; C5004–3; MC049; Phase IIa; Rig V
   Not illustrated

16 Primary flake Flint (Class 5)

Mottled medium grey flint. Fresh, unpatinated. Beach/river pebble type cortex. Plain platform; a typical and diffuse bulb of force with incipient eraillure, pronounced ripples on flake release surface. Flaking angle 111°. Direct percussion with medium hammer, apparently intentional. Length 30mm; width 48.5mm; thickness 8mm. Undiagnostic.

   A08–736; C6511–1; MC051; Phase IIa; Rig VI
   Not illustrated

17 Cortical angular fragment Flint (Class 5?)

Dark grey flint (beach pebble). Abraded, patinated, one face slightly corticated. Beach cortex, naturally broken. Dimensions 28mm by 19mm by 10mm.

   A6921; C3589–1; MC061; Phase IIb; Rig VI
   Not illustrated

18 Natural chip Flint (Class 1)

Dark red-brown flint. Abraded. No technological pattern. Dimensions 10mm by 9mm by 8mm.

   A11183a; C5021–3; P3.0a; Phase IId; Rig VI
   Not illustrated

19 Chip Flint/jasper (Class 4)

Red flint/jasper. Slightly abraded and patinated. No technological pattern. Dimensions 13mm by 10mm by 7mm.

   A11183b; C5021–3; P3.0; Phase IId; Rig VI
   Not illustrated

20 Cortical angular fragment Flint (Class 5)

Dark grey flint (beach pebble). Fresh, unpatinated. No technological pattern. Dimensions 27mm by 27mm by 10mm.

   A10473; C4498–3; M1.1a; Phase IId–IIe; Rig VI
   Not illustrated

21 Cortical angular fragment Flint (Class 3)

Medium grey flint (beach pebble). Fresh unpatinated. No technological pattern. Chalk cortex, waterworn. Dimensions 47mm by 34mm by 13mm.

   A12334; C3889–1/2; MC071; Phase IIb–IIf; Rig VI
   Not illustrated

22 Beach/river nodule Flint (Class 5)

Mottled grey flint. About one quarter of nodule present. Fresh, unpatinated. Smashed, no technological pattern. Dimensions 80mm by 48mm by 28mm.

   A6440; C3577–1; B5, North Room, Occupation(2); Phase IIa–IIff; Rig V
   Not illustrated

23 Angular fragment Flint (Class 3)

Dark grey flint. Some flake ridges and edges crushed, often heavily. 'Chalk' flint. Smashed, no technological pattern. Crushing, which has removed flakes in places, might be due to use rather than accidental. Dimensions 51mm by 45mm by 29mm.

   A8475; C2239–4; M11; Phase IIh; Rigs V and VI
   Not illustrated

24 Chalk flint nodule Flint (Class 3)

Cherty grey to black flint (broken). Chalk cortex slightly smoothed. One end of nodule broken off. Dimensions: 72mm by 32mm by 20mm.

   A9953; C2462C–3; M1.3; Phase IIi; Rig VI
   Not illustrated

25 Primary flake Flint (Class 5)

Medium-dark grey flint. Fresh, unpatinated. Waterworn ('beach'?) chalk cortex. Abnormal bulb of force, pronounced ripples on flake release surface. Plain, small platform. Flaking angle 122°. Hard/medium hammer, direct percussion. Probably intentionally flaked. Undiagnostic. Dimensions 34mm by 36mm by 9mm.

   A11305; C3874–1; MC112b; Phase IIIb; Rig VII
   Not illustrated

26 Chalk flint nodule fragment Flint (Class 3)

Dark grey flint. Fresh, unpatinated. Thick chalk cortex (up to 10mm). Smashed, no technological pattern. One face thermally (?frost) pocked all over. Dimensions 58mm by 41mm by 40mm.

   A7978; C2234–4; M1.4a(a); Phase IIIa–IIIc; Rig VI
   Not illustrated

Illus 64 *Flint reused as strike-a-light (Cat No 47) and barbed-and-tanged arrowhead (Cat No 34) found in posthole of Building B18.*

27 Two chips Flint (Class 1)
Both abraded, patinated, corticated and iron-stained. Natural.
Dimensions (a) 7mm by 6mm by 2.5mm, (b) 8mm by 5mm by 4.5mm.
A08–0286; C9246–9; P8.1c; Phase IIIc; Rig VII
Not illustrated

28 Angular fragment Flint (Class 4)
(?Grey) flint. Calcined, no technological pattern. Dimensions 37mm by 35mm by 18mm.
A06–0060; C9414–9; P8.1c; Phase IIIc; Rig VII
Not illustrated

29 Burnt cortical angular fragment Flint (Class 4)
Calcined. Small patch beach/river cortex remains. No technological pattern. Dimensions 25mm by 20mm by 12mm.
A08-0466; C9404–9; M15; Phase IIId; Rig VII
Not illustrated

30 Chalk flint nodule Flint (Class 3)
Black flint. Chalk cortex. Slightly worn. Two projections broken off and apex crushed. Breaks probably from natural causes; broken surfaces fresh and unpatinated. Dimensions 41mm by 38mm by 25mm.
A7863; C2528–3; P2.2b; Phase IVa; Rig V
Not illustrated

31 Chalk flint nodule Flint (Class 3)
Chalk cortex slightly worn and dirty. One end naturally broken off; break fresh and surface unpatinated. Dimensions 110mm by 34mm by 27mm.
A6717; C2508–3; P2.3a; Phase IVaa; Rig V
Not illustrated

32 Cortical angular fragment Flint (Class 3)
Dark grey flint (from chalk flint nodule). Fresh, unpatinated. 'Smashed'; no technological pattern. Dimensions 44mm by 39mm by 14mm.
A5705; C2222–4; MC158a, Pit 2228; Phase IVaa; Rig V
Not illustrated

33 Beach nodule fragment Flint (Class 5)
Mottled pale to dark grey flint. Some edges crushed, unpatinated. 'Smashed'; no technological pattern. Dimensions 60mm by 59mm by 30mm.
A8767; C2595–3; B2, Occupation (1a); Phase IVa,IVaa; Rig VI
Not illustrated

34 Barbed-and-tanged flint arrowhead Flint (Class 2)
Type: Sutton c. Orange brown flint. Edge unabraded, surface slightly patinated and possibly slightly iron-stained. It is thin and well-made; edges are finely but irregularly serrated and slightly convex in plan. The extreme tip and one barb seem to have been broken off in antiquity. The remaining barb tapers to a point; the tang is tapered to a rounded base. Beaker Early Bronze Age (c2100–1400BC). Dimensions 27.5mm by 20.0mm by 3.5mm.
A06–0041; C9223–9; B18 (Phase 1b), PH9242; Phase IVa,IVaa; Rig VII
Illus 64

35 Pebble fragment Flint (Class 1)
Greyish yellow-brown flint. Thermally split pebble, exterior partly smooth dark cortex, partly old flaking (natural), abraded, patinated and iron-stained. Split surface fresh unpatinated. Dimensions 16mm by 17mm by 6mm.
A06–0057; C9193–9; B18 (Phase 1b)–destruction; Phase IVa,IVaa; Rig VII
Not illustrated

36 Secondary flake Flint (Class 3)
Black cherty flint with pale grey inclusions. Fresh, unpatinated. Chalky flint, no cortex. Proximal end smashed? Marked ripples on flake release surface. Unworn burin-spall-like removal from left-hand edge, distal part. (?) Hard hammer, direct percussion. Might be naturally flaked. Undiagnostic. No dimensions available.
A06–0051; C9302–9; B18(Phase 1/2), Pit 9301; Phase IVaa,IVb; Rig VII
Not illustrated

37 Angular fragment Flint (Class 3)
Mottled dark grey flint. Fresh, unpatinated. 'Chalk' flint. 'Smashed'; no technological pattern. Dimensions 25mm by 20mm by 10mm.
A08–0687; C9111–9; B18(Phase 2a), Hall South, Occupation (1); Phase IVb; Rig VII
Not illustrated

38 Chip Flint (Class 4)
Yellow-brown flint. Edges slightly abraded, patinated. Piece of shatter, whether from natural or intentional percussion unknown. Flint colour suggests that the latter is possible. Dimensions 12.5mm by 8mm by 3.5mm.
A08–0153; C9132–9; B18 (Phase 2b), North Room/Hall/Hall South, Occupation (10); Phase IVb; Rig VII
Not illustrated

39 Angular fragment Flint (Class 3)

Black cherty 'chalk' flint. Mainly fresh and unpatinated, but one flake surface slightly eroded and patinated. Limestone cortex up to 24mm thick, probably water-eroded. Smashed; no technological pattern. Dimensions 80mm by 65mm by 49mm.

A5331; C2476–3; M1.4d; Phase IVb,IVc; Rig VI
Not illustrated

40 Flaked beach/river nodule Flint (Class 5)

One end of nodule has been struck off, with an irregular lateral flake being detached at the same time. The flake-scars are fresh and unpatinated. The heavy blow which detached the flakes need not have been intentional. Dimensions 92mm by 75mm by 60mm.

A8145; C2476–3; M1.4d; Phase IVb,IVc; Rig VI
Not illustrated

41 Cortical angular fragment Flint (Class 5)

Black flint (beach nodule). Fresh, unpatinated. Smashed; no technological evidence. Found with A8215b. Dimensions 102mm by 60mm by 37mm.

A8215a; C2476–3; M1.4d; Phase IVb,IVc; Rig VI
Not illustrated

42 Fragment Flint (Class 5)

Dark grey flint. Detached from end of nodule. Flake scars fresh and unpatinated. Heavy crushing above the well defined cone of force (without bulb) suggests 'natural' flaking. Two flakes have been detached from the edge of the main nodule with the main scar as platform; the proximal edges are crushed, again probably unintentional flaking. Found with A8215a. Dimensions 65mm by 44mm by 33mm.

A8215b; C2476–3; M1.4d; Phase IVb,IVc; Rig VI
Not illustrated

43 Cortical angular fragment Flint (Class 5)

Variegated pale to dark grey flint (beach nodule). Fresh, unpatinated. 'Smashed' by heavy blow; no technological pattern. Dimensions 58mm by 52mm by 35mm.

A8321; C2476–3; M1.4d; Phase IVb,IVc; Rig VI
Not illustrated

44 Flaked beach/river nodule Flint (Class 5)

Mottled grey flint. Flaked surfaces fresh and unpatinated. At one end, two opposed large flakes have been removed and the apex has been shattered. One flake probably removed by a hard hammer or by a similar accidental blow, the other has been struck off by a very heavy blow which has left a large, partially detached, cone of force. This blow may not have been deliberate napping. The edge formed by intersection of the flake scars bears slight abrasion and modern wear, from being drawn laterally on hard surface, possibly a nonce-tool (one use only), but could be accidental. Undiagnostic. Dimensions 119mm by 85mm by 46mm.

A12407; C2476–3; M1.4d; Phase IVb,IVc; Rig VI
Not illustrated

45 Split chalk flint nodule Flint (Class 3)

Black flint. Two conjoining halves, a few shattered pieces lacking. Chalk cortex slightly worn, break surfaces fresh and unpatinated. Split by unintentional 'blow'. One of missing pieces probably detached in modern times. Dimensions (whole nodule) 78mm by 51mm by 45mm.

A5017; C2194–4; M1.4b; Phase IVb–IVcc; Rigs V and VI
Not illustrated

46 Cortical angular fragment Flint (Class 3)

Black (chalk) flint. Fresh, unpatinated. Chalk cortex slightly worn, up to 9mm thick in places. 'Smashed'; no technological pattern. Dimensions: 40mm by 24mm by 20mm.

A08–0722; C7247–7; M9a; Phase IVc,IVcc; Rig VII
Not illustrated

47 Utilised secondary flake Flint (Class 2)

Strike-a-light? Brown flint. Bulbar end snapped off. Slightly patinated and stained. Dark staining along right-hand edge. Both edges bear steep, direct, irregular retouch, leaving small projections. Pronounced ripples on the flake release surface suggest direct percussion. Step termination at distal end. Dimensions 29mm by 23mm by 5mm. Possibly medieval/early modern.

A08–0070; C9001–9; M9a; Phase IVc,IVcc; Rig VII
Illus 64

48 Angular fragment Flint (Class 4)

Flint, burnt purplish-grey but not calcined. Fresh, unpatinated, with undetached thermal 'pot-lid' fracture on the flake surfaces. No technological pattern. Dimensions 34mm by 25mm by 9 mm.

A1646; C2116–4; M3e, Pit 2111; Phase Vdd>; Rig VI
Not illustrated

49 Secondary flake Flint (Class 5)

Light to dark grey flint. Fresh, unpatinated. Pont platform on crushed edge. Eraillure on flake release surface, hinge termination. If deliberately struck, hard hammer direct percussion used, but features and context suggest a 'natural' agency. Undiagnostic. Dimensions 19mm by 41mm by 6.5mm.

A2659; C2743–2; Building V, Pit 2743; Phase VIc-VIf; Rig V
Not illustrated

50 Primary flake/split chalk flint nodule Flint (Class 3)

Mottled dark grey/black flint. Chalk cortex waterworn and dirty. Eraillure on flake release surface. Fresh, unpatinated, unstained. One dorsal flake removed, with crushing of edge – this is unlikely to be intentional – and similar flaking at the distal end. Direct percussion with hard hammer or 'natural' blow. Dimensions 72mm by 101mm by 38mm.

A7607; C2006–3/4; U/S; Rigs V and VI
Not illustrated

North Sector

Area 5

51 Cortical angular fragment Flint (Class 4)
Pale to light grey flint. 'Smashed' piece without technological
pattern. Cortex is waterworn chalk type. Slightly abraded
and patinated. Dimensions 40mm by 14mm by 11mm.
A7487; C0493–5&A; Ditch; Phase 1(2)
Not illustrated

52 Flake Flint (Class 2)
Yellow-brown flint (?utilised). Fresh, perhaps slightly
patinated. Facetted platform, eraillure on flake release
surface. Flaking angle 117°. Two dorsal scars. The edges
and distal end bear continuous irregular inverse micro-
flaking, possibly use-wear. Dimensions 12.5mm by 11mm by
4mm. ?Prehistoric?
A7152; C0426–5&A; CG003; Phase 3
Not illustrated

References

Alcock, L 1970 'Excavation at South Cadbury Castle, 1969; a summary report', *Antiq J*, 50, 14–25.

Andersen, H H, Crabb, P J and Madsen, H J 1971 *Århus Søndervold: en Byarkaeologisk Undersøgelse*. Copenhagen.

Anderson, J 1794 *A General View of the Agriculture of Aberdeenshire*. Edinburgh.

Andrews, A H and Noddle, B A 1975 'Absence of premolar teeth from ruminant mandibles found at archaeological sites', *J Arch Sci*, 2, 137–4.

APS *The Acts of the Parliaments of Scotland*, 12 vols, Thomson, T and Innes, C (eds) 1814–75. Edinburgh.

Armitage, P L and Clutton-Brock, J 1976 'A system for classification and description of the horn cores of cattle from archaeological sites', *J Arch Sci*, 3, 329–349.

Armitage, P L 1978 *Report on the Mammalian Remains from Baynard's Castle, Blackfriars, London*. PhD Thesis, University of London.

Armitage, P L 1982 'Studies on the remains of domestic livestock from Roman, medieval and early modern London: objectives and methods' in Hall, A and Kenward, H K (eds) *Environmental Archaeology in the Urban Context*), 94–106. London (=CBA Research Report 43).

Baker, J and Brothwell, D 1980 *Animal Diseases in Archaeology*. London.

Ballard, A 1916 'The theory of the Scottish burgh', *Scot Hist Rev* 12, 16–29.

Barrow, G W S (ed) 1999 *The Charters of King David I*. Woodbridge

Bawcutt, P and Riddy, F (eds) 1992 *Selected poems of Henryson and Dunbar*. Edinburgh.

Baxter, E V and Rintoul, L J 1953 *The birds of Scotland*. Edinburgh, 2 vols.

Beith, M 2004 *Healing Threads. Traditional Medicines of the Highlands and Islands*. 2nd edition. Edinburgh.

Benson, G 1906 'Notes on an excavation, at the corner of Castlegate and Coppergate', *Annual Report Yorkshire Philos Soc*, 72–6.

Bergquist, H and Lepiskaar, J 1957 'Animal skeletal remains from mediaeval Lund' *Acta Archaeologica Lundensia* 1, 1–95. Lund. Kulturhistorika.

Bigelow, G F 1993 'Archaeological and ethnohistoric evidence of a Norse island food custom', in Batey, C E, Jesch, J and Morris, C D (eds) *The Viking Age in Caithness, Orkney and the North Atlantic*. Edinburgh.

Bil, A 1992 'Transhumance names in Perthshire', *Proc Soc Antiq Scot* 122, 383–402.

Blomquist, H 1942 'Kammar fran Lunds medeltid', *Kulturen*, 133–62.

Boessneck, J, Muller, H-H, and Teichert, M 1964 'Osteologische Unterscheidungsmerkmale zwischen Schafe (*Ovis aries* Linne) und Ziege (*Capra hircus* Linne)', *Kuhn Archiv* 78, 1–129.

Bogdan, N Q 1992 *The Perth High Street Archaeological Excavation 1975–7*. Final interim report. Old Meldrum.

Bogdan, N Q and Wordsworth, J 1978 *The medieval excavations at the High Street Perth 1975–6, an interim report*. Perth High Street Archaeological Excavation Committee. Perth.

Bowler, D P 2004 *Perth, the Archaeology and Development of a Scottish Burgh*. Perth (=Tayside Fife Archaeol Committee Monogr 3).

Bowler, D and Hall, D 1995 'Kinnoull Street' in Bowler, D, Cox, A and Smith, C (eds) 'Four excavations in Perth, 1979–84', *Proc Soc Antiq Scot* 125, 939–49.

Boyd, W E nd 'The botanical remains from Blackfriars House'. SUAT Ltd Archive report.

Boyd, W E 1986 'Minor finds of cereals at two medieval rural archaeological sites in north-east Scotland', *Circaea* 4, (1), 39–42.

Boyd, W E 1988 'Cereals in Scottish antiquity', *Circaea* 5, (2), 101–110.

Brodie, J 1872 'Notice of a collection of flint implements found in the neighbourhood of Fordoun, Kincardineshire', *Proc Soc Antiq Scot*, 9 (1870–72), 499–503.

Brown, D 1990 'Games and toys: dice, a games-board and playing pieces', in Biddle, M Goodall, I and Hinton, D A (eds) *Object and Economy in Medieval Winchester. Winchester Studies* 7 ii, 692–706. Oxford.

Brown, J Lawson 1979 'Samples examined for the Perth High Street Archaeological Excavation'. Archive report. RCAHMS (Box number 8/A/4; Folder 1).

Brown, J Lawson 1980 'Samples examined for the Perth High Street Archaeological Excavation. Supplementary report to report already submitted'. Archive report. RCAHMS (Box number 8/A/4; Folder 1).

Brown, P H 1902 *History of Scotland*. Cambridge.

Bruun, B, Delin, H, Svensson, L, Singer, A and Zetterström, D 1989 *Birds of Britain and Europe*. London.

Burnett, A (ed) 1993 *Angus and Dundee Bird report 1993*. Brechin.

Burton, J H 1877 *Register of the Privy Council of Scotland*. Edinburgh. H M General Register House.

Cachart, R 2004 'Data structure report. Archaeological excavation and watching brief at Camerons, Skinnergate, Perth'. Unpublished archive report. SUAT Ltd.

Campbell, M 1965 'Goat keeping in the old Highland economy – 3', *Scottish Studies*, 9, 182-6.

Carus-Wilson, E 1963 'The medieval trade of the ports of the Wash', *Medieval Archaeology* 6–7, (1962–3), 182–201.

Carver, M O H 1979 'Three Saxo–Norman tenements in Durham City', *Med Arch* 23, 1–80.

Cerón-Carrasco, R 1994 'Feathers from Deposit F23 in the stone-lined pit (F22)' in McCormick, F 'Excavations at Pluscarden Priory, Moray', *Proc Soc Antiq Scot* 124, 414.

Chandler, A C 1916 'Study of the structure of feathers with reference to their taxonomic significance'. *University of California Publications in Zoology* 13, 243–446.

Chaplin, R E 1971 *The Study of Animal Bones from Archaeological Sites*. London.

Chaplin, R E and Barnetson, L 1978 'Report on the animal bones from mediaeval and later horizons in the High Street, Edinburgh', *Proc Soc Antiq Scot* 107, (1975–76), 229–240.

Chmielowska, A 1971 *Grzebebienie Starozytne i Średniowieczne z Zien Polskich*. Lodz (=Acta Archaeol Lodziensia 20).

Clapham, A R, Tutin, T G and Warburg, E F 1962 (2nd edition) *Flora of the British Isles* Cambridge.

Clarke, H and Carter, A 1977 *Excavations in King's Lynn 1963–1970*. London (=Soc Med Arch Monogr Ser 7).

Clason, A T 1967 *Animal and Man in Holland's Past*, Vols A and B. Groningen.

Coleman, R J 1996 'Burgage plots of medieval Perth: the evidence from excavations at Canal Street', *Proc Soc Antiq Scot* 126, 689–732.

Cooper, M R and Johnson, A W (eds) 1984 *Poisonous Plants in Britain and their Effects on Animals and Man*. London (=Ministry of Agriculture, Fisheries and Food Reference Book 161).

Cornwall, I W 1974 *Bones for the Archaeologist*. London.

Coupar Angus Rental 1880 Rogers, C R (ed) *Rental Book of the Cistercian Abbey of Cupar-Angus*, 2 vols. London (Grampian Club).

Cox, A 1996 'Backland activities in medieval Perth: excavations at Meal Vennel and Scott Street', *Proc Soc Antiq Scot*, 126, 733–821.

Cox, A 1996 'Stone objects' in Cox, A 'Backland activities in medieval Perth: excavations at Meal Vennel and Scott Street', *Proc Soc Antiq Scot*, 126, 783–5.

Cox, A 1997 'The artefacts' in Coleman, R and Moloney, C 'The development of a medieval street frontage: the evidence from excavations at 80–86 High Street, Perth', *Proc Soc Antiq Scot*, 127, 740–67.

Cox, A 2000 'Spindle whorls' in Perry, D R *Castle Park, Dunbar. Two thousand years on a fortified headland*, 140–1. Edinburgh. (=Soc Antiq Scot Monogr Ser, 16).

Cox, A and Smith, C 2007 'The wood' in Cox, A 'Excavations at the Horse Cross, Perth' *Tayside Fife Archaeol J*, 13, 169–170.

Crone, A and Barber, J 1987 'Structural timber' in Holdsworth, P (ed) *Excavations in the Medieval Burgh of Perth 1979–81* , 87–8. Edinburgh. (=Soc Antiq Scot Monogr Ser, 5).

Cross, J F and Bruce, M F 1989 'The skeletal remains' in Stones 1989, 119–41.

Curle, A O, Olsen, M and Shetelig, H 1954 'Civilisation of the Viking settlers in relation to their old and new countries' in Shetelig, H (ed) *Viking Antiquities in Great Britain and Ireland*, 6. Oslo.

Davidson, C F 1932 'The Arctic clay of Errol, Perthshire', *Trans Proc Perthshire Natur Hist Soc* 9, 35–68.

Day, M G 1965 'Identification of hair and feather remains in gut and faeces of stoats and weasels', *Proceedings of the Scientific Meetings of the Zoological Society of London* 148, (1966), 201–7.

Dickinson, W C 1961 *Scotland from the Earliest Times to 1603* Vol 1. London.

Dickson, J H 1973 *Bryophytes of the Pleistocene*. Cambridge.

Dickson, C 1996 'Food, medicinal and other plants from the 15th century drains of Paisley Abbey, Scotland' *Vegetation History and Archaeobotany* 5, 25–31.

Dickson, J 2000 'Some especially noteworthy finds from the drain' in Malden, J (ed) *The Monastery and Abbey of Paisley*, 225–229. Glasgow.

Dickson, J H, Dickson, C A and Breeze D J 1979 'Flour or bread in a Roman military ditch at Bearsden, Scotland', *Antiquity* 53, 47–51.

Dimbleby, G W 1978 *Plants and Archaeology*. 2nd edition. London.

Dodgshon, R A 1993 'Strategies of farming in the western highlands and islands of Scotland prior to crofting and the clearances', *Economic History Review* XLVI, 4 (1993), 679–401.

Donaldson, A 1979 'Plant life and plant use in three Saxo-Norman tenements in Durham city', *Med Arch* 23, 1–81.

Donaldson, J 1794 *A General View of the Agriculture of the Carse of Gowrie in the County of Perth*. London.

Driesch, A von den 1976 *A Guide to the Measurement of Animal bones from Archaeological Sites*. Harvard, Massachusetts. (=Peabody Museum Bulletin 1).

Driesch, A von den and Boessneck, J A 1974 'Kritische Anmerkungen zur Widerristhohenberechnung aus Langenmassen vor undfruhgeschichtlichen Tierknochen', *Saugetierkundliche Mitteilungen* 22, 4, 325–48.

Duncan, A A M 1974 'Perth: the first century of the burgh', *Trans Perthshire Soc Natur Sci* (Special Issue), 30–50.

Duncan, A A M 1975a *Scotland: the Making of the Kingdom*. Edinburgh.

Duncan, A A M 1975b 'Burghs before 1296' in McNeill, P and Nicholson, R (eds) *A Historical Atlas of Scotland*, 31–2. St Andrews.

Dunkeld Rentale 1915 *Rentale Dunkeldense 1505–1517*, Hannay, R K (ed). Edinburgh (=Scottish History Society).

Dyer, J 1974 'The excavation of two barrows on Galley Hill, Streatley', *Bedfordshire Archaeol J*, 9, 13–34.

Eagles, J L M 1995 *The 'Chronicle of Perth': an Historical and Archaeological Study*. PhD Thesis, University of St Andrews.

Emmet, B (ed) 1969 *Montogomery Ward & Co. Catalogue and Buyers' Guide No 57, Spring and Summer 1895*. New York.

English, P, Burgess, G, Segundo, R and Dunne, J 1992 *Stockmanship. Improving the Care of the Pig and other Livestock*. Ipswich.

ERS 1878-1908 *The Exchequer Rolls of Scotland*. Stuart, J, Burnett, G, Mackay, A J G and MacNeill, G P (eds). Edinburgh, 23 vols, 1264–1600.

Evans, D 1987 *Digging up the Coopie. Investigations in the Gallowgate and Lochlands*. Aberdeen Art Gallery and Museums Interim Report. Aberdeen.

Evans, J 1872 *The ancient stone implements, weapons, and ornaments of Great Britain*. London.

Ewbank, J M, Phillipson, D W, Whitehouse, R D and Higgs, E S 1964 'Sheep in the Iron Age. A method of study', *Proc Prehist Soc* 30, 423–6.

Fairweather, A 1992 'Report on samples from Canal Street III, Perth'. SUAT Ltd Archive Report.

Fairweather A 1996a 'Botanical remains' in Cox, A (ed) 'Backland activities in medieval Perth: excavations at Meal Vennel and Scott Street', *Proc Soc Antiq Scot*, 126, 795 and 813–14.

Fairweather, 1996b 'Botanical remains' in Coleman, R J 'Burgage plots of medieval Perth: the evidence from excavations at Canal Street', *Proc Soc Antiq Scot*, 126, 726–7.

Fairweather, A 1997 'The environmental remains' in Coleman, R and Moloney, C 'The development of a medieval street frontage: excavations at 80-86 High Street, Perth', *Proc Soc Antiq Scot*, 127, 773–74.

Fenton, A S 1976 *Scottish Country Life*. Edinburgh.

Findlay, W M 1956 *Oats, their Cultivation and Use from Ancient Times to the Present Day*. Aberdeen University Studies 137, Edinburgh.

Fittis, R S 1891 *Sports and Pastimes of Scotland*. Paisley.

Fock, J 1966 *Metrische Untersuchungen an Metapodien Einiger Europäischer Rinderassen*. Universität München Inaugural-Dissertation.

Forbes, R J 1966 *Studies in Ancient Technology 5*. Leiden.

Ford, B 1987a 'Bone objects' in Holdsworth, P (ed) *Excavations in the Medieval Burgh of Perth 1979–81*, 150–1. Edinburgh (=Soc Antiq Scot Monogr Ser, 5).

Ford, B 1987b 'The wooden objects' in Holdsworth, P (ed) *Excavations in the Medieval Burgh of Perth 1979–81*, 141–7. Edinburgh (=Soc Antiq Scot Monogr Ser, 5).

Ford, B 1987c 'Stone objects' in Holdsworth, P (ed) *Excavations in the Medieval Burgh of Perth 1979–81*, 147–50. Edinburgh. (=Soc Antiq Scot Monogr Ser, 5).

Ford, B 1995 'Bone and antler objects', in Bowler, D, Cox, A and Smith, C (eds) 'Four excavations in Perth, 1979–84', *Proc Soc Antiq Scot*, 125, 917–99.

Ford, B and Robinson, D 1987 'Moss', in Holdsworth 1987, 153–4.

Foreman, M 1991 'The objects of stone and fired clay', in Armstrong, P, Tomlinson, D and Evans, D H *Excavations at Lurk Lane Beverley, 1979–82*, 105–14. Beverley. (=Sheffield Excavation Reports 1).

Fraser, A F 1980 *The Days of the Garron. The Story of the Highland Pony*. Loanhead, Midlothian.

Fraser, M J 1981 *A Study of the Botanical Material from Three Medieval Scottish sites*. MSc Thesis, University of Glasgow.

Fraser, M J and Dickson, J H 1982 'Plant remains' in Murray, J C (ed) *Excavations in the medieval burgh of Aberdeen 1973–8*, 239–43. Edinburgh (=Soc Antiq Scot Monogr Ser, 2).

Froissart, J 1867 *Les Chroniques de Froissart*, 2. Paris.

Gastaldi, B 1865 *Lake habitations and prehistoric remains in the urbaries and marl-beds of North and Central Italy*, trans C H Chambers. London.

Gelling, P S 1958 'Close ny Chollagh: an Iron Age fort at Scarlett, Isle of Man', *Proc Prehist Soc*, 24, 85–100.

Gerard, J 1597 *The Herball or General Historie of Plants*. London.

Gilbert, J M 1975 *Hunting Reserves in Medieval Scotland*. PhD Thesis, University of Edinburgh.

Gilbert, J M 1979 *Hunting and Hunting Reserves in Medieval Scotland*. Edinburgh.

Godwin, H and Bachem, K 1959 'Excavations in Hungate, York. Appendix III, Plant material', *Archaeological Journal*, 116, 109–13.

Goodridge, J F (trans) 1966 *Piers the Ploughman by William Langland*. Harmondsworth.

Goodwin, P J 1985 *The River and the Road. Journal of a Freshwater Pearl-fisher*. London.

Graham, H G 1969 *The Social Life of Scotland in the Eighteenth Century*. London, 5th ed.

Grant, I F 1930 *The Social and Economic Development of Scotland before 1603*. Edinburgh.

Grant, I F 1934 *The Economic History of Scotland*. London.

Grant, I F 1961 *Highland Folk Ways*. London.

Green, B 1973 'A Romanesque ivory object from Norwich', *Antiq J*, 53 (1973), 287–9.

Green, H S 1980 *The Flint Arrowheads of the British Isles*. 2 vols. Oxford (=B A R Brit Ser 75).

Greig, J R A 1976 'The plant remains' in Buckland, P C (ed) *The Environmental Evidence from the Church Street Roman Sewer System*, 23–8. London. (=*The Archaeology of York*, 14/1).

Grigson, C 1974 'The craniology and relationships of four species of Bos 1' *J Arch Sci* 1, 353–379.

Grigson, G 1975 *The Englishman's Flora*, 2nd edition. St Albans.

Guy, I 1986 'The Scottish export trade' in Smout, T C (ed) *Scotland and Europe 1200–1850*, 63–81. Edinburgh.

Haldane, A R B 1981 *The Great Fishmonger of the Tay. John Richardson of Perth and Pitfour*. Dundee (=Abertay Historical Society Publication 21).

Hall, A R and Kenward, H K 1980 'An interpretation of biological remains from Highgate, Beverley' *J Arch Sci* 1 (1979), 33–51.

Hall, D W 1989 'Perth: the excavations' in Stones 1989, 99–110.

Hall, D W 2006 *Scottish Monastic Landscapes*. Stroud.

Hall, M A 2001 'An ivory handle from the High Street, Perth: consuming ritual in a medieval burgh', *Med Arch*, 45, 169–88.

Hamer, D (ed.) 1931 *The Works of Sir David Lindsay of the Mount 1490–1555*, vol 2. Edinburgh (=Scottish Text Society, 3rd Series).

Hamilton-Dyer, S 1993 'Fish and bird bones from 16–18 Netherkirkgate'. Aberdeen Art Gallery and Museums Archive Report.

Hamilton-Dyer, S 1994 'Bird and fish bones from Gallowgate Middle School'. Aberdeen Art Gallery and Museums Archive Report.

Hamilton-Dyer S, McCormick F, Murray H K and Murray J C 1993 'The bone assemblage and animal husbandry' in Murray, H K and Murray, J C 'Excavations at Rattray, Aberdeenshire, a Scottish deserted burgh', *Med Arch* 37, 203–5.

Hamilton-Dyer, S, Smith, C, Bullock, A E and Jones, A K G 2001 'The fish and bird bones' in Cameron, A S and Stones, J A *Aberdeen: an In-depth View of the City's Past*, 276–280. Edinburgh. (=Soc Antiq Scot Monogr Ser, 19).

Handley, J E 1953 *Scottish Farming in the Eighteenth Century*. London.

Harcourt, R A 1974 'The dog in Prehistoric and early historic Britain', *J Arch Sci* 1, 151–175.

Harris, M 1986 *Good to Eat*. London.

Harvie-Brown, J A 1906 *A Fauna of the Tay Basin and Strathmore*. Edinburgh.

Hastie, M and Holden, T 2000 'The plant remains' in Brown, G and Roy, M 'Excavations at 27–35 Panmure Street/72–8 Murraygate, Dundee', *Tayside Fife Archaeol J*, 6, 63–66.

Hastie, M and Holden, T 2001 'The plant remains' in Moloney, C and Baker, L 'Evidence for the form and nature of a medieval burgage plot in St Andrews: an archaeological excavation of the site of the Byre Theatre, St Andrews', *Tayside Fife Archaeol J*, 7, 77–9.

Hazlitt, W C 1995 *Dictionary of Faiths and Folklore*. London (facsimile of 1905 edition).

Heddle, M F 1901 *The Mineralogy of Scotland*. Vol 1. Edinburgh.

Hencken, H O'N 1938 *Cahercommaun, a stone Fort in County Clare*. Dublin.

Hencken, H O'N 1950 'Lagore Crannog: an Irish royal residence of the 7th to 10th centuries AD', *Proc Royal Irish Acad*, 53C, 1–247.

Henderson, D C 1990 *The Veterinary Book for Sheep Farmers*. Ipswich.

Hinton, D 1982, 'Stone', in Coad, J G, and Streeten, A D F, 'Excavations at castle Acre Castle, Norfolk, 1972–7: Country House and castle of the Norman Earls of Surrey', *Archaeol J* 1390 (1982), 138–301.

Hinton, P 1991 'Weed associates of recently grown *Avena strigosa* Schreber from Shetland, Scotland', *Circaea* 8, (1) (1990), 49–54.

HMC Mar and Kellie 1904 *Historical Manuscripts Commission. Report on the Manuscripts of the Earl of Mar and Kellie preserved at Alloa House, N.B.* London (HMSO).

Hodgson, G W I 1967 in G Jobey 'Excavation at Tynemouth Priory and Castle', *Archaeologia Aeliana*, Fourth Series, 65, 94–95.

Hodgson, G W I 1968 'A comparative account of the animal remains from Corstopitum and the Iron Age site of Catcote near Hartlepools, County Durham', *Archaeologia Aeliana*. Fourth Series, 66, 127–62.

Hodgson, G W I 1977 *The animal remains from excavations at Vindolanda 1970–1975*. Hexham.

Hodgson, G W I 1980 *A Comparative Analysis of Metrical Data Derived from Mammalian Remains from Selected Historic Sites in Britain*. PhD Thesis. University of Dundee.

Hodgson, G W I 1983 'The animal remains from mediaeval sites within three burghs on the eastern Scottish seaboard' in Proudfoot, B (ed) *Site, Environment and Economy*, 3–32. Oxford. (=B A R Int Ser 173).

Hodgson, G W I and Jones, A 1979 'The animal remains from four sites in Elgin', unpublished archive report. Historic Scotland.

Hodgson, G W I and Jones, A 1982a 'The animal remains' in Thoms, L M 'Trial excavations at St Ann's Lane, Perth', *Proc Soc Antiq Scot*, 112, 437–54.

Hodgson, G W I and Jones, A 1982b 'The animal bone' in Murray, J C (ed) *Excavations in the medieval burgh of Aberdeen 1973–81*, 229–8. Edinburgh (=Soc Antiq Scot Monogr Ser, 2).

Hodgson, G W I and Jones, A 1984 'Report on the animal remains from the medieval levels' in Blanchard, L 'An excavation at 45 Canal Street, Perth, 1978–79', *Proc Soc Antiq Scot*, 113, 514–7.

Hodgson, G W I and Smith, C 1982 'The animal remains', in Wordsworth, J 'Excavations of the settlement at 13–21 Castle Street, Inverness, 1979', *Proc Soc Antiq Scot*, 112, 375–8.

Hodgson, G W I and Smith, C 1983 'The animal remains from 1 Bank Street/5–7 Townhall Street' in Wordsworth, J 'Excavations in the burgh of Inverkeithing, 1981', *Proc Soc Antiq Scot*, 113, 542–4.

Hoffman, M 1964 *The Warp-weighted Loom*. Oslo.

Holden, T 1999 'Assessment of soil samples and the charred plant identifications from 77–79 High Street, Arbroath' in Perry, D R 'Excavations at 77–79 High Street, Arbroath' *Tayside Fife Archaeol J*, 5, 66–68.

Holden, T 2000 'The plant remains' in Cachart, R 'Excavations at 106–110 South Street, St Andrews', *Tayside Fife Archaeol Journal*, 6 (2000), 131–2.

Holdsworth, P (ed) 1987 *Excavations in the Medieval Burgh of Perth 1979–81*. Edinburgh. (=Soc Antiq Scot Monogr Ser, 5).

Howard, M M 1963 *The Metrical Determination of the Metapodials and Skulls of Cattle*. Royal Anthropological Institute Occasional Paper.

Hruby, V 1957 'Slovanské Kostsné Pšedmšty a Jejich Výroba na Moravš', *Památky Archaeologické* 48 (1957), 118–217.

Hume Brown, P 1978 *Early Travellers in Scotland*. Edinburgh (facsimile reprint of 1891 edition).

Innes, C (ed) 1854 *The Acts of Parliament of Scotland*. Edinburgh (=Scottish Burgh Records Society).

Innes, C 1868 *Ancient Laws and Customs of Burghs in Scotland 1124–1424*, vol 1. Edinburgh (=Scottish Burgh Records Society).

James, H and Yeoman, P 2008 *Excavations at St Ethernan's Monastery, Isle of May, Fife 1992-7*. Perth (=Tayside Fife Archaeol Committee Monogr 6).

James, N D G 1982 *The Forester's Companion*. Oxford, 3rd edition.

Jennings, D L 1976 'Raspberries and blackberries' in Simmonds, N W (ed) *Evolution of Crop Plants*. London.

Jensen, H A 1979 'Seeds and other diaspores in medieval layers in Svendborg' in *The Archaeology of Svendborg, Denmark, 2*. Odense.

Jewell, P A 1962 'Changes in size and type of cattle from prehistoric to mediaeval times in Britain', *Z Tierz Zuch Biol* 77, 159–67.

Jones, A K G 1982 'Bulk-sieving and the recovery of fish remains from urban archaeological sites' in Hall, A R and Kenward, H K (eds) *Environmental Archaeology in the Urban Context*, 79–85. London (=CBA Research Report 43).

Keith, T 1913 'The trading privileges of the Royal Burghs of Scotland', *Eng Hist Rev* 28, 454–71.

Kenward, H and Hall, A 2001 'Plants, intestinal parasites and insects' in Cameron, A S and Stones, J A *Aberdeen. An In-depth View of the City's Past*, 280–97. Edinburgh (=Soc Antiq Scot Monogr Ser, 19).

Kenworthy, J B 1982 'The flint' in Murray, J C *Excavations in the Medieval Burgh of Aberdeen 1973-81*, 200–15. Edinburgh (=Society of Antiquaries of Scotland Monogr, Ser 2).

Kevill-Davies, S 1991 *Yesterday's Children. The Antiques and History of Childcare*. Woodbridge.

King, A 1978 'A comparative survey of bone assemblages from Roman sites in Britain', *Institute of Archaeology Bulletin* 15, 207–32.

Kunz, G F and Stevenson, G H 1993 *The Book of the Pearl*. New York (facsimile reprint of 1908 edition).

Kunz, G F 1971 *The Curious Lore of Precious Stones*. New York (facsimile reprint of 1913 edition).

Lamb, H H 1995 *Climate, History and the Modern World*. London, 2nd edition.

Lasko, P 1984 'Ivory carvings' in Zarnecki, G, Holt, J and Holland, T (eds) *English Romanesque Art 1066–1200*. London.

Lawrie, A C 1910 *Annals of the Reigns of Malcolm and William AD 1153–1214*. Glasgow.

Livingstone, S 1997 *Scottish Festivals*. Edinburgh.

LMMC London Museum Medieval Catalogue 1940, Ward-Perkins, J B.

Lockwood, B L 1984 *The Oxford Book of British Bird Names*. Oxford.

Longnan, J and Cazelle, R 1969 *Les Très Riches Heures du Duc de Berry*. London.

Love, J A 1983 *The Return of the Sea Eagle*. Cambridge.

Lynch, M, Spearman, M and Stell, G (eds) 1988 *The Scottish Medieval Town*. Edinburgh.

McCormick, F nd The mammal bones from Rattray Castle. Unpublished Archive Report.

McFadyean, J 1884 *The Comparative Anatomy of the Domesticated Animals* Part 1. *Osteology and arthrology*. London.

MacGregor, A G 1976 'Finds from a Roman sewer system, and an adjacent building in Church Street', in Addyman, P V (ed) *The Archaeology of York* 17, 1–30. London.

MacGregor, A G 1978 'Industry and commerce in Anglo-Scandinavian York', in Hall, R A (ed) *Viking Age York and the North* 37–57. London (=CBA Research Report 27).

MacGregor, A G 1979 'Taking the lid off the past', *Interim* 6 No 3 (1979), 6–8.

MacGregor, A G 1982 *Anglo-Saxon finds from Lloyds Bank, Pavement and other sites*. London (*The Archaeology of York. The Small Finds* 17/3).

MacGregor, A G 1985 *Bone, Antler, Ivory and Horn*. London.

MacGregor, A G 1995 'Roman and early medieval bone and antler objects', in Phillips, D and Heywood, B *Excavations at York Minster*1 Part2, *The Finds*, 414–27. London.

MacGregor, A G, Mainman, A J and Rogers, N S H 1999 *Craft, Industry and Everyday Life. Bone, Antler, Ivory and Horn from Anglo-Scandinavian and Medieval York. The Archaeology of York* 17/12: *The Small Finds*. York.

Mackinnon, J 1920 *The Social and Historical History of Scotland*. London and Glasgow.

Mabey, R 1979 *Plants with a Purpose*. Glasgow.

Major, *History* 1892 J Major, *A History of Greater Britain*, Constable, A (ed). Edinburgh (Scottish History Society).

Margeson, S 1982 'Worked Bone' in Coad, J G, and Streeten, A D F 'Excavations at Castle Acre Castle, Norfolk, 1972–7: Country House and Castle of the Norman Earls of Surrey', *Archaeol J* 139 (1982), 138–301.

Martin, A 1995 *Fishing and Whaling*. Edinburgh.

Matthews, J R 1955 *Origin and Distribution of the British Flora*. London.

Mathewson, A 1879 'Notes on stone cists and an ancient kitchen midden near Dundee', *Proc Soc Antiq Scot*, 13 (1878–9), 303–7.

Melrose Liber 1837. *Liber Sancti Marie de Melros: munimenta vetusitoria Monasterii Cisterciensis de Melros*, ed Innes, C. Edinburgh (Bannatyne Club).

Mennerich, G 1968 *Römerzeitliche Tierknochen aus drei Fundorten des Niederrheingebiets*. Universitat München Inaugural-Dissertation.

Millar, R H 1961 *Scottish Oyster Investigations 1946–1958*. Department of Agriculture and Fisheries for Scotland, Marine Research No 3. Edinburgh.

Moffat, B and Penny, M 2001 'Residues from a ceramic vessel and stone mortar' in Cameron, A and Stones, J A (eds) *Aberdeen: an In-depth View of the City's Past*, 297–9. Edinburgh (=Soc Antiq Scot Monogr Ser, 19).

Mowat, S no date *The Port of Leith*. Edinburgh.

Muir, R 1975 'The development of Sheriffdoms' in P McNeill and R Nicholson (eds) *A Historical Atlas of Scotland*. University of St Andrews.

Murdoch, R and Lewis, J 1999 'Excavations at the St Monans saltpans 1990–96' in Lewis, J Martin, C, Martin, P and Murdoch, R *The Salt and Coal Industries at St Monans, Fife, in the 18th and 19th centuries*, 5–27. Glenrothes (=Tayside Fife Archaeol Committee Monogr 2).

Munro, R 1879 'Notice of the excavation of a crannog at Lochlee, Tarbolton, Ayrshire', *Proc Soc Antiq Scot*, 13 (1878–79), 175–252.

Murray, J C 1982 *Excavations in the Medieval Burgh of Aberdeen 1973–81*. Edinburgh (=Soc Antiq Scot Monogr Ser, 2).

NMI 1973 *Viking and Medieval Dublin: National Museum excavations 1962–1973*. Dublin (National Museum of Ireland).

Nicolas, N H 1826 'A narrative of the progress of King Edward the First in his invasion of Scotland in the year 1296', *Archaeologia* 21, 478–98.

Noddle, B A 1973 'Determination of the body weight of cattle from bone measurement' in Matolcsi, J (ed) *Domestikationforshung und Geschichte der Haustiere* 377–89. Budapest.

Noddle, B A 1974 'Ages of epiphyseal closure in feral and domestic goats', *J Arch Sci* (1974), 1, 195–204.

Noddle, B A 1975a 'A comparison of the animal bones from eight mediaeval sites in Southern Britain' in Clason, A T (ed) *Archaeozoological Studies*, 248–259. Amsterdam.

Noddle, B A 1975b 'The animal bones' in Platt, C and Coleman-Smith, R *Excavations in mediaeval Southampton* 1, 332–40. Leicester.

Noddle, B A 1976 'Report on the animal bone' in Elvey, G R 'Saxon and medieval Walton, Aylesbury: excavations 1973–74', *Records of Buckinghamshire*, 20, Part 2, 269–86. Aylesbury.

Noddle, B A 1977 'Mammal bone' in Clarke, H and Carter, A *Excavations in King's Lynn 1963–70*. Leeds (=Soc Med Arch Monogr Ser, 7).

Noddle, B A 1984 'Exact chronology of epiphyseal closure in domestic mammals of the past: an impossible proposition', *Circaea* 2 (1), 21–27.

NSA 1845 *The New Statistical Account of Scotland 1845, Vol 10. Perth*. Edinburgh and London.

O'Connor, T P 1989 *Bones from Anglo-Scandinavian levels at 16–22 Coppergate. The Archaeology of York* 15:3. London.

Ødymn, S 1965 'Germination of ancient seeds. Floristic observations and experiments with archaeologically dated soil samples', *Dansk Bot Arc* 24 (2), 1–68.

OSA 1977 *The statistical account of Scotland, 1791-1799. Vol. 12, North and West Perthshire; edited by Sir John Sinclair*, (Gen Eds) Withrington, D J and Grant, I R. Wakefield.

Ottaway, P and Rogers, N 2002 *Craft, Industry and Everyday Life: Finds from Medieval York* York (=*The Archaeology of York. The Small Finds* 17/15).

Payne, S 1973 'Kill-off patterns in sheep and goats', *J Anatolian Studies* 23, 281–303.

Penney, S H 1976 'Axes, arrowheads and other antiquities in Irish folklore', *Ulster Folklife*, 22, 70–75.

Penny, G 1836 *Traditions of Perth*. Perth.

Percy, T (ed) 1905 *Northumberland Household Book*. London.

Perry, D 2005 *Dundee Rediscovered. The Archaeology of Dundee Reconsidered*. Perth (=Tayside Fife Archaeol Committee Monogr 4).

Perry, D R and Coleman, R J forthcoming 'St John's Square, Perth'. SUAT/Historic Scotland.

Perthshire Bird Report 1976–8 1979. Perth.

Platt, C and Coleman-Smith, R 1975 *Excavations in Mediaeval Southampton 1953–69, 2. The Finds*. Leicester.

Pope, S T 1974 *Bows and Arrows*. London.

Proudfoot, V B 1961 'The economy of the Irish Rath', *Med Arch* 5, 94–122.

Prummel, W 1982 'The archaeozoological study of urban sites in the Netherlands' in Hall, A R and Kenward, H K (eds) *Environmental Archaeology in the Urban Context*. London (=CBA Research Report 43).

Prummel, W 1983 *Early Medieval Dorestad, an Archaeozoological Study. Excavations at Dorestad 2*. Nederlands Oudhouden 11, Kromme Rijn Projekt 2.

Pullar, P 1972 *Consuming Passions*. London.

Raven, J and Walters, M 1956 *Mountain Flowers*. London.

Remnant, G L 1969 *A Catalogue of Misericords in Great Britain*. Oxford.

Reynolds, P J 1987 *Ancient Farming*. Aylesbury.

RMS Registrum Magni Sigilli Regum Scotorum. The Register of the Great Seal of Scotland. 11 vols, 1306–1668, Thomson J M et al. (eds) Edinburgh (1984 reprint).

Roberts, J 2005 'The human remains' in Fyles, C, Roberts, J and Hall, D 'Watching brief on environmental improvements around St John's Kirk, Perth', *Tayside Fife Archaeol J* 11, 27–41.

Roberts, J 2007 'The human remains' in Cox, A et al 'Excavations at the Horse Cross, Perth', *Tayside Fife Archaeol J* 13, 179–86.

Robertson, J 1799 *General View of the Agriculture in the County of Perth: with Observations on the Means of its Improvement*. Perth.

Robertson, J 1843 *Collections for a History of the Shires of Aberdeen and Banff*. Aberdeen (=Spalding Club).

Robinson, D nd 'The botanical remains from King Edward Street and Mill Street', SUAT Archive Report.

Robinson, D 1987a 'Botanical remains' in Holdsworth, P (ed) *Excavations in the Medieval Burgh of Perth 1979–1981*, 199–209. Edinburgh (=Soc Antiq Scot Monogr Ser, 5).

Robinson, D 1987b 'Spice and famine food? The botanical analysis of two post-Reformation pits from Elgin, Scotland', *Circaea* 5 (1), 21–7.

Robinson D 1995 'The botanical remains: Mill Street and King Edward Street' in Bowler, Cox, A and Smith, C (eds) 'Four excavations in Perth 1979–84', *Proc Soc Antiq Scot*, 125, 990–93.

Robinson, D and Boyd, W 1997 'Botanical report' in Rains, M J (ed) *Excavations in St Andrews, 1980–89. A Decade of Archaeology*, 137–40. Glenrothes (=Tayside Fife Archaeol Committee Monogr 1).

RRS Regesta Regum Scottorum, Barrow, G W S et al (eds). Edinburgh, 8 vols, 1960–.

Russell, J C 1948 *British Medieval Population*. Albuquerque.

Ryder, M L 1961 'The animal remains from four medieval sites in Yorkshire', *Agricultural History Review* 9, 105.

Ryder, M L forthcoming 'The wool and hair' in *The leather and textiles. Perth High Street Archaeological Excavation 1975–77. Fascicule 2*.

Samuel, A M 1918 *The Herring; its Effect on the History of Britain*. London.

Schmidt, P 1969 'Zum heidnischen und frühchristlichen Bestattungsbrauch auf den frühmittelalterlichen Gräberfeld von Dunum, Ostfriesland', *Frühmittelalterliche Studien* 3, 257–76.

Schofield, J and Vince, A 1994 *Medieval Towns*. Leicester.

Serjeantson, D 1989 'Animal remains and the tannery trade' in Serjeantson, D and Waldron, T (eds) *Diet and Crafts in Towns*, 129–46. Oxford (=B A R Brit Ser, 199).

Shaw, J 1979 'Sumptuary legislation in Scotland', *Juridical Review*, New Ser XXIV, 81–115.

Shaw, J 1994 'Manuring and fertilising the Lowlands 1650–1850' in Foster, S and Smout, T C *The History of Soils and Field Systems*, 111–18. Aberdeen.

Shepherd, H D 1979 'Dog bowies: the use of dogskins for fishing floats', *Scottish Studies* 23, 83–6.

Silver, I A 1969 'The ageing of domestic animals', in Brothwell, D and Higgs E S (eds) *Science in Archaeology*, 2nd edition, 283–302. London.

Simon, A L 1983 *A Concise Encyclopedia of Gastronomy*. London.

Sissons, S 1964 *The Anatomy of the Domestic Animals*. London.

Skene, J 1609 *Regiam Maiestatem Scotiae*. London.

Smith, A J E 1978 *The Moss Flora of Britain and Ireland*. Cambridge.

Smith, B D 1975 'Toward a more accurate estimation of the meat yield of animal species at archaeological sites' in Clason, A T (ed) *Archaeozoological Studies*, 99–106. Amsterdam.

Smith, C 1989 'The animal remains' in J A Stones (ed) *Three Scottish Carmelite Friaries*, mf 13: F2–13. Edinburgh (=Soc Antiq Scot Monogr Ser, 6).

Smith, C 1995a 'The animal bone' in Bowler, D, Cox, A and Smith, C 1995 (eds) 'Four excavations in Perth 1979–1984' *Proc Soc Antiq Scot*, 125, 986–9.

Smith, C 1995b 'The animal bone' in Hall, D W 'Archaeological excavations at St Nicholas Farm, St Andrews, 1986–87', *Tayside Fife Archaeol, J* 1, 67–73.

Smith, C 1996a 'Animal bone' in Cox, A (ed) 'Backland activities in medieval Perth: excavations at Meal Vennel and Scott Street', *Proc Soc Antiq Scot*, 126, 792–5 and 812–3.

Smith, C 1996b 'Animal bone' in Coleman, R J 'Burgage plots of medieval Perth: the evidence from excavations at Canal Street', *Proc Soc Antiq Scot*, 126, 725–6.

Smith, C 1997 'Animal bone' in Moloney, C and Coleman, R 'Excavations at 80–86 High Street, Perth', *Proc Soc Antiq Scot*, 127, 767–73.

Smith, C 1998 'Dogs, cats and horses in the Scottish medieval town', *Proc Soc Antiq Scot*, 128, 859–85.

Smith, C 2000a 'A Grumphie in the Sty: an archaeological view of pigs in Scotland', *Proc Soc Antiq Scot*, 130, 705–724.

Smith, C 2000b 'The animal bone' in Perry, D R *Castle Park, Dunbar. Two Thousand Years on a Fortified Headland*, 194-297. Edinburgh (=Soc of Antiq Scot Monogr Ser, 16).

Smith, C 2006 'Animals' in Storrier, S (ed) *Scottish Life and Society. A Compendium of Scottish Ethnology, Vol 6. Scotland's Domestic Life*, 581–96. Edinburgh.

Smith, C unpublished 'The animal bone from six sites in Ayr', SUAT/Historic Scotland Archive Report.

Smith, C forthcoming 'The 'Poor Man's Mart': history and archaeology of goats in Scotland'.

Smith, C and Hodgson, G W I 1984 'The animal bone' in Murray, H 'Excavations at 45–47 Gallowgate, Aberdeen', *Proc Soc Antiq Scot*, 114, mf4:A11.

Smith, C and Hodgson, G W I 1987 'Animal bone' in Holdsworth, P (ed) *Excavations in the medieval burgh of Perth 1979–1981*, 196–9. Edinburgh (=Soc Antiq Scot Monogr Ser, 5).

Smith, C, Dixon, D and Cox, A 2007 'Stone artefacts' in Cox, A 'Excavations at the Horse Cross, Perth', *Tayside Fife Archaeol J*, 13, 167–9.

Smith, C and McCormick, F 2001 'The mammal bone' in Cameron, A S and Stones, J A (eds) *Aberdeen: an in-depth view of the city's past*, 271–5. Edinburgh (=Soc Antiq Scot Monogr Ser, 19).

Smith, T no date *The Master Book of Poultry and Game*. London.

Smout, T C 1963 *Scottish Trade on the Eve of Union 1660–1707*. Edinburgh and London.

Smout, T C 1965 'Goatkeeping in the old Highland economy – 4' *Scottish Studies* 9, 186–9.

Smout, T C 1993 'Woodland history before 1850' in Smout, T C (ed) *Scotland since Prehistory. Natural Change and Human Impact*, 40–49. Aberdeen.

Spearman, R M 1988 'Workshops, Materials and Debris – Evidence of Early Industries' in Lynch et al 1988, 134–47.

Stavert, M L 1993 *The Perth Guildry Book 1452–1601*. Edinburgh (= Scottish Record Society New Series 19).

Stevenson, R B K 1967 'A Roman period cache of charms in Aberdeenshire', *Antiquity*, 41, 143–45.

Stevenson, S J and Torrie, P D 1988 *Historic Dundee. The Archaeological Implications of Development*. Scottish Burgh Survey. Edinburgh.

Stones, J A 1989 *Three Scottish Carmelite Friaries. Excavations at Aberdeen, Linlithgow and Perth 1980–86*. Edinburgh (=Soc Antiq Scot Monogr Ser, 6).

Stuart, M (ed) 1987 *The Encyclopedia of Herbs and Herbalism*. London.

Tait, E S R 1947 *Shetland Folk Book* 1, Lerwick.

Tallantire, P A 1979 'Late Viking and early medieval plant material from Trondheim–a problem in interpretation', *Archaeo-Physika* 8, 295–301.

Taylor, K 1971 '*Rubus chamaemorus* L. Biological flora of the British Isles', *J Ecol* 59, 293–306.

Taylor, L B 1972 *Aberdeen Shore Work Accounts 1596–1670*. Aberdeen.

Teichert, M 1975 'Osteometrische Untersuchungen zur Berechnung der Widerristhohe bei Schafen' in Clason, A T (ed) *Archaeozoological Studies*, 51–69. Amsterdam.

Thom, V M 1986 *Birds in Scotland*. London.

Thomas, K 1983 *Man and the Natural World. Changing Attitudes in England 1500–1800*. London.

Thoms, L M 1982 'Trial excavation at St Ann's Lane, Perth', *Proc Soc Antiq Scot* 112, 437–54.

Thomson, K and Grime, J P 1979 'Seasonal variations in the seed banks of herbaceous species in ten contrasting habitats', *J Ecol* 67, 893–921.

Trewin, N 1982 'Stone objects' in Murray, J C (ed) *Excavations in the Medieval Burgh of Aberdeen, 1973–81*, 184–5. Edinburgh (=Soc Antiq Scot Monogr Ser, 2).

Twinch, C 1985 *Poultry. A Guide to Management*. Marlborough.

Tyler, P F 1882 *History of Scotland*. Edinburgh.

Uerpmann, H P 1973 'Animal bone finds and economic archaeology: a critical study of osteo-archaeological method', *World Archaeology* 4, (3), 307–22.

Walker, F 1961 *Tayside Geology*. Dundee.

Walton Rogers, P 1997 *Textile Production at 16–22 Coppergate*. York (=*The Archaeology of York. The Small Finds* 17/11).

Walton Rogers, P 2000 'Stone spindle whorls' in Mainman A J and Rogers, N S H *Craft, Industry and Everyday Life: Finds from Anglo-Scandinavian York*, 2530–4. York (=*The Archaeology of York. The Small Finds* 17/14).

Warden, A J 1872 *The Burgh Laws of Dundee*. London.

Waterman, D M 1959 'Late Saxon, Viking and early medieval finds from York', *Archaeologia*, 97 (1959), 59–105.

Watson, E V 1968 *British Mosses and Liverworts*, 2nd edition. Cambridge.

Webster, B 1975 *Scotland from the 11th century to 1603*. Worcester.

West, B 1982 'Spur development: recognizing caponized fowl in archaeological material' in Wilson, B, Grigson, C and Payne, S (eds) *Ageing and Sexing Animal Bones from Archaeological Sites*. 255–61. London (=B A R Brit Ser, 109).

Whatley, C A 1984 *The Salt Industry and its Trade in Fife and Tayside c1570–1850*. Dundee. (=Abertay Historical Society Publication 22).

Wheeler, A C 1969 *The Fishes of the British Isles and North-west Europe*. London.

Wheeler, A C 1978 'Problems of identification and interpretation of archaeological fish remains' in Brothwell, D R, Thomas, K D and Clutton-Brock, J (eds) *Research Problems in Zooarchaeology*, 69–75. London (=Institute of Archaeology Occasional Paper No. 3).

Wheeler, A C and Jones, A K G 1976 'The fish remains' in Rogerson, A (ed) *Excavations on Fuller's Hull, Great Yarmouth*, 208–224. Gressenhall (=East Anglian Archaeology Report No. 2).

White, F B W 1893 'Local names and uses of Perthshire plants', *Proceedings of the Perthshire Society of Natural Sciences* 1, (1886–93), lxix–lxxxi.

White, F B W 1898 *The Flora of Perthshire*. Edinburgh.

Whyte, I 1979 *Agriculture and Society in Seventeenth-century Scotland*. Edinburgh.

Wiberg, C 1977 'Horn og bematerialet fra 'Mindets tomt'', in Hoeg, H I et al *De Arkaeologiske Utgravninger i Gamlebyen Oslo 1. Feltet 'Mindets tomt'*. Oslo.

Wickham-Jones, C R and Collins, G H 1978 'The sources of flint and chert in northern Britain', *Proc Soc Antiq Scot*, 109, (1977–78), 7–21.

Wilkinson, M R 1979 'The fish remains' in Maltby, M *Faunal Studies on Urban sites. The Animal Bones from Exeter 1971–1975*, 74–81. Sheffield (=Exeter Archaeological Reports Vol. 2).

Williamson, P 1982 *An introduction to medieval ivory carvings*. London.

Wilson, D 1863 *The Prehistoric Annals of Scotland*. London (2nd edition, 2 vols).

Wilson, D M and Hurst, D G 'Medieval Britain in 1965', *Med Arch*, 10 (1966), 168–219.

Wyness, F 1966 *City by the Grey North Sea: Aberdeen*. Aberdeen.

Yealland, S and Higgs E S 1966 'The economy' in Hilton, R H and Rahtz, P 'Upton, Gloucestershire, 1959–1964', *Trans Bristol and Gloucestershire Arch Soc* 85, 139–43.

Yonge, C M 1960 *Oysters*. London.

Appendix 1 *Glossary*

A Accession number given to artefacts.

Area The excavation was divided into ten areas, each of which was administered by a supervisor. Areas 1-6 were excavated during the 1975-6 Season; 7-10 during the following season. Area 1 lay on the High Street frontage, Areas 5 and 6 on the Mill Street frontage

Building (with letter) Standing structures, ie those standing and surveyed in 1975 (see CD insert in Fascicule 1); (with number) excavated timber and stone buildings (see Dr Murray's report in Fascicule 1)

byre Scottish term for a cow shed

c circa; about/approximately

C Context number – a reference number assigned to every feature and layer during the excavation

close Scottish term for a lane/path between buildings

Context/Feature Index Index of the Context Numbers (arranged numerically) and including the following fields of information: 1/ Context/Feature Number; 2/ Rig(s); 3/ Area(s); 4/ Context Group Designation; 5/ Context Group Sequence Number; 6/ Feature Designation and Reference Number; 7/ Phase(s); 8/ Matrix Level(s); 9/ Figure Numbers; 10/ Page Numbers of description/discussion. Deposited in site archive

Context Group (CG) One or more contexts grouped together on the basis of interpretation, eg Buildings, Paths etc, and/or their relationship to other context groups (indicated by the prefix CG)

Context Group Designation The Context Groups were divided on the basis of interpretation into twenty-one categories

Context Number Reference number (indicated by the prefix C) assigned to every feature and layer during the excavation; see Context Index in archive for full list

D
Drain; a Feature Category

Drains
Feature Category (indicated by the prefix D)

ft
feet (Imperial measurement)

Gully (Gullies) Feature Category (indicated by the prefix T)

H Hearth; a Feature Category

HBF Highland Boundary Fault

Hearth Feature Category

Lade The Town Ditch/Moat; Context Group Designation within North Sector

layers Those Context Numbers which were not designated as Features

MC Miscellaneous Context Group; Context Group Designation within the South Sector

MF Miscellaneous Feature; a Feature Category

Midden Context Group Designation (indicated by the prefix M)

Miscellaneous Context Group(s) Context Group Designation (indicated by the prefix MC)

Miscellaneous Features Feature Category (indicated by the prefix MF)

Miscellaneous Wood Feature Category (indicated by the prefix MW)

mm millimetre(s)

MW Miscellaneous Wood

Natural Context Group Designation (Undisturbed fluvio-glacial sand)

North Sector That part of the site containing Areas 5 and 6 and Trenches A and B

occ Occupation layer(s)

OPH Old Parliament House

ORS Old Red Sandstone

Oven Context Group Designation within Area 5

PA Post Alignment(s)

Path(s) Context Group Designation (indicated by the prefix P)

Period Chronological division

Period I pre-1150

Period II 1150–c1200

Period III c1200–c1250

Period IV c1250–c1300

Period V c1300–1350>

Period VI Post-medieval and/or modern

Phase *i* Chronological division; sub-division of a Period reflecting a variation in the site's structure/path pattern *ii* Phases of buildings

PH Post Hole(s)

PHSAE Perth High Street Archaeological Excavation

PHSAEC Perth High Street Archaeological Excavation Committee

Pit(s) Feature Category

Post Alignment(s) Feature Category (indicated by the prefix PA)

Post Hole(s) Feature Category (indicated by the prefix PH). This category includes post pits and robbed postholes

Post Pits Pits dug to insert a post/stake; see PW below

Post(s) Feature Category (indicated by the prefix PP)

PP Post(s)/stake(s); Feature Category

PW Post Pits with timber in situ; Feature Category

RCAHMS Royal Commission on the Ancient and Historical Monuments of Scotland

rig(s) Property (division)

SA Stake Alignment(s)

SDD Scottish Development Department (of Scottish Office)

sondage Machine-cut pit

South Sector That part of the site containing Areas 1–4 and 7–10

Stake Alignment Feature Category (indicated by the prefix SA)

SUAT Scottish Urban Archaeological Trust

T Trench/Gully; Feature Category

TS Tree Stump; Feature Category within the South Sector

Trench(es) Feature Category (indicated by the prefix T)

US Unstratified

vennel(s) Scottish term for a Lane/Path.

Wall Stone Wall(s); Feature Category.

Wattle Wall(s) Feature Category (indicated by the prefix WW) within the South Sector

WW Wattle Wall(s)

Wynd Scottish term for a Lane/Path

yd yard (Imperial measurement)

Acknowledgements

Environmental reports

Because of the length of time which passed between excavation and publication, many people were involved in this project, some now sadly deceased. Dr George Wharton Ian Hodgson (Illus 65) died in 1986, Nicholas Quentin Bogdan in 2002, David Heppel in 2004 and James B Kenworthy in 2011. Therefore, on behalf of all the authors, living and dead, grateful thanks are extended to the following individuals and institutions from whose expert knowledge the contributors to this volume benefitted. Thanks are particularly extended to Olwyn Owen of Historic Scotland, for her patient yet determined approach to publishing this material, to David Perry for his retentive memory of the site over more than thirty years and to the members of Tayside and Fife Archaeological Committee (TAFAC) who have supported this project from its earliest days.

Mammal bone

Especial thanks are due to Rose Smith, Administrator of the Perth High Street Archaeological Excavation for administering the research, typing various drafts of the manuscript and unfailing support and friendship over the decades.

Dr David Breeze and Christopher Tabraham of the (then) Ancient Monuments Branch of the Scottish Development Department (now Historic Scotland).

Barbara Wishart, Duncan of Jordanstone College of Art, for her relentless pursuit of documentary evidence and her considerable efforts in their translation.

Dr Juliet Clutton-Brock of the British Museum (Natural History) for her help in identifying difficult specimens.

Dr M L Ryder and John Woolliams (Animal Breeding Research Unit, Rosslyn, Midlothian), the late Barbara Noddle (University of Cardiff), Dr A L Long (Hancock Museum, Newcastle), David Geddes (Paisley College of Technology), Dr P L Armitage (British Museum (Natural History)), Tom Oliver (Town Planning Department, University of Dundee), Dr Sebastian Payne and Dr R A Harcourt for discussing zoological details of this work and its possible agricultural implications.

Colin Buy of the Computing Department, University of Dundee.

Illus 65 *George Wharton Ian Hodgson, osteologist, 1970s (on left of photograph) contemplates the High Street assemblage.*

Mr Buchanan of Messrs Millar and McKay, Perth for access to the records of the Fleshers Guild.

Professor G W S Barrow, St Andrews University for advice on interpreting some of the original literary sources.

Marion Stavert for access to her transcriptions of the Perth Guildry Book.

J Jackman, Trent Bridge Leather Works, Nottingham for information on the preparation of leather; the Governors of the former Duncan of Jordanstone College of Art, Dundee for the provision of accommodation for the project over a ten year period.

Gertie Whittet, Mary Bell and Dennis Chapman of Duncan of Jordanstone College of Art for their administrative, technical and moral support.

The library staff at Dundee University, Duncan of Jordanstone College of Art, and the Sandeman and A K Bell Libraries, Perth.

Staff of the Natural History Department, National Museums Scotland, particularly Dr Jerry Herman and Dr Andrew Kitchener.

The staff and volunteers of the original excavation who washed and marked each one of the many bone fragments, in particular, the late Mrs Catherine Coventry.

Bird bone

Staff of the Natural History Departments at the National Museums Scotland, Edinburgh, Perth Art Gallery and Museum and Dundee Museums (Barrack Street Collections Unit) for access to the skeletal collections, particularly Bob McGowan of NMS.

RSPB, Vane Farm; Brian Cowling, SSPCA; Liz Pawley, SNH; present and former colleagues at SUAT Ltd and Alder Archaeology (particularly Fraser Stewart, Calum McWilliam, James McCusker, Jen Anderson, Ray Cachart, David Bowler, Derek Hall, David Perry, Johanna Schofield, Carol Milne, Frank Moran); and Charles Rooney, Chic Nicoll, Leah Cece, Robert Smith, Jennifer Smith, the family cats and all those others who have helped keep a watchful eye open for road kills and other casualties suitable for conversion into comparative material.

Barbara West, Dept of Zoology, British Museum (Natural History) and Professor Don Brothwell, Dept of Archaeology, University of York for information regarding chicken sizes.

Fish bone

John Lock, formerly of the Environmental Archaeology Unit, University of York, for sieving the soil samples and extracting the fish remains; expending considerable time and effort ordering the hand-excavated bones, which were packed by accession number, into contexts; also cataloguing the vertebral centra from the 1977 excavation and preparing computer data files; and John Carrott of the EAU for help in locating original records.

Nicholas Q Bogdan, George W I Hodgson, Allan Hall, Harry Kenward and Terry O'Connor all of whom made helpful comments on the first draft of this report.

Plant remains

Thanks are due to Prof James H Dickson of the Department of Botany, University of Glasgow and to John Lock, York for sieving and extracting the plant remains from the raw soil samples.

Mollusc report

Claire Pannell, Assistant Curator Mollusca, National Museums Scotland for her comments on the text.

William Finlayson and Kathleen McSweeney for sorting and making prelimiminary lists of the molluscan material.

Brian Spencer, Department of Medieval Antiquities, Museum of London for his comments on scallop pilgrim badges.

David Perry for historical advice regarding the Tain mussel fishery.

Feather report

Olwyn Owen of Historic Scotland for arranging the feather analysis.

Dr Andrew Kitchener of the Natural History Section of the National Museum of Scotland, Edinburgh, for his input and reference material for this study.

The worked bone

Catherine Smith gratefully acknowledges the help provided by Dr Jerry Herman of National Museums Scotland in facilitating access to the animal bone assemblage, on various occasions throughout the years, and allowing SUAT Ltd to borrow several fragments of worked bone which had not previously been recorded. Thanks also to museum volunteers who reboxed the animal bone assemblage.

Mark Hall would like to thank Duncan Brown, Mark Simmons, Jeremy Duncan, Doreen Hall, Malcolm Jones, Dave Munro (illustration of ivory knife handle), Paul Adair (photography) and Historic Scotland for their sponsorship of the original paper on the ivory knife handle.

The stone, flint and glass

Thanks are due to Mark Hall and Mark Simmons of
Perth Museum and Art Gallery, for arranging access
to the collections and corroboration of geological
identifications. Torben Ballin kindly commented on
the flint. Thanks also to Iain Fraser of RCAHMS
for archive advice.

Photography and illustration

For those photographs supplied by Perth Museum and
Art Gallery, thanks are due to Mark Hall and Paul
Adair (Illus 31, 33, 34, 42, 44, 64). (Illus 31 and 34 are
attributable to the studio of Magnus Jackson, Perth).
Other photographs were taken by staff of the Perth
High Street Archaeological Excavation team, Denis
Chapman of Duncan of Jordanstone College of Art,
Dundee, and by SUAT Ltd and Alder Archaeology, in
particular, David Bowler, Tamlin Barton, Adrian Cox,
Derek Hall, Becky Smith and Catherine Smith.

Maps, diagrams and illustrations of the worked bone
(Illus 1, 2, 19, 38, 50–54) are by Dave Munro of SUAT
Ltd. Illus 55–63 and the back cover photograph of the
stone whorls are by Tamlin Barton. Thanks are also
due to Tamlin Barton and Sapphire Sherwood for help
in scanning and editing graphics. The original version
of Illus 19 was drawn by David Harrison, draughtsman
on the Perth High Street Archaeological Excavation.
The cover painting and reconstruction of the medieval
pig (Illus 9) are by Maureen Rooney Mitchell, the
medieval midden (Illus 47) by Steve Earl and the
backland reconstruction (Illus 49) by Roger Dennis.

The Excavation and publication

For information regarding the PHSAE Committee
and the excavation itself, readers are referred to the
Acknowledgement section of Fascicule 1, where we
extend grateful thanks and appreciation to all those
who contributed to the PHSAE project from inception
to publication.

The post-excavation process was managed by Derek
Hall, formerly of SUAT Ltd, from 2004-11.

This fascicule was collated and prepared for publication
by Catherine Smith who is grateful to the Tayside and
Fife Archaeological Committee Editors, Lisbeth Thoms
and Derek Hall and to all colleagues who offered
comments and corrections on the texts.

'a good report maketh the bones fat'
(Proverbs 15:30, King James version)

Index to Perth High Street Archaeological Excavations 4

Notes

1 Bibliographical references are not generally indexed.

a

Abbot of Unreason 103
Aberdeen 8, 17
Aberdeen, 16–18 Nethergate (Phases 1–4) 18, 25, 30, 31
Aberdeen, 42 St Paul Street 16, 18, 42, 43
Aberdeen, 45–47 Gallowgate (Phases I–III) 16, 18, 42, 43
Aberdeen, 53–59 Gallowgate (Phases II–III) 16, 30, 31, 41, 42, 43
Aberdeen, Broad Street 129
Aberdeen, Carmelite Friary 92
Aberdeen, Gallowgate 45–75 18
Aberdeen, Gallowgate 85
Aberdeen, Gallowgate Middle School (Phase 2) 16, 18, 19, 30, 31, 42, 43
Aberdeen, Queen Street 16, 18, 42, 43
abnormal bones 28
Achillea millefolium L 70
acorn 70, 78
Agrostemma githago L 70,78, 90
Ajuga reptans L 73
alder 84
ale 76
alveolar recession, 30
Alyth (Perth and Kinross) 82
amethyst 128
anaerobic 68
Anas clypeata 45, 51
Anas penelope 45, 51
Anas platyrhynchos 45, 50, 63, 64, 65
Anatidae 63, 64, 65
Ancient Monuments Department (SDD) 3
Andersmass Fair 19
Ane satire of the thrie Estatis 91
angiosperm 67
Anguilla anguilla L 53, 54
annual knawel 71
annual meadow grass 71
Anser anser 45, 49, 63, 64
Anser brachyrhynchus 45, 50
Anser fabalis 50
Anseriformes 63, 64, 65
Anthemis cotula L 70
anthropomorphic ivory handle 102, 113
Antitrichia curtipendula (Hedw) Brid 74, 79
antler 19, 105
antler
    comb 100, 108, 109, 110, 112, 114
    dice 101, 102, 108, 110, 112, 114
    fragments 12
    handle 102, 108
    offcuts 101, 105, 109, 114
    tine 12
    working 89, 99, 101

apple 69, 77
Aquila chrysaetos 45
Arbroath 86
Arbroath, 77–79 High Street 75, 76
Ardea cinerea 45
Artica islandica 60, 61
ash 82, 84
Assisa de tolloneis 38, 44
Atholl 85
Auchterarder (Perth and Kinross) 82
Aucupi 85
Aulacomnium palustre (Hedw) Schwaegr 74
Autumnal hawkbit 70
Avena fatua 70, 75, 76
Avena sativa L 69, 75, 83
Avena strigosa 75, 76
Aylesbury (Buckinghamshire) 17, 37
Ayr, Harbour Street 32

b

bacon 8
Balcormac quarry (Perth and Kinross) 128
bale pin 103
Balmerino (Fife) 87
Baltic 37
bannocks 90
bantam 45, 52
barbed-and-tanged flint arrowhead 139, 143
barley 68, 69, 75
barrels 91
Baynard's Castle (London) 17, 28
bead 98, 105, 119
beaming knives 39
bean goose 50
beans 75, 83
bear-baiting 94
Bearsden Roman fort 78
beef 17, 41, 44
bell heather 72
Bemys knyffis 39
bere 75, 76, 82, 83
Berwick upon Tweed 43
Betula pubescens Ehrh 73
Beverley (Yorkshire) 78
    Lurk Lane 138
Bidens tripartita L 73, 79
birch 73, 82, 84
bird bone 45
Birnam oak 82
Bishopric of Dunkeld 85
bittern 49
black bindweed 71

Black Death 43

black grouse 45, 46, 51, 85

blackthorn 77

blaeberry 70, 77, 78

blawin (blowing) of meat 91

blinks 73

bobbins 97, 98, 104, 113

bog heather, cross-leaved heather 72

bog myrtle 72, 78, 85

bog pondweed 73

bogbean 68, 73, 78, 86

Bogdan, Nicholas Q xii

bone fracture

    cat 33

    cattle 32

bone working 97

boned salt pork 8

Bordeaux (France) 77

botanical remains 67

bottle, glass 122, 123, 124, 125

bowies 87

Brachythecium rutabulum cf Bryum sp 74

bracken 72

bramble 70, 77, 84

Brassica 69, 75, 76, 83

Brassica campestris L 69, 76

Brassica Eu-campestri 76

Brassica oleracea 76

Breadalbane (Perth and Kinross) 85

bristle club-rush 68, 73

bristle oat 75, 76, 86

British Museum 97

broken mouth 30

Bromus mollis agg 70

brooch moulds 84

Broughty Ferry (Dundee) 87

Bryophyte 67

Buccinum undatum 60, 61

buckie/whelk 60, 61, 62, 87

bugle 73

Building B18 78, 97, 103

Building B4 88, 92

Building B53 79

Bullace 69, 77, 84

bulls 22

bur-marigold 73, 79

burnisher 105

butchery 37, 41, 89

Buteo buteo 45

buzzard 6, 45, 46, 51, 52, 81, 85

byre 88, 92

c

cabbage 76

Cahercommaun (Ireland) 103

Caill 76

Callander (Stirling) 83

Calluna vulgaris 72, 77

Caltha palustris L 73

campion 71

candles 35

capercaillie 85

capon 45, 46, 47

Capreolus capreolus 7

Capsella bursa-pastoris (L) Medic 70

carcass weight 41

Carex spp distigmatae 73

Carex spp tristigmatae 73

carrion crow/rook 45, 46

Carse of Gowrie (Perth and Kinross) 61, 76, 82, 83

casket mount 97, 98, 99, 107

Castle Acre Castle (Norfolk) 138

castrates 17

cats 6, 7, 14, 19, 21, 22, 30, 33, 41, 81, 89, 93

cat's ear 70

cattle 6, 7, 8, 9, 17, 22, 27, 28, 33, 35, 43

celery-leaved crowfoot 74

Centauera cyanus 78

Cerastium fontanum Baumg 70

Cerastoderma cf edule 60, 61

Ceratodon purpureus (Hedw) 74

cereals 75

Cervus elaphus 7

cess pits 68, 81

chalk 128

chalk flint ballast 139,140

charlock 71

cheese 85

cheese-making 83

Chenopodium album L 70

chickweed 68, 71

Chronicle of Perth 87

Chrysanthemum segetum L 70, 78

Ciconia ciconia 51

Cirsium arvense (L) Scop 70

Cirsium vulgare (Savi) Ten 70

Cistercian monks 22

Claviceps purpurea 90

cloudberry 70, 77

clover 68

Clupea harengus L 53, 54

coal mining 84

Cock and the Fox, The 94

Cockenzie (East Lothian) 62

cock-fighting 47, 93

cockle 60, 61, 62

cock-throwing 93

cod 53, 54, 56, 62, 81, 87

codling 87

Colonsay (Argyll and Bute) 79

comb 98, 99, 100, 108, 109, 110, 112, 114

    double-sided 101, 108

    single-sided 101, 108

common spike-rush 73

Compositae 72

corn 75

corn cockle 70, 78, 90

corn marigold 70, 78

corn spurrey 68, 71

cornflower 68, 78

Corsie hill quarry (Perth and Kinross) 129

Corvidae 63, 64

Corvus corax 45, 51

Corvus corone/fragilegus 45

Corylus avellana L 69, 78

cotton grass 72

Coupar Angus (Perth and Kinross) 82

Coupar Angus, Cistercian Abbey 46, 49, 51, 52, 83, 84

cows 22

Craigie (Perth and Kinross) 83

crane 45, 46, 49, 51, 52, 86

creeping buttercup 71

creeping thistle 70

Cribra orbitalia 92

cross-bows 35

Crossraguel Abbey (Ayrshire) 84

crows 6, 63, 65

crystalline limestone 128

Culross Abbey (Fife) 84

curled dock 71

Customs Accounts 38

Custume portuum 38

Cygnus cygnus 45, 64, 65

Cygnus olor 51

d

Daphnia 68

David I (King) 34, 38, 82

David II (King) 34, 38, 82

deadly nightshade 78

decorative terminal 101

deer 84

Den Bosch, Netherlands 35

Denmark 78

dice 101, 102, 108, 110, 112, 114

Dicranum scoparium Hedw 74

die

    bone 98, 99, 113

      chalk 138

docks 68, 97

dogs 6, 7, 13, 19, 20, 21, 30, 33, 41, 43, 81, 89, 93

    or fox 14

dog rose 70

dog whelk 60, 61, 62

dog-fighting 93

domestic fowl 45, 52

Dorestad, Netherlands 35

Dornoch Firth (Highland) 61

Dublin (Ireland) 101

ducks 45, 50, 63

Dunbar, Castle Park (East Lothian) 17, 94, 129

Dundee 38, 61, 82, 87, 88

Dundee harbour 62

Dundee, 23–35 Panmure Street/72–8 Murraygate 75

Dundee, Duncan of Jordanstone College of Art 3

Dundee, St Nicholas Craig 87

Dundee, Stannergate 62

Dundee, West Ferry 87

Dunfermline Abbey 84

Dunkeld Rental 92

Durham 79, 104

e

eagle 45

earne 51

Edinburgh 17, 25

Edinburgh, High Street 8, 37

Edinburgh, Merchants of 89

Edinburgh, National Museums 3

Edinburgh, Royal Scottish Museum 45

Edinburgh, Tron Kirk 37

Edward Balliol 6

Edward I (King) 43

Edward III (King) 43

eel 53, 54, 56, 81, 85

eggshell 52, 81

eider 45, 46, 51, 70

elder 77

elderberry 84

Eleocharis palustris (L) Roem & Schult 73

elephant ivory, 116

elf shot 140

Elgin (Moray) 8, 17, 77, 78, 90

Elgin, High Street 8, 16, 18, 35, 42, 43

Emden, Ostfriesland (Germany) 100

Epilobium parviflorum Schreb 73

ergot 90

Erica cinerea L 72

Erica tetralix L 72

Eriophorum vaginatum L 72, 77

Errol (Perth and Kinross) 61, 79, 86

Euphorbia helioscopia L 70

Eurhynchium pralongum (Hedw) BrEur 74

ewes 28

Exchequer Rolls of Scotland 37, 44

Exeter Cathedral 103

f

fat hen 68, 70, 87

feather, covert 63

feathers 63

Felis silvestris 20

Ficus carica L 69, 77

field penny cress 71

figs 69, 75, 77, 90

    seeds 68

Filipendula ulmaria (L) Maxim 73

finger-ring 128

fish 41

fish bone 53

fish hooks 87

flatfish/plaice/flounder 53, 54, 56, 87

flax 69, 87, 89

Flesher Incorporation of Perth 37

flesher's market 39

Flesher's Vennel 39

flint 128, 139

floating sweet-grass 73

Forest Law 35

forget-me-not 70

forked implement 98, 105

fowler 85

fox (tod) 6, 7, 31, 45, 93
Fragaria vesca L 69, 77
free forest grant 84
freshwater pearl mussel 60, 62, 86
Freswick, Caithness 104

g
Gadus morhua L / Gadid 53
Galeopsis tetrahit agg 70
Galium palustre L 73
Galliformes 63
Galium saxatile L 72
Gallus gallus 45, 64, 65
game
    birds 41
    greater 35
    lesser 35
garron 19, 26
gastropod limestone 128
Gavia stellata 45, 51
gean, wild cherry 69, 77, 84
geese 45, 49, 63, 88, 89
gelding 26
Germany 37
Gibbula cineraria 60, 61
gipsywort 79
githagism 90
Glasgow University 3
glass
    beads 119
    mounts 119
    medieval 119
glue and neats foot oil 89
Glyceria fluitans (L) RBr 73
goat 7, 11, 26, 27, 28, 35, 43, 44, 77, 83, 84, 104
golden eagle 45, 46, 51
Goltho (Lincolnshire) 97, 129
goosander 45, 46, 51, 86
grain 34
Graminae 72
grape 77, 90
grease 35
great plantain 71
green men 103
grey heron 45, 46, 51, 86
greylag 45, 46, 49, 50, 63, 86
groundsel 71
Grus grus 45, 51
Guildry Incorporation of Perth 86
gun flints 139
gypsy wort 73

h
haddock 53, 54, 56, 87
Hadrian's Wall 25
hair 35, 37
Haliaetus albicilla 45
halibut 53, 54, 56, 87
handles 98, 99, 102, 113
hare 7, 15, 35, 41

hawthorn 103
hazel 69, 78, 84
hazelnuts 78, 84
heath bedstraw 72
heath rush 72
heather 68, 72
heckle comb 89
hedge woundwort 71
Helen de Morville 22, 25
hemp-nettle 68, 70
henbane 69, 78, 87
herring 53, 54, 87
herring gull 52
hides 17, 34
Highland Boundary Fault (HBF) 127
Hippoglossus hippoglossus L 53
Holyrood Abbey 84
hones 135
Hordeum vulgare 69, 75, 83
Hordeum vulgare tetrastrichum 76
horn cores 35, 36, 37, 44
    cattle 23, 33, 97, 105
    goat 26, 97, 105
    perforated 105
    sawn 36, 37
horn
    terminal 98, 113
    working 89
hornbeam 103
horner's workshop 101
horse 7, 12, 19, 26, 27, 29, 41, 83, 93
    hair 87
hugstairs (hucksters) 87
human bone 59, 92
husbandry 92
Hydrocotyle vulgaris L 73
Hylocomium brevirostre (Brid) BrEur 74
Hylocomium splendens 74, 79
Hyoscyamus niger 69, 78
Hypnum cupressiforme 74, 79
Hypochaeris radicata L 70

i
Ice skate 98, 105, 113
Iceland cyprina 60, 61, 62
Inchcolm Abbey (Fife) 84
Inchcoonans (Perth and Kinross) 61
infant's teether 99, 106, 113
Inverkeithing (Fife) 17, 43
Inverness (Highland) 17, 43
Inverness, Castle Street 19
Iona (Argyll and Bute) 138
Iris pseudocorus 73, 79, 86
Isla 86
Isle of Man, Close ny Chollagh 105
Isle of May (Fife) 62
Isolepsis setacea (L) RBr 73
Isothecium myosuroides Brid 74
ivory handle 98, 102–3, 111

j

Jacob sheep 25, 83
James I (King) 57
James VI (King) 61
jasper 139, 141
jointed rush 73
Juglans regia L 69, 77
Juncus articularis L 73
Juncus bufonius L 70
Juncus effusus L 73
Juncus sp 73
Juncus squarrosus L 72

k

kail 76
Kersgrange (Perth and Kinross) 83
Kettins (Angus) 82
Kincarrathie quarry (Perth and Kinross) 128
Kinfauns (Perth and Kinross) 86
King's Lynn (Norfolk) 17, 26, 37, 139
kingcup 73
Kinnoull Hill (Perth and Kinross) 129
Kirriemuir (Angus) 82
kittens 28
knight 6
knotgrass 71

l

Labiatae 72
lade 68
Lagopus mutus 45, 51
Lagore Crannog (Ireland) 103
lamb 28, 51, 92, 93
Lanark 89
Lapsana communis L 70
latrine 68
    pit 91
leather manufacture 89
Leges Quatuor Burgorum 88
legume 68, 75
Leith 62
Leontodon autumnalis L 70
leprosy 90
Lepus capensis 7
lesser clubmoss 72
lesser spearwort 74
limestone 135, 136, 137, 138
limpet 60, 61, 62, 87
Lincoln Cathedral 103
Lindores Abbey (Fife) 84
linen smoothers 119
ling 53, 54, 56, 62, 87
Linlithgow, Carmelite Friary 92
Linum usitatissimum L 69
Littorina littorea 60, 61
liverwort 75
Loch Rannoch (Perth and Kinross) 52
Lochlee Crannog (Ayrshire) 105
London, City of 8
long-headed poppy 70

lop-grass 70
Low Countries 37
Ludgershall Castle (Wiltshire) 100
luis 84
Lund, Sweden 17, 101
Luzula multiflora (Retz) Lej 72
Lycopus europaeus L 70, 73
Lynchnis flos-cuculi L 73
Lyrurus tetrix 45, 51

m

Major, John 19, 25, 26
mallard / domestic duck 45, 46, 50, 65, 86
Malus silvestris sl 69, 77
Margaritifera margaritifera 60, 61, 62
Marks and Spencer 3
marsh bedstraw 73
marsh cinquefoil 73
marsh pennywort 73
marsh ragwort 74
marsh violet 74
marten 41
May festivities 103
meadow grass 68, 71
meadowsweet 68, 73
Melanogrammus aeglefinus L 53, 54
Melrose Abbey (Scottish Borders) 22, 25, 102
Menyanthes trifoliata 73, 78, 86
Mergus merganser 45, 51
metal working 84
metapodials
    cattle and sheep 17, 22, 34, 37, 38
    deer 20
    horse 19, 105
    pig 17, 104
micaceous schist 131, 133, 134, 138
mice 91
middens 81
    Midden M9a 79
milk 83
Mnium hornum Hedw 74
mollusc 61
Molva molva 53
Montia fontana L ssp fontana 73
Montrose Basin 51, 61
Moravia 104
mortar, stone 137-8
moss rope 70, 79, 81
mosses 68, 79
moulds, metal-working 135, 136, 137
mount
    bone 97, 99-100, 106
    glass 119, 120, 121
mouse-ear chickweed 70
mudstone 128
Mull (Argyll and Bute) 86
mussel 60, 61, 62, 86, 87
mute swan 51
mutton 17, 41, 44
Myosotis arvensis (L) Hill 70

Myrica gale L 72, 78
Mytilus edulis 60, 61

n

Neckera complanta (Hedw) Hub 74
needles 103
Nethermills (Moray) 90
nettles 68, 87
Newbattle Abbey (Midlothian) 84
Newburgh (Fife) 86
Newhaven 62
nipplewort 70
Norfolk 103
Northumbrian Chillingham bulls 17
Norwich 97
Nucella lapillus 60, 61
nuts 68

o

oats 68, 69, 75, 76, 82
Odontites verna (Bell) Dum 70
offcut 98
opium poppy 69, 78
orchards 83
Oslo, Norway 101
Osmerus eperlanus L 53, 54
osteoarthritis 32, 33
osteomyelitis 33
Ostrea edulis 60, 61
otter 41
oxen 17, 22, 27
Oxford, Greyfriars 47
oyster 60, 61

p

Paisley Abbey drain 75, 77 78, 79
pale persicaria 71
pannnage 84
pansy 72
Papaver dubium L 70
Papaver somniferum 78
Paris, France 86
Parva custuma 38
Passeriformes 63, 64
Patella cf vulgata 60, 61
Pavo cristatus 45, 49
peafowl 45, 46, 49
peas 75, 83
Pecten maximus 60, 61, 62
Pedicularis palustris L 73
perforated bones 98, 106
periodontal disease 30
periwinkle/wulk 60, 61, 62
Persicaria 68
Perth Guildry Book 76, 86, 87
Perth Museum and Art Gallery 4
Perth
    103 High Street 3
    1–5 High Street 138
    80–86 High Street 3, 17, 18, 19, 20, 31, 84, 129

Baptist Church 3
Blackfriars House 3, 18
Burghmuir 88
Canal Street I (Phase III) 3, 16, 18, 42, 43, 51
Canal Street II 3, 17, 18, 75, 76
Canal Street III (Phases 1–5) 3, 18, 31, 75, 76, 89
Carmelite Friary 92
Cow Causeway 88
Dominican Friary 92
floods 87
Glover Incorporation 41
harbour 79
High Street backlands 93
Horse Cross 92, 138
Horse Cross, St Laurence's Chapel 92
King Edward Street 3, 17, 18, 19, 27, 28, 31, 32, 51, 75, 76, 79, 101, 106
Kinnoull Street 3, 18, 31
Kirk Close 3, 17, 18, 37, 75, 76, 79, 84, 90, 91, 97
Kirk Close latrine 76
Meal Vennel (Phases 1–3) 3, 16, 17, 20, 27, 30, 32, 41, 42, 43, 51
Meal Vennel (Phases 1–5) 18
Merchant Guildry of 41
Mill Street 3, 17, 18, 19, 27, 28, 32, 43, 76, 77, 78, 87
North Inch 88, 89
Parliament Close 119
PHSAE 3, 16, 18, 42, 43
Pullar's Mill Street 3
Scott Street 3, 18, 27, 32
Skinnergate 3
South Inch 88, 89
South Methven Street 3, 17, 18, 35, 75, 76, 78
South St John's Place 3
St Ann's Lane 3, 8, 16, 17, 18, 42
St John's Kirk 39, 92
St John's Square 89, 101
Whitefriars 19, 41
pets 93
pheasant 45, 85
Phragmites 86
pig 7, 8, 11, 19, 28, 29, 33, 84, 88, 92, 104
    fibula pins 103
pike 56
pilgrim's badge
pins 98, 99, 103
pin-beaters 98, 104, 113
pine 82
pine marten 84
pinkfooted goose 45, 46, 50, 86
pit 7230 79
Plagiochila asplenoides (L) Dum 75
Plagiomnium affine (Funck) Kop 74
Plantago lanceolata L 71
Plantago major L 71
playing piece 102, 113
Pleuronectid 53, 54
Pleurozium schreberi 74, 79
Plumatella 68
Pluscarden Priory (Moray) 85

Poa annua L 71
Poa spp 68
Poa trivialis L 71
polecat 41
Pollachius virens L 53
Polygonum aviculare L 71
Polygonum convolvulus L 71
Polygonum persicaria L 71
Polygonum lapathifolium L 71
Polytrichum commune 70, 74, 79
Polytrichum formosum Hedw 74
Pontefract (Yorkshire) 8
pork 17, 41
porridge 90
pot lids, stone 138
Potamogeton polygonifolius Pourr 73
Potentilla erecta (L) Rausch 72
poultry 41
Prestonpans (East Lothian) 62
prickly sow-thistle 71
Prunella vulgaris L 71
Prunus avium 69,77
Prunus domestica ssp institia 69, 77
Prunus spinosa 77
Pseudoscleropodium purum (Hedw) Fleisch 74
ptarmigan 45, 46, 51, 85
Pteridium aquilinum (L) Kuhn 72
puppies 28
Purbeck marble 128, 138
pynnouris (shoreporters) 90

q
Quercus sp 70, 78
querns 138

r
rabbit 41
rabies 89
ragged robin 73
Rannoch 85
Ranunculus flammula L 74
Ranunculus repens L 71
Ranunculus sceleratus L 74
Ranunculus sp subgenus Batrachium 74
Raphanus raphanistrum L 71
raspberry 70, 77, 84
rats 6
Rattray Castle (Aberdeenshire) 18, 25, 28
ravens 6, 45, 46, 51, 52, 63, 65, 81
red clover 71
red deer 7, 12, 19, 22, 30, 35, 84
red grouse 45, 85
red rattle, (bartsia) 70, 73
redshank 68, 71
red-throated diver 45, 46, 51, 52, 86
reeds 86
Res nullius 34, 35
Reseda luteola L 70
Rhianthus sp 71
Rhytidiadelphus loreus (Hedr) Want 74

ribwort plantain 71
Richardson, John 86
ring bone 30
ring moulds 84
River Eden 61
River Forth 61
River Tay 34, 45, 50,57, 86, 87
River Ythan 62, 86
roach 56
Robert the Bruce (King) 43
Robin Hood 103
roe deer 7, 12, 22, 35, 84
Rosa canina 70, 77
rose 77
rosehip 84
Rouen, France 68
roundworm 68, 90
Rowan 70, 77, 84, 103
Royal Forest 35
Rubus chamaemorus 70,77
Rubus fruticosus 70, 77
Rubus idaeus 70, 77
Rumex acetosa 71
Rumex acetosella agg 71
Rumex crispus L 71
Rumex sp 71
Rumex cf *conglomeratus Murr* 71
rushes 68, 86
Rutherford's map of Perth 38, 39
rye 68, 69, 75, 75, 82, 83

s
Saint James the Great 62
Saint Johns (Perth) 19
Saithe 53, 54, 56, 87
Salix sp 73
Salmo salar L 53
Salmo trutta L 54
salmon 74, 85, 86, 92
Salmonid 53, 54
salt 75, 91
Sambucus nigra 70, 77
sandstone 128
Santiago de Compestela, Spain 62, 87
Saynt Johns 43
Scaffingyr (Scaffie) 90
scallop 60, 61, 62, 87
scentless mayweed 72
Schleswig, West Germany 102
Scleruthus anuus L 71
Scone 82
    Abbey 76
Scots sow 19
Scottish pearls 86
screw shell 60, 61, 62
scudding knives 39
Secale cereale 69, 75, 83
sedges 68, 73, 86, 87
Selachii 53
Selaginella selaginoides (L) Link 72

self heal 71

Senecio cf aquaticus Hill 74

Senecio cf vulgaris L 71

sewing needles 97, 113

sharp dock 71

shearling tup 28

sheep 7, 17, 25, 27, 43, 44, 83, 92

    four horned 25

    polled 25

    polycerate 25

    two horned 25

sheep/goat 8, 10, 30, 33, 106

    culling pattern 24

sheep's sorrel 68, 71

shellfish 41

shepherd's purse 70

shoulder heights (horse, dog) 19

shoveler 45, 46, 51, 86

Silene sp (Melandrium Roehl) 71

silk textiles 6

siltstone 119

Sinapis arvensis L 71

Skinner Gate 39

Skinners Yard 39

skinning 41, 43, 89

skins 34

Skye 138

sloe 77, 84

small nettle 72

smelt (sparling) 53, 54, 56, 81, 85, 86

soap 35

soft rush 73

Somateria mollisima 45, 51

Sonchus asper (L) Hill 71

Sonchus oleraceus L 71

Sorbus aucuparia 70, 77

sorrel 71

South Cadbury Castle (Somerset) 100

Southampton (Hampshire) 17, 37, 101

Southern Uplands 82

Sowter, John of Mylnhourn 49

sow-thistle 71

spavin, in cattle 31

spear thistle 70

Spergula arvensis L 71

Sphagnum 74, 85

spindle whorls 127

Spisula solida 60, 61

split fish 54

spurs (gilt) 6, 7, 19

St Andrews

    106–110 South Street 75, 76

    134 Market Street 75, 76

    Byre Theatre, Abbey Street 75, 76, 77, 79

St Anthony's Fire 90

St Bartholomew 39, 41

St Kilda 25

Stachys cf sylvatica L 71

Stellaria media (L) Vill 71

stinging nettle 72

stinking mayweed 68, 70

Stirling 86

stockmanship 92

stone objects 127

    mortar 138

    whorls 129, 130, 132

stork 46, 51, 86

Strathearn 82

Strathmore 82

strawberry 77, 84

Streatley, Bedfordshire 101

strike-a-light 140, 143

stye 88

sugar 77

sumptuary law 129

sun spurge 70

swans, feathers 63

t

Tain (Highland) 61

tallow 35

tally stick 97, 113

tapers 35

tapeworm 90

Tayport (Fife) 61

The Dirige 86

The Wash (Norfolk) 77

Thlaspi arvense L 71

Thuidium tamariscinum 75, 79

tile, marble 138

Tiree 138

toad rush 70

tod (fox) 93

toggle (s) 98, 99, 104, 113

toilet paper 79, 90

tools 39

top shell 60, 61, 62

Torilis japonica (Houtt) DC 71

tormentil 68, 72, 85

tree stumps 88

Trichuris 68, 81, 90

Trifolium pratense L 71

Trifolium repens L 71

Tripleurospermum indorum L Schutz-Bip 72

Triticum aestivum sl 69, 75, 83

Trondheim, Norway 77

trough shell 60, 61

trout 54

tufted vetch 72

turnip 69, 76

turnip-rape 76

Turritella communis 60, 61

Tynemouth 8

u

Ulota crispa (Hedr) Brid 75

Umbelliferae 72

umbrella handle 99, 102

upright hedge-parsley 71

Urtica dioica L 72

Urtica urens L 72

v

Vaccinium myrtillus 70, 77
venison 17, 41, 85
vessel glass 119
Vicia cf cracca L 72
Vicia sp 72
Vindolanda 28
Viola palustris L 74
Viola sp *Subgenus Melanium* 72
Viola sp *subgenus Viola* 73
violet 73
Vulpes vulpes 7

w

walnuts 69, 75, 77
walrus ivory 102, 111
Walton 17
water crowfoot 74
wattle pathway 80
wedders 25, 28
weld, dyer's rocket 70
Western Isles 76
Wharram Percy 8
wheat 68, 69, 75, 76, 83
whipworm 81, 90
white clover 71
white-tailed sea eagle 45, 46, 51
whooper swan 45, 46, 51, 65, 86
whooping cough 78
whorls bone 98, 99, 104
whorls, stone 129–134
wigeon 45, 46, 51, 86
wild boar 35, 85

wild cat 35, 41
wild cherry 77
wild navew 76
wild oat 70
wild radish 71
wild strawberry 69
wild turnip 76
William I (King) 76
William the Lion (King) 22, 34, 82
William, Count of Holland 57
willow 73, 84
willowherb 73
Winchester 101
window glass 119
wine 34
withers heights (cattle, sheep, pig) 17
wolves 93
wood rush 72
wool 6, 8, 34, 35, 38, 83, 103
woolfells 6, 8, 17, 28, 34, 38, 43, 83
Worcester Cathedral 103
Wormit 87

y

yarn spinning 89
yarrow 70
yellow flag 73, 79, 86
yellow-rattle 71
York 81, 97, 101
    16–22 Coppergate 52, 100, 129
    Bedern 138
    Coppergate 100, 101
    Environmental Archaeology Unit 3
    Minster 100